THE HARPERCOLLINS DICTIONARY OF ASTRONOMY AND SPACE SCIENCE

THE HARPERCOLLINS DICTIONARY OF ASTRONOMY AND SPACE SCIENCE

Dianne F. Moore

Series Editor, Eugene Ehrlich

HarperPerennial
A Division of HarperCollins*Publishers*

HarperCollins books may be purchased for educational, business, or sales promotional use. For information, please call or write: Special Markets Department, HarperCollins Publishers, Inc., 10 East 53rd Street, New York, NY 10022. Telephone: (212) 207-7528; Fax: (212) 207-7222.

FIRST EDITION

Library of Congress Cataloging-in-Publication Data

Moore, Dianne F,

The HarperCollins dictionary of astronomy and space science / Dianne F. Moore. — lst ed.

p. cm.

ISBN 0-06-271542-9 — ISBN 0-06-461023-3 (pbk.)

1. Astronomy—Dictionaries. 2. Space sciences—Dictionaries.

I. Title.

QB14.M59 1992

520'.3—dc20 91-55394

---

92 93 94 95 96 ◆/RRD 5 4 3 2 1

With love, to my parents, who were there at the beginning, and to Rebecca P. and Peggy M., my two mentors and loving friends who patiently listened and encouraged, and to my astronomy students, who believe in tomorrow.

The HarperCollins Dictionary of Astronomy and Space Science

A

Abenezra a lunar crater 27 miles in diameter. It is located at 21° S and 12° E on the near side of the moon.

aberration 1. a defect of lenses and curved mirrors that results in a blurred image of a star under observation;

2. an apparent change in the position of a star due to Earth's motion in space. Announced in 1729 by English astronomer James Bradley (1693–1762), this phenomenon provided the first observational proof of the Copernican hypothesis that the sun is the center of the universe. See COPERNICUS.

ablation the process by which heat shield material of a spacecraft reentering the atmosphere is melted or removed. The HEAT SHIELDS of space vehicles such as the SHUTTLE have outer layers that are designed to shed in order to prevent excessive heating of the craft's interior.

Able a type of liquid propellant rocket that formed the upper stage of early space vehicles.

absolute magnitude (M) **1.** the brightness of a star;

2. the apparent visual magnitude a star would have if it were ten parsecs from Earth.

absolute temperature scale a temperature scale that has the same divisions as the Celsius scale, but in which the hypothetical lowest limit of physical temperature is assigned the value zero. Degrees on this scale are given as K, short for Kelvin, after Lord Kelvin, the physicist who devised the scale. See ABSOLUTE ZERO.

absolute zero the lowest temperature theoretically possible. At this temperature molecular motion almost ceases. A point of temperature equal to -273.15°C, -459.67°F, or 0 K.

absorption line (or **band**) a dark line in a spectrum produced by the absence of photons that have been absorbed by adjacent atoms or molecules. See SPECTRUM.

absorption nebula see DARK NEBULA.

absorption spectrum a spectrum made of dark lines against a bright, continuous background. The sun has an absorption spectrum. In this case, the bright background is due to the sun's brilliant photosphere, and the dark absorption lines are produced by the solar atmosphere. These dark lines occur because the atoms in the solar atmosphere absorb certain characteristic wavelengths from the continuous spectrum of the photosphere.

Acamar the common name for the brilliant white double star Theta Eridani, located in the lower bend of the meandering southern constellation Eridanus, the River, near Fornax. Acamar, 17 parsecs from Earth, has a magnitude of 2.92. See ERIDANUS.

acceleration (a) the rate of increase in velocity with time, expressed in units such as meters (m) per second (sec) squared. When a body falls to the ground, it experiences an acceleration due to gravity of 9.8 m/sec squared.

acceleration of gravity (g) **1.** the acceleration of an object falling freely without air resistance to the center of a PLANET (or any other natural SATELLITE);

2. the acceleration due to downward motion in a gravitational field. Italian astronomer Galileo Galilei, known as Galileo, (1564–1642) showed that all objects fall at the same rate. See GALILEO.

accretion the gradual sticking together of MASS, as by a planet forming by the building up of colliding particles in the SOLAR NEBULA.

accretion disk a disk of hot material spiraling into a compact massive object, such as a NEUTRON STAR OR BLACK HOLE. An accretion disk is usually detected by its emission of X-rays.

Achernar the common name for Alpha Eridani (a Eri), a conspicuous bluish-white star—ninth brightest in the sky and brightest in the southern constellation Eridanus, the River, near Tucan. Eridanus meanders from the foot of Orion deep into the southern hemisphere, ending with Achernar. Its distance from Earth is 35 parsecs. See ERIDANUS.

Achilles (Asteroid 588) the first member of the so-called TROJAN GROUP of asteroids to be discovered; in 1906. It lies east of JUPITER. Beginning with Achilles, most of the Trojans have been named after heroes of the two sides of the Trojan War.

achondrite a type of meteorite. Achondrites contain very little iron or nickel. *Stony meteorites* are usually more coarsely crystallized.

Acidalia Planitia the main dark area in the northern hemisphere of MARS.

acoustic velocity see SPEED OF SOUND.

Acrux also called Alpha Crucis (a Cru), the brightest star in the constellation Crux, or Southern Cross. Acrux is the 14th brightest star in the sky. This conspicuous white SUBGIANT STAR is a visual BINARY. Alpha and Gamma Crucis point toward the SOUTH CELESTIAL POLE. See CRUX and SOUTHERN CROSS.

actinometer any device that measures the intensity of radiation capable of effecting photochemical changes, particularly of the sun. A familiar example is the photographic exposure meter.

active galaxy **1.** a type of GALAXY that emits large amounts of ENERGY.

2. any galaxy emitting unusually large amounts of energy from a very powerful source, possibly accounted for by a central supermassive black hole, tearing stars apart by tidal forces. Other examples are SEYFERT GALAXY and RADIO GALAXY.

Adonis (Asteroid 2101) a member of the APOLLO GROUP of MINOR PLANETS (asteroids) discovered in 1936. Adonis (0.6 mile in diameter) missed Earth by 1,553,000 miles in 1936. It was seen again in 1977 but passed at a much greater distance.

Adrastea JUPITER'S 15th SATELLITE, discovered by a VOYAGER PROBE in 1979. Its MAGNITUDE is 18.9. This small moon is 36 kilometers in diameter.

Aeneas 1. one of the Trojan asteroids. It has a diameter of 81 miles and a period of 11.7 years.

2. a crater on Saturn's satellite Dione.

aeon or **eon** a passage of time numbering one thousand million years.

aerolite a stony meteorite. See ACHONDRITE.

aeronomy the physics and chemistry of the upper atmosphere of a planet, dealing with such considerations as its temperature, density, motions, composition, chemical processes, and reactions to solar and cosmic radiation.

aerospace Earth's atmosphere and space beyond. The word was coined from *aeronautics* and *space*. Aerospace research is concerned with developing vehicles that can operate in space as well as in the atmosphere.

aerospace vehicle see SPACE-AIR VEHICLE.

Agena 1 one of the most successful United States rockets, used extensively from 1961 to 1970 for launching satellites, such as the Mercury spacecraft, and as a second stage for lunar and planetary probes.

Agena 2 also called Beta Centauri, second brightest star in the southern constellation Centaurus.

air see ATMOSPHERE.

airglow the faint, infrared glow caused by air molecules being excited by solar radiation in the upper atmosphere. Even on the clearest of nights, when there is no moon, the sky between the stars is not absolutely dark.

airlock a chamber in a spacecraft in which the atmospheric pressure can be adjusted. Astronauts may use an airlock when they leave their pressurized spacecraft to perform a walk in airless space. It enables them to avoid depressurization of the entire craft.

air pressure see ATMOSPHERIC PRESSURE.

Alba Patera possibly the largest central-vent volcanic structure of Mars.

Its central CALDERA is enclosed by a ring of fractures 600 km in diameter. Associated lava flows cover an area more than 1500 km across.

albedo an indication of the reflecting power of a planet or planetary surface, expressed as the ratio of the light reflected by the planet (or satellite) to the light received by it. In the case of the moon, it is the extent to which the moon reflects sunlight. Values range from 0 (perfectly black) to 1 (perfect reflector). Our moon has a very low albedo (0.07), while that of Venus is high (0.6).

Albireo the common name for the orange giant star Beta Cygni. With a magnitude of 5.4, this orange giant star is found in the northern constellation CYGNUS, the Swan. It is a beautiful double star with a deep blue companion star.

Alcaid also called Alkaid, Benetnasch, and Eta Ursae Majoris. This blue-white star, magnitude 1.86, is among the brightest in the Plow (Ursa Major). Alcaid is 70 parsecs from Earth. See ALKAID, BIG DIPPER, URSA MAJOR.

Alcor the white star 80 Ursae Majoris, the naked-eye companion to Mizar. Alcor lies in the northern constellation Ursa Major. See BIG DIPPER, URSA MAJOR.

Alcyone the star Eta Tauri. With a magnitude of 2.87, this bluish-white double is the brightest member of the Pleiades cluster. Alcyone is 125 parsecs from Earth. See PLEIADES and TAURUS.

Aldebaran also called Alpha Tauri, a conspicuous red giant, magnitude 0.85, and the brightest star in the northern constellation Taurus, near Orion. A slow irregular variable, it is also considered a visual binary star, with an 11th magnitude red dwarf companion. It lies 21 parsecs from Earth. Alpha Tauri appears to lie in the Hyades cluster, but it is not considered a true member of the group. See TAURUS.

Aldrin, Edwin E. "Buzz" (1930–) American astronaut assigned to Apollo 11 as Lunar Module pilot. On July 20, 1969, he became the second man to walk on the moon. The first was Neil Armstrong.

Alfven's theory a theory proposed in 1942 by Swedish physicist Hannes Alfven (1908–) that the planets formed out of material captured by the sun from space gas and dust. See ALFVEN WAVES.

Alfven waves the hydromagnetic shear waves found in the solar wind and in Earth's magnetosphere. They are named after Hannes Alfven, winner of the 1970 Nobel Prize for Physics.

Algol called the Demon Star and the Winking Demon, one of the most famous variable stars in the northern sky, near Andromeda and Auriga, and a prototype of a class of eclipsing binaries. This white star is the second brightest in PERSEUS.

Alinda (Asteroid 887) an Amor type of asteroid, only a few kilometers in diameter. See AMOR GROUP.

Alkaid a star also called Benetnasch, ALCAID, and Eta Ursae Majoris. It is located in the Big Dipper, 70 parsecs from Earth, and its magnitude is 1.86. See BIG DIPPER and URSA MAJOR.

Almagest a work of astronomy compiled by Ptolemy about 140 AD. Its 13 volumes cover all of astronomy as conceived in ancient times, with a detailed description of the Ptolemaic conception of the solar system. It also includes a star catalog giving positions and magnitudes of 1022 stars.

Almanon a crater in the 4th quadrant of the moon, at -17° S and +16° E. Almanon is 30 miles in diameter and has walls rising some 10,000 feet. It lies west of Mare Nectaris.

Alnilam a star also called Epsilon Orionis. It is located in Orion's belt and has a magnitude of 1.70. Its distance from Earth is 1200 light-years. See ORION.

Alpha (α) the first letter of the Greek alphabet, used first by German astronomer Johann Bayer (1572–1625) to designate the brightest star in a constellation.

Alpha Capricornids a minor meteor stream that is active from mid-July until mid-August. Its average rate is six meteors per hour.

Alpha Centauri a triple star, magnitude -0.01, that is the brightest star in the constellation Centaurus, the third brightest star in the entire sky, and second nearest star to our sun. Its distance from Earth is 1.31 parsecs. See CENTAURUS.

Alpha Piscis Austrini see FOMALHAUT.

Alphonsus a walled lunar plain in the 3rd quadrant, at -14° S and -3° W, in Mare Nubium.

Alpine Valley or **Alpinus Vallis** a conspicuous gash 83 miles long and from three to six miles wide, cutting perpendicularly through the lunar Alps, at +49° N and +2° E, in the moon's first quadrant, on the north-western border of Mare Imbrium.

Altair a conspicuous white star in the northern constellation Aquila. Its distance from Earth is 5.1 parsecs. With a magnitude of 0.77, this first-magnitude star forms one of the three stars of the so-called summer triangle. Altair is ten times as luminous as the sun, and one of the closest of the bright stars. See AQUILA.

Altai Scarp or **Altai Escarpment** a lunar cliff following a circular arc from Piccolomini Crater on the south into Mare Tranquillitatis 600 miles to the north. Altai averages about 1 mile high, but exceeds 2 miles at some points. It lies at longitude +22° E and latitude -24° S, in the 4th quadrant of the moon's near side.

Altar the common name for the southern constellation Ara. See ARA.

altitude (alt) the distance of a star or planet above a surface (horizon).

Amalthea the largest of the four innermost moons of Jupiter. It was discovered in 1892 by American astronomer Edward Emerson Barnard (1857–1923) and was the last of the Jovian satellites to be discovered by Earth-based observers. The remaining Jovian moons were not detected until the Voyager flybys of 1979, when the orbit of Amalthea was mapped with sufficient accuracy to enable special observations by Voyager 1, March 5, and Voyager 2, July 9. Because of its dark red color, the heavily cratered moon has a low ALBEDO. Its largest crater spans a distance of 56 miles.

Amirani an active volcano on Jupiter's satellite Io.

Amor group of asteroids a group of more than 16 known minor planets, asteroids also called *Mars crossovers*, that come within the perihelion distance of Mars. Ganymede and Eros are two of them. Discovered in 1932 by American astronomer Eugene J. Shoemaker, this group is named after the minor planet Amor. See GANYMEDE and EROS.

Ananke the smallest of Jupiter's moons, diameter 18.6 miles, discovered in 1951 by American astronomer Seth B. Nicholson (1891–1963). It has been suggested that this satellite, which has retrograde motion, may be a captured asteroid.

anatase see OCTAHEDRITE.

Andromeda a large constellation of the Northern Hemisphere. It is located close to Pegasus. Its bright stars include Alpheratz, Mirach, and Almaak. The most famous object in the constellation is the Great Spiral Galaxy, M31. The open cluster NGC 752 is also an easy binocular object. In mythology, Andromeda was the Ethiopian princess of the Perseus legend, a daughter of Cassiopeia and wife of Perseus, who rescued her from a sea monster.

Andromeda Galaxy (M31, NGC 224) the largest of the close galaxies and part of the Local Group of galaxies. The spiral galaxy is one of the few visible to the naked eye. It is perceived as an oval patch of light in the Andromeda. See LOCAL GROUP.

Andromedids see BIELIDS.

angstrom (*abbreviation* A or Å) a unit of length—one-tenth of a millimicron, or 10^{-10} meters—used primarily to express the wavelength of light.

annular eclipse a solar eclipse in which the solar photosphere appears around the edge of the moon in a bright ring. The CORONA, CHROMOSPHERE, and prominences cannot be seen during an annular eclipse.

anomalistic month the average period of revolution of the moon from perigee to perigee: a period of 27 days, 13 hours, 18 minutes, and 33.2 seconds.

ansae the handle-shaped portions of Saturn's rings that are telescopically visible on either side of the planet as seen from Earth.

Antares also called Alpha Scorpii, a red supergiant star whose distance from Earth is 130 parsecs. It is the brightest star in the southern constellation Scorpius. Antares (a rival of Ares, the Greek god of war—identified with Mars) is a visual binary; its reddish hue is similar to the color of Mars. Its companion star, Antares B, appears green and is a peculiar hot radio source.

Antlia (Ant) the Pump, one of the constellations of the southern sky that were introduced in 1756 by French astronomer Nicolas-Louis de Lacaille (1713–1762). He called the constellation *Machine Pneumatique*, the air pump—in German it is called *Luft Pumpe*. Antlia is a faint mid-southern group adjoining the Milky, in Pyxis and Vela. Its brightest stars are only 4th magnitude.

Antoniadi Dorsa a steep cliff extending along the edge of a plateau in the northern hemisphere of Mercury, at latitude +24° and longitude 164°, east of the Caloris Basin.

Apennines also called Montes Apenninus, a mountain range in the 2nd quadrant of the moon, at +20° N and -2° W. Apollo 15 landed here in summer 1971. These lunar mountains rise to 2-1/2 miles above the lava shores of Mare Imbrium and dwindle to hills 870 miles to the southeast.

aphelion the point in the orbit of a planet, comet, or artificial satellite in solar orbit that is farthest from the sun. Earth is at aphelion on or about July 3. See Fig. 1.

Aplan, Peter (1495–1552) German geographer and astronomer who observed that the tails of comets point away from the sun.

apogee 1. the point in the orbit of the moon or an artificial satellite at which it is farthest from Earth. When a spacecraft or satellite reaches apogee, its rockets can be fired to boost it into a more nearly circular orbit or to enable it to escape from Earth orbit. See Fig. 2.

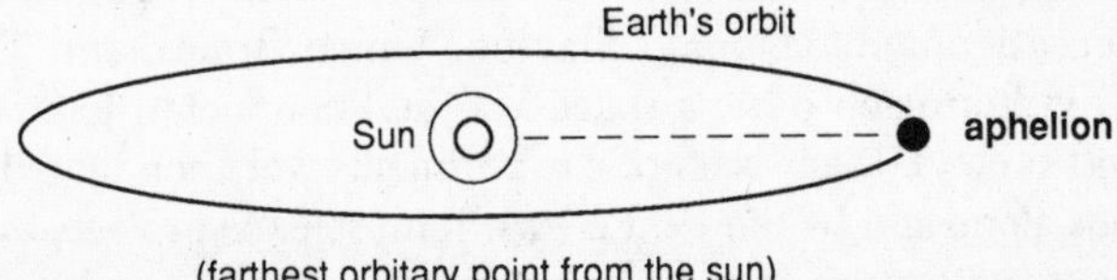

Fig. 1. **Aphelion.** The orbitary point farthest from the sun.

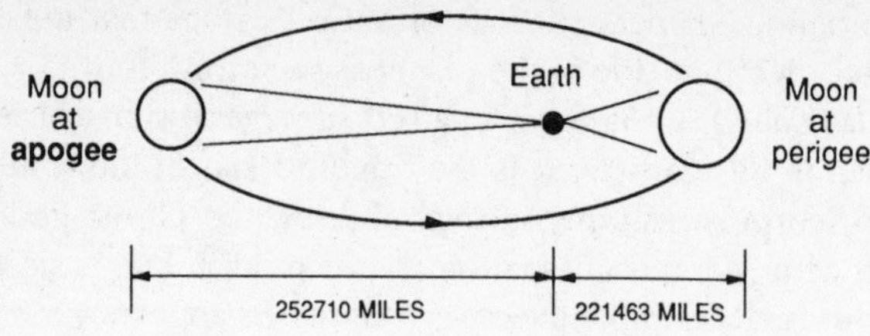

Fig. 2. **Apogee.** An observer at a location above the North Pole of Earth, over a lunar month, would see the moon describe an ellipse in a counterclockwise direction. The moon is shown here in its orbit about Earth. Both its apogee—the farthest point from Earth—and its perigee—the closest point to Earth—are shown.

2. the highest point above Earth's surface that is attained by a rocket.

Apollo the United States space program, six space missions between 1968 and 1972, that landed humans on the moon. See LUNAR EXCURSION MODULE.

Apollo asteroids see APOLLO GROUP.

Apollo group or **Apollo asteroids** a group of some 28 or more known asteroids, including Hermes and Icarus, that have Earth-crossing orbits. Most are very small and observable only when close to Earth. See PERIHELION.

Apollo-Soyuz Test Project (APTP) the first international manned space flight, conducted by the United States and the USSR from July 15 to July 24, 1975. It was designed to test the compatibility of rendezvous and docking systems of American and Soviet spacecraft, as a means for opening the door for international space rescue and for future joint manned flights. Apollo 18 and Soyuz 19 were launched into Earth orbit on July 15 and successfully rendevoused and docked at an altitude of 225 km on July 17.

The crews of two cosmonauts (Alexei Leontov and Valery Kubasov) and three astronauts (Donald Slayton, Vance Brand, and Thomas Stafford) visited each other's spacecraft and conducted joint experiments and surveys. Many scientific experiments were conducted by the Americans alone and by the joint crews. Joint science projects included experiments with zone-forming fungi and a microbial exchange test. United States experiments included microorganism growth, fish embryonic development, and seed genetic experiments. In two medical experiments, an electric field was used to separate blood samples into their constituents to help determine whether the space environment offers an improved means of isolating viruses, enzymes, and other small particles for analysis.

Apollo spacecraft the spacecraft that took United States astronauts to the moon (1968–1972). See LUNAR EXCURSION MODULE.

apparent magnitude the brightness of a star. See MAGNITUDE.

apparent position the true position of a star.

apparent solar time time measured by reference to observed motion of a star.

April Lyrids See LYRIDS.

APS *abbreviation of a*scent *p*ropulsion *s*ystem, a rocket engine designed to propel astronauts back to the orbiting mother ship after they have landed on the moon.

apsides (singular: apsis) **1.** the points in an orbit closest to (*periapsis*) and farthest from (*apoapsis*) the focus of gravitational attraction. The velocity of an orbiting body is maximal at periapsis and minimal at apoapsis;

2. in regard to the orbit of the moon the line of apsides connecting perigee and apogee.

Apus (Aps) also called the Bird of Paradise, a star group lying close to the south celestial pole, between Octans and Triangulum Australe, and containing no bright stars.

Aquarids the two active meteor showers having their apparent origin in AQUARIUS. Those called *Eta Aquarids* maximize on or about May 4 and have a peak duration of 10 days; those called *Delta Aquarids* maximize on or about July 19 and have a peak duration of about 20 days.

Aquarius (Aqr) the Water Bearer, a constellation in the Southern Hemisphere near Pegasus. It contains a planetary nebula NGC 7009 (Saturn Nebula) and NGC 7293 (Helix Nebula), and the globular clusters M2 and M72. Aquarius contains several spiral galaxies above 13th magnitude.

Aquila (Aql) the Eagle, a small inconspicuous constellation in the Northern Hemisphere south of Cygnus. Altair, a first-magnitude star, is the brightest in the constellation. Two open clusters, NGC 6709 and NGC 6755, are visible with binoculars. In mythology, Aquila was the eagle sent to collect the young shepherd Ganymede to become cupbearer of the gods.

Ara the Altar, a southern constellation between Scorpius and Triangulum Australe.

Aratus a Greek poet (310?–240? BC) who wrote *Phaenomena*, a poem dealing with astronomy.

Arcturus also called Alpha Boötes, in the northern sky a conspicuous red giant, magnitude -0.06, that is the brightest star in the constellation Boötes, the Herdsman. Arcturus is 11 parsecs from Earth. See BOÖTES.

Arecibo Vallis a valley southeast of Kuiper Crater in the southern hemisphere of Mercury, at latitude -27° and longitude 29°.

areography 1. the study of the air or atmosphere;
2. the geography of Mars.

Arethusa (Asteroid 95) a very dark asteroid in the main asteroid belt, discovered in 1867. Arethusa's diameter is 143 miles, its opposition magnitude is 12.1, and its revolution period is 5.37 years.

Argo or **Argo Navis** formerly a large southern constellation between Canis Major and the Southern Cross. Argo is one of many ancient constellations, no longer recognized by astronomers, that appear on old star maps. Only the stern of the ship Argo is shown in the sky.

People are often puzzled by the concept of a disused constellation, thinking that a constellation is either there or is not there. However, the patterns we see in the stars are no more than a product of human imagination, so humans are free to amend the patterns as they choose, and astronomers did just that during the heyday of celestial mapping in the 17th and 18th centuries. Argo, named for Jason's ship of Greek mythology, is a constellation that is not so much disused as dismantled. It was one of the 48 constellations known to Greek astronomers, as listed by Ptolemy, but 18th-century astronomers considered it to be too large and so divided it into three parts: CARINA, PUPPIS, and VELA, respectively, the Keel, the Stern or Poop, and the Sails.

Argyre I a circular feature on the surface of Mars. It was probably formed by a meteoroid impact that created its 9800-foot rim. In 1971, Mariner 9 observations showed it to be a basin with a featureless floor covered by dust deposits.

Ariel a moon of Uranus, discovered in 1851 by English astronomer William Lassell (1799–1880). Ariel's 580 square-mile surface shows numerous impact craters, linear grooves suggestive of tectonic activity, and smooth patches indicative of deposition of material. The satellite was observed during the Voyager 2 flyby in 1986 and was seen to have the brightest and geologically youngest surface in the Uranian system.

Aries the Ram, a north-equatorial constellation whose brightest stars include Hamal (Arabic for *sheep*), Sheratan (Arabic for *sign*—it marked the vernal equinox at the time of Hipparchus), Mesarthim (Hebrew for *ministers*), and Botein (*belly*). The golden fleece of the ram was the prize ultimately carried off by Jason, leader of the Argonauts.

A ring the outermost ring of Saturn visible from Earth with the help of a small telescope. Pioneer 11, flying by Saturn in 1979, discovered a narrow ring just outside the A ring that came to be called the F ring. There is a gap between the dusky A ring and the brighter B ring. The gap is known as CASSINI'S DIVISION. See also F RING.

Arizona meteorite crater also called Winslow Crater, the impact explosion crater measuring 1280 meters in diameter and 180 meters in depth that was formed about 6000 years ago by a 250,000-ton meteorite, 70 meters in diameter. The meteorite vaporized almost completely—with only a few hundred tons of tiny iron spherules left scattered over 80 square kilometers around the crater. It was the first crater on Earth's surface identified as resulting from meteoritic impact. It is situated on a flat plateau lying between Flagstaff and Winslow, Arizona.

Armstrong, Neil Alden (1930–) the first astronaut, in 1969, to set foot on the moon. Edwin Aldrin was the second. Michael Collins waited in the spacecraft's command module, which was in lunar orbit, for their return from the moon's surface and the team's subsequent trip back to Earth. The location of this first lunar landing is now officially named Station Tranquillitatis.

Arrakis Mu Draconis, called the Danger star. This white dwarf binary is 100 light-years from Earth and has a luminosity 8 times that of the sun. Its period is 1090 years. See DRACO.

Arsia Mons a shield volcano 19-km high, 400-km wide at latitude -9° and longitude 121°, at the edge of the THARSIS RIDGE of Mars. It has the largest summit CALDERA of the volcanoes on Mars.

artificial satellite a manufactured object, such as a spacecraft, that is boosted into a closed orbit around Earth, the moon, or other celestial body. The Space Age began on October 4, 1957, when the Soviet Union launched the first artificial satellite (Sputnik I) into orbit around Earth. See Fig. 3.

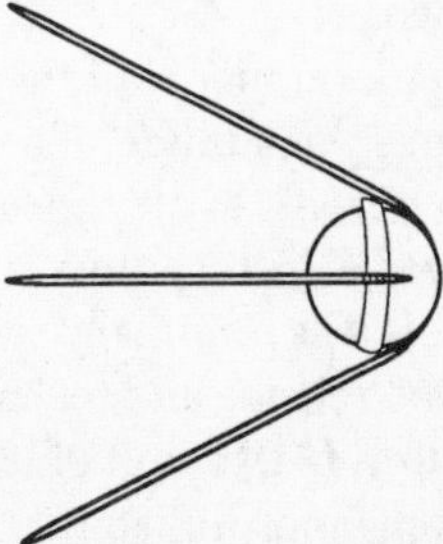

Fig. 3. **Artificial satellite.** With the dramatic 1957 Earth-orbiting flight of the USSR's Sputnik I, shown here, the Space Age began, with the United States apparently scrambling to catch up.

ascent stage the upper portion of the lunar module of a spacecraft, for example, the Apollo. The ascent stage houses the crew, controls, and ascent engine.

Ascraeus Mons a shield volcano 19-km high at latitude +12° and longitude 104°, in Mars' THARSIS province. It is 400 km wide at its base and has a summit CALDERA that is 50 km across.

ashen light **1.** earthshine on the moon;

2. the dim coppery glow observed sometimes on the dark side of Venus when it is in its crescent phase. Ashen light may be similar to Earth's northern lights. The cause of ashen light may be found in an electrical phenomenon in the upper atmosphere of Venus.

association a loose group of young stars, which occur in regions rich in gas and dust in the spiral arms of the Milky Way galaxy.

A stars the stars of spectral type A, characterized by the great strength of the hydrogen absorption lines in their spectra. On the main sequence they range in surface temperature from 7500 K up to 9900 K.

asteroid a minor planet, the rocky bodies that, for the most part, orbit the sun between Mars and Jupiter. Italian astronomer Giuseppe Piazzi (1746–1826) in 1801 discovered the largest asteroid (Ceres), confirming the prediction in BODE'S LAW that a planet of some size would be discovered near 2.8 AU. German astronomer Carl Gauss (1777–1855), taking this lead, formulated a method of calculating orbits that is still used.

asteroid belt a zone between the orbits of Mars and Jupiter that contains the majority of minor planets. See Fig. 4.

Astraea (Asteroid 5) the fifth minor planet to be discovered, in 1845.

astrobleme an erosional scar, usually ancient, left in a planet's crust by the impact of a meteorite. The largest astroblemes on Earth are Vredefort, South Africa (40-km diameter); Nordlinger Ries, Germany (25-km diameter); Deep Bay, Saskatchewan, Canada (14-km diameter); Lake Bosumtwi, Ghana (10-km diameter); and Serpent Mound, Ohio (64-km diameter).

astrochemistry the study of the chemistry of celestial bodies and regions of space.

astrolabe a medieval model of the heavens invented by the Greeks and used to measure the altitude of a celestial object. The term astrolabe is derived from Greek, with the meaning "instrument for taking the stars". During the 15th century, mariners used the astrolabe to determine latitude. It was eventually replaced by the SEXTANT.

astronautics the science and technology of spaceflight.

astronomical unit (AU) a unit of length equal to the mean distance from Earth to the sun, approximately 93 million miles. The astronomical unit

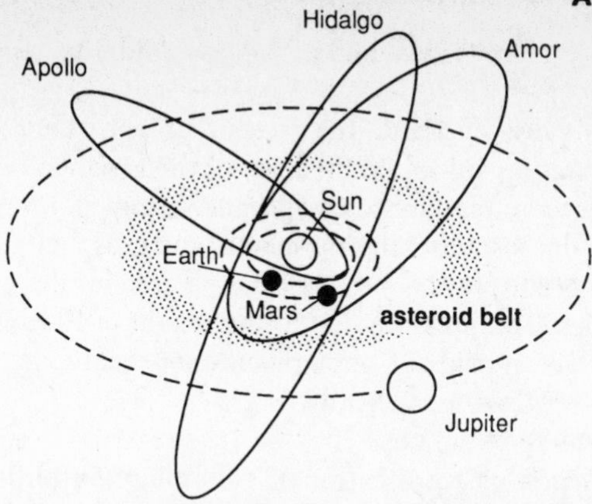

Fig. 4. **Asteroid belt.** This belt contains the majority of asteroids that orbit the sun. Other minor asteroid groups, such as Apollo, Hidalgo, and Amor, have independent orbits around the sun.

is used for indicating distances within a solar system (star system).

astronomy the study of celestial bodies and space, as well as the universe as a whole.

astrophysics the study of energy from stars: x-rays, ultraviolet, infrared, etc.

Aten asteroids a family of asteroids with semimajor axes smaller than Earth's. They lie primarily inside Earth's orbit, less than 1 AU, but may cross outside near aphelion. The only known Aten asteroids are Aten (2062), Ra-Shalom (2100), Hathor (2340), and 1984 QA.

Atla Regio the eastern section of Aphrodite Terra, on Venus. Atla Regio appears to be a sinuous mountain belt with features that are prominent on radar. Its conical mountains include Maat Mons and Ozza Mons, 16,000 feet high.

Atlas[1] a 1st-quadrant lunar crater some 55 miles in diameter, at +46° N and +45° E. Atlas contains multiple peaks—the tallest is 2600 feet—and the highest point on the crater wall is 10,000 feet.

Atlas[2] the innermost satellite of Saturn. It is the so-called shepherd satellite of the A-ring. This Saturnian satellite was discovered in 1980 by Richard J. Terrile, using a 100-inch telescope at Las Campanas Observatory in Chile.

Atlas[3] the star 27 Tauri, in the Hyades; magnitude 3.63. See HYADES.

Atlas[4] an intercontinental ballistic missile (ICBM) rocket modified to launch the Mercury spacecraft, some with upper stages (Able, Agena, and Centaur).

atmosphere (atm) the layers of gases around a planet, star, or moon. The gaseous envelope surrounding Earth, which rotates with Earth, consists of oxygen, nitrogen, and other gases and extends to a height of about 22,000 miles.

atmospheric layers on Earth, the gaseous layers that are divided into a series of regions organized on the basis of the variation of temperature with altitude. Examples are the troposphere, tropopause, stratosphere, ozonosphere, mesosphere, thermosphere, and exosphere. See Fig. 5.

atmospheric pressure the force per unit of area for the gases that surround a planet. The pressure due to the weight of Earth's atmosphere is equal at sea level to about 14.69 pounds per square inch.

atmospheric window see WINDOW.

atomic nucleus see NUCLEUS.

ATS *abbreviation of* Applications Technology Satellites, satellites designed for use in weather prediction, navigation, and communications assistance. They are also used for relaying signals from other satellites back to Earth.

AU *abbreviation of* *a*stronomical *u*nit.

audiofrequency a frequency—between 15 Hz and 20,000 Hz—within the range of normally audible sound.

augmentation (aug) an apparent increase, as observed from Earth, in the semidiameter of a celestial body as its altitude increases. The term is used principally in reference to the moon.

Auriga (Aur) the Charioteer, a large constellation of the Northern Hemisphere in the form of a kite, between Perseus and Gemini. Auriga contains three star clusters: M36 (NGC 1960), M37 (NGC 2099), and M38 (NGC 1912). Capella is Auriga's brightest star. In mythology Auriga represents Erechthonius, the son of Vulcan, who became King of Athens and was the inventor of the four-horse chariot.

aurora the diffusion of light at the poles that is commonly known as the *northern lights* (aurora borealis) and the *southern lights* (aurora australis). This glow in a planet's upper atmosphere is caused by incoming charged particles (protons and electrons) from the sun that interact with the planet's ionosphere. The color is mostly green, but may also be white, yellow, or blue. The lower border of the display may have a red fringe.

aurora borealis see NORTHERN LIGHTS.

autumnal equinox that point occupied each year on or about September 22, when Earth's declination changes from north to south; also called September equinox. See Fig. 6.

axis the imaginary line that passes through the center of a body such as a planet, moon, or star; it is about this imaginary line that a rotating body turns.

azimuth (az) a horizontal coordinate system. The azimuth of an object in

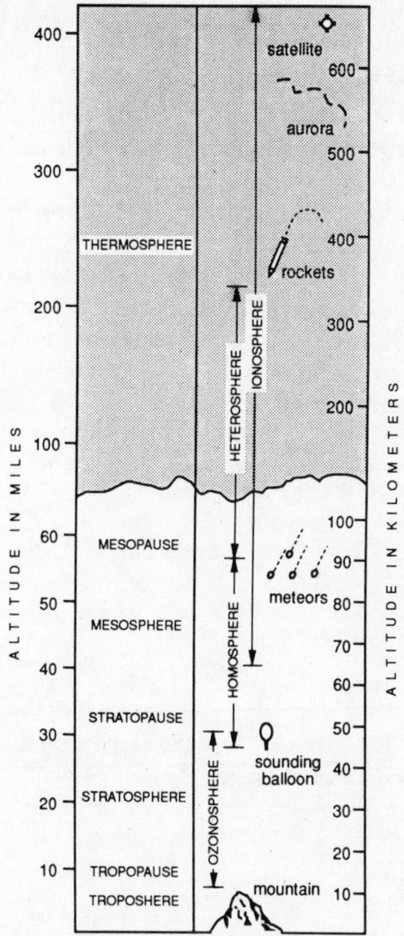

Fig. 5. **Atmospheric layers.** Regions of Earth's atmosphere can be designated by gaseous structure and by use.

the sky is its angular distance measured eastward along the horizon from the north point to the intersection of the horizon with a meridian (vertical circle) running through the object. See Fig. 7.

B

Baade's star another name for Crab pulsar, the star whose explosion produced the Crab nebula and is now a young optical pulsar identified as the Crab pulsar in 1967. Its pulsations are also observed at radio, infrared, x-ray, and gamma-ray wavelengths. Baade's star is the powerhouse for the CRAB NEBULA.

background radiation 1. cosmic background radiation.
2. microwave background radiation.

Baily's beads the spots of light that appear to encircle the moon as the moon eclipses the sun. As an eclipse occurs, the sun's crescent becomes slimmer and slimmer until finally only a narrow line of light is left. Just before this narrow line disappears, it breaks up into what are known as Baily's beads. They were first described, in 1836, by British astronomer Francis Baily (1774–1844) as "a row of lucid points, like a string of bright beads around the moon's limb."

ballistic missile see MISSILE, GUIDED.

barium stars G and K giant stars with excesses of barium and other heavy elements in their atmospheres.

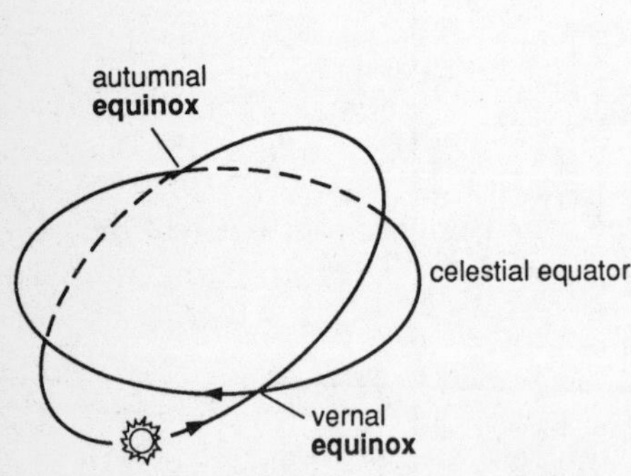

Fig. 6. **Autumnal equinox.** As Earth travels around the sun, Earth's path forms a plane that is known as the *ecliptic*. Because of Earth's 23.5° axis tilt, seasonal changes are produced. During the vernal and autumnal equinoxes, the days and nights are of equal length.

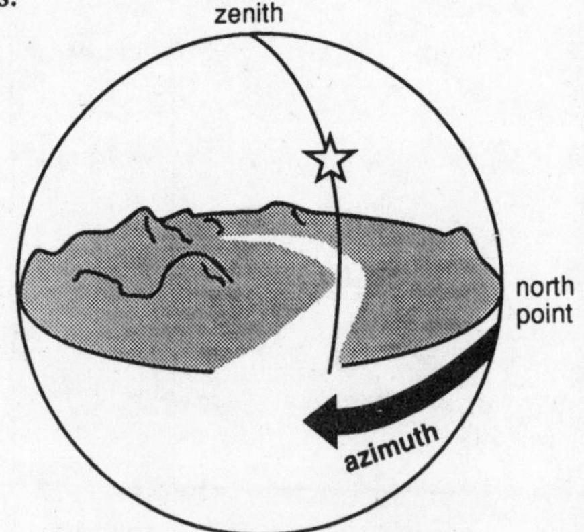

Fig. 7. **Azimuth.** A horizontal direction or bearing, one means of enabling astronomers to designate the location of a celestial event or object.

Barnard Regio a plain on Jupiter's satellite Ganymede.

Barnard's star a red dwarf star in the equatorial constellation Ophiuchus. At a distance of 1.83 parsecs, it is the fourth-nearest star to the sun. The red dwarf was discovered in 1916 by American astronomer Edward Emerson Barnard (1857–1923).

barred spiral galaxy a spiral galaxy with a center in the form of an extended bar. Normal spiral galaxies have dense round nuclei, while barred spiral galaxies have arms that wind outward from the ends of a central bar. Some have arms that sweep around so they nearly touch both ends of the central bar. Examples are M58 (NGC 4579) in Virgo and M95 (NGC 3351) in Leo.

barycenter the center of mass of the Earth-moon system. Also called the *center of inertia*. See Fig. 8. See also CENTER OF MASS.

basin or **lunar basin 1.** any of the huge ringed crater structures on the moon that are several hundred kilometers in diameter and were caused by asteroidal bodies.

2. a crater on the moon, for example, Mare Imbrium.

beam a well-defined elongated region of space down which energy is passing.

Beehive, the see PRAESEPE.

Beethoven a 388-mile diameter crater at latitude -20° N and longitude 124° in the southern hemisphere of Mercury, near the Schoenberg Crater.

Bellatrix (Gamma Orionis) a distant luminous blue-white giant star, third brightest in the northern constellation ORION, 140 parsecs from Earth. Bellatrix is named for an Amazon.

belt-zone circulation the atmospheric circulation typical of Jovian planets (the moons of Jupiter). Dark belts and bright zones encircle the planet parallel to its equator.

Berenice's Hair see COMA BERENICES.

Berenice's Cluster see COMA CLUSTER.

Bessel, Friedrich W. (1784–1846) the German astronomer who made the first authenticated measurement of the distance to a star, 61 Cygni.

Be stars 1. stars showing hydrogen emission lines. One example is Gamma Cassiopeia;

2. irregular binaries of stellar type B, that show bright emission lines during spectrum analysis. The stars are rotating very rapidly and lose mass, forming a gaseous shell around the star. Be stars are identical with shell stars.

Beta Cassiopeiae see CAPH.

Beta the second letter (ß) of the Greek alphabet, used in to designate

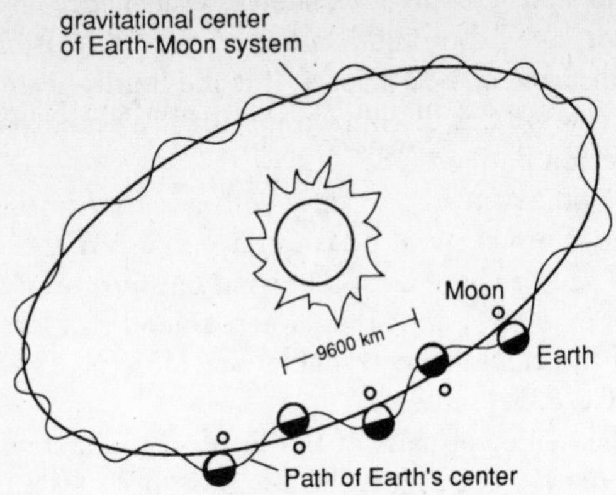

Fig. 8. **Barycenter.** Planet Earth and its moon revolve around the sun like a single body. And like a single body, the Earth-moon system has its own center of gravity, called the *barycenter*.

the second brightest star in a constellation. Beta Auriga is an example.

Beta Centauri a luminous, remote, blue-white giant star, second brightest in the Centaurus constellation. See CENTAURUS.

Beta Cephei stars a small group of variable stars, for example, stars in the Canis Major constellation. See VARIABLE STARS.

Beta Leporis see NIHAL.

Beta Lyrae stars a class of eclipsing binaries. See BINARY.

Betelgeuse a first-magnitude red supergiant star, the second-brightest in the northern constellation ORION, where it sits on the right shoulder of the Hunter. Its distance from Earth is 180 parsecs.

Biela's comet (1852 III) a comet first observed on March 8, 1772, and on November 10, 1805. It was seen again, on February 27, 1826, by Wilhelm von Biela (1782–1856), an Austrian army officer and amateur astronomer, who calculated the comet's orbit period, 6.6 years. It appeared again in 1832 and 1845. On December 19, 1845, the comet appeared once again and soon split in two. By March 3, 1846, it was determined that the two parts were over 150,000 miles apart. At its next return, in 1852, the separation had increased to 1.25 million miles. The comet has not reappeared since then, but in 1872 and 1885, two showers of Andromedid meteors were seen on the anniversary of the disintegration of Biela. See BIELIDS.

Bielids or **Andromedids** a meteor shower with its radiant in the Andromeda constellation. It is named after Biela's comet, which disintegrated after 1852. Little has been seen of the Bielids since 1885.

big bang (theory) the theory that the universe began with a violent explosion from which the expanding universe of galaxies eventually formed.

Big Dipper (the Plow) a group of stars in Ursa Major that contains the seven brightest stars in that northern constellation.

binary a double star, a pair of stars that are revolving about a common center of mass under the influence of their mutual gravitational attraction. Binary stars are very common in the Milky Way galaxy. See Fig. 9. See also ECLIPSING BINARY.

binary galaxy **1.** a double galaxy;
2. two galaxies observed in close proximity.

Biot, Jean B. (1774–1862) a French physicist who first demonstrated, in 1803, the extraterrestrial origin of meteorites. He also accompanied Gay-Lussac on a balloon flight in 1804 to collect scientific data about Earth's upper atmosphere.

Birkeland a large crater on the moon's far side, adjacent to the Van de Graff Crater.

black dwarf the end state of a white dwarf, which is a star about the size of Earth that has cooled. Black dwarfs are the coldest stars and give off no light.

Black-eye Nebula (M64, NGC 4826) a 9th-magnitude spiral galaxy 12 million light years off. M64 is found in COMA BERENICES.

black hole a theoretical massive object so collapsed that its escape velocity exceeds the velocity of light, first described by Einstein in his General Theory of Relativity, for which he won the Nobel Prize in Physics in 1921. Once formed, a black hole can only be detected by its gravity. Black holes may appear as x-ray sources in binary star systems. Some astronomers believe that black holes may be located in Cygnus X-1 and LMC X-3.

blueshift in starlight the shift of the spectral lines toward the blue end

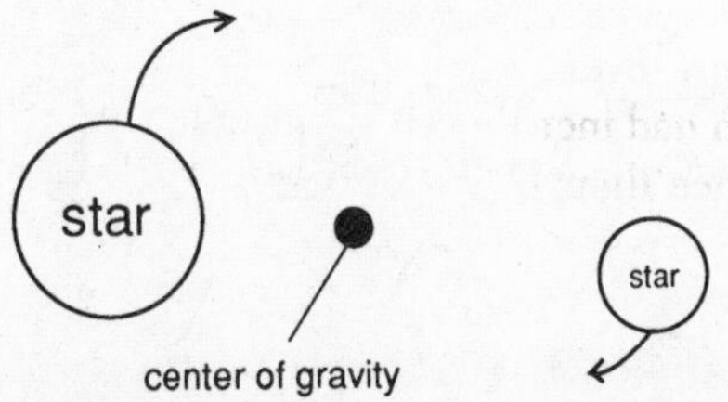

Fig. 9. **Binary.** Two stars close to one another and held together by a gravitational force and revolving like a dumbbell about a common center of gravity are called a *binary*. The center of a binary is closer to the more massive star.

of the spectrum. Blueshift indicates that the star is traveling toward Earth. See Fig. 10 and REDSHIFT.

blue-sky scale see LINKE SCALE.

Bode's Law according to a theory of German astronomer Johann Bode (1747–1826), the relationship between the distance of planets from the sun can be estimated in a sequence of 0, 3, 6, 12, 24 . . . . In this series, each number (except the 3) is twice the previous number if one adds 4 to each, and divides by 10. The resulting progression of 0.4, 0.7, 1.0, 1.6, 2.8, 5.2 . . . is similar to the actual distances of most planets from the sun, expressed in astronomical units (AU).

The actual distances are as follows: Mercury, 0.39 AU; Venus, 0.72 AU; Earth, 1.00 AU; Mars, 1.52 AU; Jupiter, 5.2 AU; Saturn, 9.54 AU; Uranus, 19.18 AU; Neptune, 30.06 AU; and Pluto, 39.44 AU. If you wonder what happened to the fifth number in the progression (2.8) given in the first paragraph of this entry, you will find comfort in knowing that there is an asteroid belt at 2.8 AU.

bolide a major fireball, or brilliant meteor, especially one that explodes. About 5000 are seen in Earth's atmosphere annually.

Bond, William Cranch (1789–1859) American astronomer, for a time director of the Harvard University observatory, who with his associates discovered Hyperion, a satellite of Saturn.

Boötes (Boo) a large constellation known as the Herdsman, from *Boötes*, the Greek word for ox-driver. The star group, seen as having the shape of a kite, is found in the Northern Hemisphere, near Ursa Major. Its brightest star is Arcturus, which is also the brightest star in the northern sky. The area also contains 3C-295, one of the most distant radio galaxies.

bow shock a phenomenon that may be thought of as an *interplanetary*

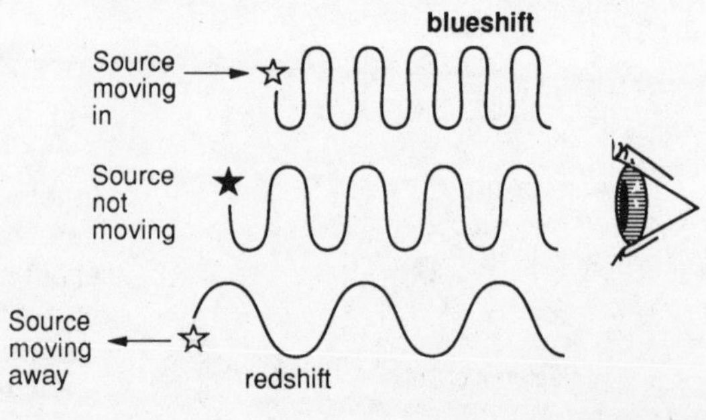

Fig. 10. **Blueshift.** An overall shift toward shorter wavelengths of the spectral lines in a spectrum. Blueshifts are observed in the spectra of celestial objects approaching Earth, redshifts in the spectra of objects moving away from Earth.

shock front in the medium comprised of the matter contained in the solar system in the space between the planets. The region contains ionized gas, or solar wind, that blows outward from the sun at supersonic speeds and is sometimes called an *interplanetary magnetic field.* A planet also moves at supersonic speed relative to the interplanetary medium, thus creating the *bow shock*, rather like that set up on the surface of the sea alongside the advancing bow of an ocean liner. See Fig. 11.

Brahe, Tycho (1546–1601) Danish astronomer who accurately observed the five planets known in 1570. Two years later, he observed a type I supernova in the constellation Cassiopeia. See TYCHO'S STAR.

brightest stars the stars with the greatest apparent visual magnitude.

brightness the intensity of light or radiation emitted from a celestial body such as a star.

brown dwarf a star whose mass is too low to ignite nuclear fusion and is heated by contraction.

B star any of the hot blue stars exhibiting the properties of the B-type spectrum—hydrogen emission lines. With temperature ranges of 10,000 to 28,000 K, B stars are extremely bright.

Bull, the the common name for the Taurus constellation. See TAURUS.

burst a brief flux of intense radiation with a sudden onset and rapid decay, as is observed from Jupiter and from the sun at radio wavelengths.

burster see X-RAY BURSTER.

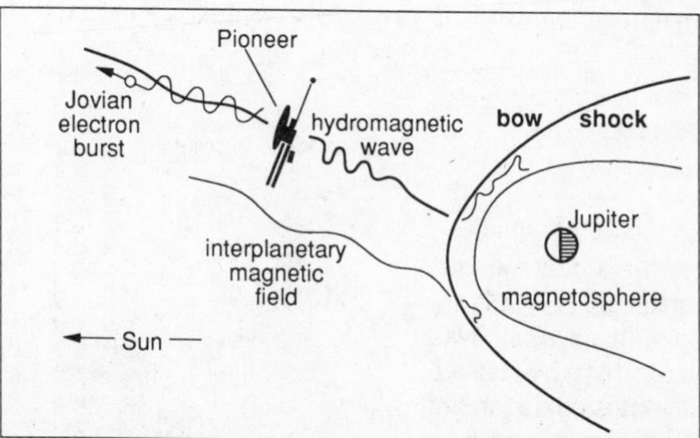

Fig. 11. **Bow shock.** The interaction of solar wind with an individual planet creates a shock front, called a *bow shock.*

C

Caelum (Cae) a small southern constellation, known as the Chisel or as the Sculptor's Tool, between Columba and Eridanus. In winter in mid-northern latitudes, it is just visible above the southern horizon. The Chisel is the tool of Sculptor, a constellation west of Eridanus. French astronomer Nicolas Louis de Lacaille (1713–1762) formed Caelum from stars between Columba and Eridanus.

caging the process of orienting and mechanically locking the spin axis of a gyro to an internal reference position.

caldera a large crater formed when part of a volcano falls into the magma chamber below the ground surface.

calendar 1. a system of reckoning time;

2. a method of determining the beginning, length, and divisions of a year and for arranging the year into days, weeks, and months. The ancient Egyptians used a calendar based on a solar year, while the Babylonians used a lunar year of twelve months.

calendar year 1. an interval of time that is the basis of a calendar;

2. the year of the Gregorian calendar—the calendar we use—which has an average of 365.2425 days.

California Nebula (IC 1499) an EMISSION NEBULA in the constellation Perseus.

Calippus a crater nineteen miles in diameter, located at +39° N and +11° E, in the northern end of the moon's Caucasus Mountains.

Callisto 1. the fourth and faintest Galilean satellite of Jupiter. Locked into a synchronous orbit, it revolves in a nearly circular orbit in the

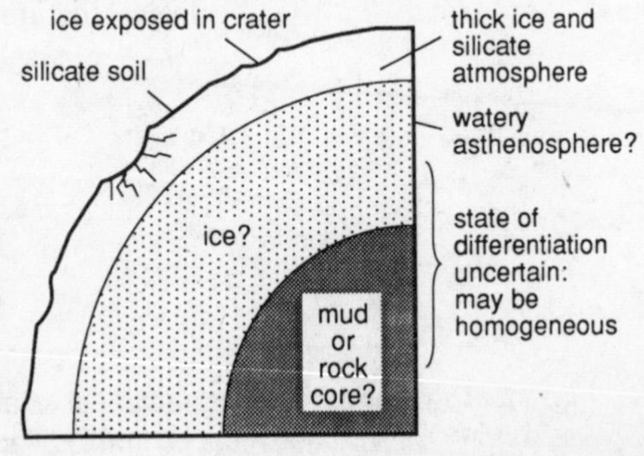

Fig. 12. **Callisto.** One of Jupiter's four largest moons (Galilean Satellite IV, also called Jupiter IV), Callisto was discovered in 1610 by Galileo. Callisto's crust is composed of ice, with rocks exposed. Its interior contains water ice and rock.

equatorial plane of Jupiter. Callisto is the second largest of the moons of Jupiter, with a diameter of 4900 km, almost identical with the diameter of the planet Mercury. Callisto, a dark moon, is covered with impact (meteorite) craters. Valhalla, the largest of these craters, has a bright central region about 370 miles in diameter. See Fig. 12.

2. in mythology, a nymph who had a love affair with Zeus and was punished by being changed into a bear and then into the stars forming the constellation URSA MAJOR.

Caloris Basin or **Caloris Planitia**, a large circular structure, latitude +22° and longitude 180°, on the illuminated hemisphere of Mercury. In photographs taken by Mariner 10, this 800-mile diameter basin appears to be a modified scar left by the impact of a space body of asteroid size.

Caloris Montes the mountainous boundary of Mercury's Caloris Basin.

Caloris Planitia see CALORIS BASIN.

Calypso a small satellite (moon) of Saturn discovered in 1980 by Pascu, Seidelman, Baum, and Currie, who were studying Voyager 1 and 2 photographs of the Saturn moon system and rings at the Jet Propulsion Laboratory, in Pasadena, California. Calypso co-orbits with TETHYS and Telesto.

Camelopardalis (Cam) also known as the Giraffe or Camelopardus, a northern constellation, introduced by the German astronomer Johannes Hevelius (1611–1687) in 1690. With no star brighter than magnitude 4, it adjoins Cassiopeia on one side, Ursa Major on the other.

Campbell, William W. (1862–1938) an American astronomer who, while serving as director of Lick Observatory, in California, discoverd 339 spectroscopic binaries. See SPECTROSCOPIC BINARY STAR.

Campo del Cielo Meteorite an Argentinian shower of large iron meteorites in 1933.

canals the name given to perceived hazy lines on the surface of Mars by the Italian astronomer Giovanni Schiaparelli (1835–1910) in 1877. They are now thought to be geological features. See VALLES MARINERIS.

Cancer (Cnc) an inconspicuous constellation in the Northern Hemisphere, near Ursa Major. One of the multiple stars is Zeta Cancri. Cancer also contains the open cluster Praesepe (M44, or the Beehive), which is visible to the naked eye; and the fainter M67, a very old open cluster. Cancer also has the strong radio source NGC 2623. The bright stars of Cancer include Alpha Cancri (Acubens), Beta Cancri (Al Tarf), and Gamma Cancri (Asellus Borealis).

Cancer, a zodiacal constellation commonly known as the Crab—*cancer* in Latin means *crab*—lies between Gemini and Leo. In legend, a crab was sent by Juno, queen of the gods, to rescue the multiheaded hydra that was locked in battle against Hercules.

Canes Venatici (CVn) the Hunting Dogs, a dim constellation in the Northern Hemisphere, near Ursa Major and Boötes. The constellation represents the dogs Asterion and Chara, which are held by the Herdsman, Boötes. Its brightest stars include Alpha Venatici (Cor Caroli, the heart of Charles), which is a 3rd magnitude binary, and Beta Venatici (Chara or Asterion). The constellation contains the bright globular cluster M3 and several galaxies, including M94 and the famous WHIRLPOOL GALAXY M51.

Canis Major (CMa) the Great Dog, a conspicuous constellation in the Southern Hemisphere, between Puppis and Orion. It contains Sirius, the bright Dog Star, which is one of the nearest stars to Earth. Its other bright stars include Adhara, Wezea, Mirzam, Aludra, and Phurad. M41 (NGC 2287), a very prominent OPEN STAR CLUSTER, lies close to Sirius.

Canis Minor (CMi) the Little Dog, a small constellation in the Northern Hemisphere, east of Orion and near Gemini. Its brightest star is the bright visual binary Procyon, which makes the Little Dog easy to identify.

Cannon, Annie J. (1863–1941) an American astronomer who made an outstanding contribution to the classification of stellar spectra. She classified more than 225,000 stars brighter than 9th or 10th magnitude.

canonical time unit for geocentric orbits the time required by a satellite to move one radian in a circular orbit of Earth's equatorial radius: 13.447052 minutes.

Canopus a conspicuous supergiant near Volans and Vela. Canopus, magnitude -0.9, is the brightest star in Carina (Carinae) and the second brightest star in the entire sky. Alpha Carinae, also called Suhel, is a yellow supergiant that lies 30 parsecs from Earth. See ERIDANUS.

Capella also called Alpha Aurigae and Alhajoth, a conspicuous yellow giant star, magnitude 0.08, that is the brightest in the northern constellation Auriga. The star's distance from Earth is 13.7 parsecs.

Caph or **Beta Cassiopeiae** the second brightest star in the northern constellation Cassiopeia. Arabian astronomers seeing the constellation as resembling a hand called it *Caph*, Arabic for hand. Caph, a white star, has an apparent magnitude of 2.4 and lies 45 light-years from Earth.

Capricorn or **Capricornus** (Cap) the Sea Goat, a zodiacal constellation in the Southern Hemisphere's so-called *sea* of the sky, along with other so-called *watery* constellations. In Greek legend, the god Pan, in order to escape the giant Typhon, leaped into the Nile River. During the leap, his head—still above water—became the head of a goat, and his immersed lower body became the rear portion of a fish, thus creating the Sea Goat. In the time of Hipparchus (2nd century BC), the sun in midwinter was in Capricorn; thus, Hipparchus gave the name *tropic of Capricorn* to the parallel of latitude at the southern limit of the sun's annual path. Capricorn's bright stars include Alpha Capricorni (Giedi, or the Goat); Beta Capricorni (Dabih, or the slaughterers); Gamma Capricorni (Nashira, or bringing good tidings); and Delta Capricorni (Deneb Algedi, or tail of the goat).

Capricornids a minor meteor shower that appears to originate in the Capricorn constellation. The shower maximizes on or about August 1.

Capricornus see CAPRICORN.

capture (in regard to a central force field, as that of a planet) to overcome by gravitational force the velocity of a passing body, for example, a meteor, and bring the body under control of the central force field, in some cases absorbing its mass.

captured rotation see SYNCHRONOUS ROTATION.

carbonaceous chondrite a rare class of meteorites that contain hydrated minerals and organic compounds.

carbon dioxide (CO_2) a colorless, odorless gas formed when carbon burns. Carbon dioxide is heavier than air and, though not toxic to humans, can cause suffocation. Plants absorb carbon dioxide during photosynthesis, while animals give it out during respiration. There is a worry that currently rising carbon dioxide levels in Earth's atmosphere may result in what is called the GREENHOUSE EFFECT, which would bring about appreciable warming of Earth's climate. The heavy atmosphere of planet Venus is about 97% carbon dioxide, compared with only .03% on Earth, and Martian air is 95% carbon dioxide gas.

carbon stars or **C stars** the rare red giant stars of low temperature whose surface composition contains more carbon than oxygen. Many stars expand when they age, and their surfaces cool, thus becoming red giants. WZ Cassiopeia is an example. Carbon stars are rare in the MILKY WAY, but common in the MAGELLANIC CLOUDS.

Carina (Car) the Keel, a star group once considered part of the southern constellation Argo Navis (the Ship Argo). The brightest star in Carina is Canopus (Alpha Carinae, or Suhel), which has a visual magnitude of -0.72. Tureis (Iota Carinae) has a visual magnitude of 2.2. Carina is associated with the magnificent Keyhole Nebula, NGC 3372. See ARGO.

Carme (Carame) Pan, a small natural satellite (moon) of Jupiter, discovered in 1938 by American astronomer Seth Nicholson (1891–1963). It has retrograde orbital motion and a diameter of 25 miles.

Casatus a lunar crater located at -72° S and -21° W, in the far southern hemisphere of the moon. It has a diameter of 65 miles.

cascade shower a group occurrence of cosmic rays, also called an *air shower*.

Cassegrain telescope also called *Cassegrainian telescope*, a reflecting telescope named after the 17th-century French physicist N. Cassegrain, who invented it in 1672. This was the second successful mirror-based telescope after Isaac Newton's.

Cassini, Giovanni Domenico (Jean Dominique) (1625–1712) an Italian-born French astronomer who made many important contributions to astronomy. For example, he discovered the four satellites of Saturn—Rhea, Iapetus, Dione, and Tethys—and later he observed the rotation of Mars and Jupiter. He described the structure of Saturn's ring and noted the famous gap in the rings of Saturn that bears his name—CASSINI'S DIVISION. Cassini was one of the first astronomers to argue that these rings were not a solid disk, but were made up of individual small moons. He also obtained Earth's distance from Mars and deduced a value for the distance from the sun (86,202,600 miles) that was far more accurate than previous estimates. He is claimed to have made the earliest systematic observation of zodiacal light.

Cassini's division a break (space) about 2500 miles wide between Saturn's rings. The division was discovered in 1675 by French astronomer Jean-Dominique CASSINI (1625–1712). It is 2500 miles wide and separates Saturn's A ring from the brighter B ring. Long thought of as being devoid of material, the well-defined rings within the Cassini division were an unexpected discovery of Voyager 1. See SATURN'S RING SYSTEM.

Cassiopeia (Cas) the Queen, a prominent northern constellation. It is visible above the horizon throughout the night. Cassiopeia is circumpolar as far south as latitude 50° north. Five bright stars in the constellation form a W-shape in the night sky. Some see in this formation the shape of a chair, thus called Cassiopeia's Chair. The stars of Cassiopeia include Schedar, Chaph, Ruchbah, Segin, and Achird. The area contains some open star clusters (M52, M103, and NGC 457), globular clusters, and the remnants of two recent supernovas—Tycho's star and the radio source Cassiopeia A. The constellation is crossed by the Milky Way.

In mythology, Cassiopeia was the wife of Cepheus, mother of Andromeda, and queen of ancient Ethiopia. In the sky she hangs in her chair head downward half of the time, as punishment for her boasting, which got Andromeda into trouble. See QUEEN.

Cassiopeia A a very strong source of radio emissions about three kiloparsecs distant in the northern constellation Cassiopeia. It may be the remnant of a supernova, probably of a supernova explosion (unrecorded) in the late 17th century. Cassiopeia A has a ring-like structure and is a source of x-rays.

Castor Alpha Geminorum, a white star and second brightest in the northern constellation Gemini. Castor is a magnitude 1.6 star and part of a visual trinary; its distance from Earth is 14 parsecs. See VISUAL TRINARY.

cataclysmic variables a group of stars that erupt. As a group these variable stars are known as CV's (see, for example, CV SERPENTIS). They include novas, supernovas, flare stars, and other erupting stars, of which some 200 are known.

Catharina Crater a lunar crater 55 miles in diameter that is located at -18° S and +24° E. The crater is in the Theophilus chain.

Caucasus Mountains a famous lunar mountain range, at +36° N and +8° E, between Mare Imbrium and Mare Serenitatis. Its peaks rise to 12,000 feet.

Ceginus Phi Boötis, a G5 type yellow star in the northern constellation Boötes. It has an apparent magnitude of 5.4.

Celaeno a bright star in the Pleiades (Beehive) star cluster. Designated as star 16 Tau in the northern constellation Cancer, Celaeno has an apparent magnitude of 5.4.

celestial pertaining to the sky.

celestial body any aggregation of matter in space constituting a unit for astronomical study—the sun, moon, a planet, comet, star, nebula, etc.

celestial coordinates coordinates that specify the position of an object on the CELESTIAL SPHERE. They are structural equivalents of the longitude and latitude coordinates of Earth. The primary great circle is the equator, whose poles are the North and South poles of Earth. Lines of equal latitude are small circles of a sphere parallel to the equator. Meridians of longitude are all great circles passing through the poles. These coordinates are fixed with respect to Earth's surface.

celestial equator a great circle on the celestial sphere located in the same plane as Earth's equatorial plane.

celestial guidance automatic celestial navigation, the process of directing movements of an aircraft or spacecraft, especially in the selection of a flight path, by reference to celestial bodies.

celestial latitude the angular distance of a heavenly body from the plane in which Earth moves around the sun.

celestial longitude the arc of the ecliptic measured eastward from the vernal equinox to the point at which the ecliptic is intersected by the great circle through the star, planet, etc. and the poles of the ecliptic.

celestial map a star chart or star map. Constellation figures appear in Egyptian royal tomb paintings from the second millennium BC and, though none has survived, star maps and globes were known to have been used in classical Greece. The earliest star chart known to have survived is in a Chinese manuscript of c.940 AD.

celestial mechanics the study of the motions and equilibria of celestial bodies subjected to mutual gravitational forces. Satellite and planetary motions, tides, precession of Earth's axis, and lunar libration are all described by these laws.

celestial meridian the great circle on the celestial sphere that passes through the north and south celestial poles. It is the projection of the observer's terrestrial meridian onto the celestial sphere.

celestial navigation a process of directing a craft from one point to another by reference to celestial bodies of known coordinates. See CELESTIAL GUIDANCE.

celestial observation in navigation the measurement of the altitude of a celestial body, or the measurement of azimuth, or measurement of both altitude and azimuth. Also called *sight*.

celestial poles intersecting points of the celestial sphere with the axis of Earth's rotation. The north celestial pole lies in Ursa Minor, near the star Polaris. See CELESTIAL SPHERE.

Celestial Police a nickname given to a team of astronomers, between 1802 and 1807, discovered three asteroids: Pallas, Juno, and Vesta.

celestial sphere an imaginary sphere of infinite diameter containing the entire universe, and on which all celestial bodies appear to be projected. The center of the celestial sphere is an observer's position on Earth. See Fig. 13.

Centaurus (Cen) an extremely large and brilliant constellation in the Southern Hemisphere near Vela and Lupus. Centaurus, one of Ptolemy's original 48 constellations, includes three star clusters: NGC 5045, an open cluster; NGC 5139, a naked-eye globular cluster; and NGC 5662, an open star cluster. It is known especially for its brightest star, Alpha Centauri, which is actually a triple star composed of Alpha Centauri, the remote 1st magnitude Beta Centauri, and Proxima Centauri.

Alpha and Beta are known as the Pointers because they indicate the direction of the Southern Cross. Alpha Centauris, which has no official proper name, though it has been called Rigel Kent or Toliman, is a splendid binary. Proxima is the nearest star to the sun. Centaurus con-

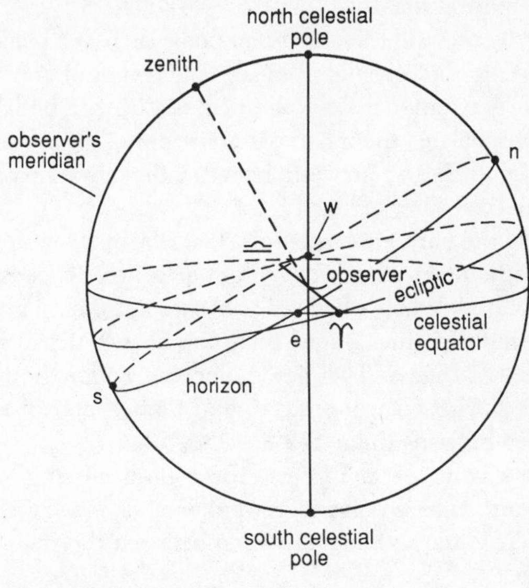

Fig. 13. **Celestial sphere.** A celestial sphere is a convenient reference structure on which to draw and study the directions of heavenly bodies in the sky. A star or other celestial body of interest may thus be thought of as a point projected on the reference circle. The principal points include the poles and the equinoxes. The observer is shown in the diagram as located at the sphere's center, with all points projected outward. The observer and Earth, for this purpose, are as one.

tains the naked-eye globular cluster Omega Centauri, the easiest to see with the naked eye in the entire sky, as well as being a strong radio source. Two bright open clusters, NGC 5460 and NGC 3766, as well as a fine planetary, NGC 3918, are found in the constellation.

Centaurus A (NGC 5128) a large radio galaxy also known as NGC 5128. The obscured nucleus of the galaxy emits a huge amount of energy at x-ray, optical, and radio wavelengths. The galaxy is located about 10 million light-years from Earth. In 1986 Robert Evans, an Australian amateur astronomer, observed a supernova in this galaxy.

Centaurus X-3 an x-ray pulsar discovered in 1971 by the UHURU satellite. In 1974 the optical companion star was identified as a 13th-magnitude supergiant. Rapid pulsation of the x-ray source at a 4.8-second period is widely interpreted as being associated with the rotation of a magnetized neutron star.

center of gravity the point in a material body, such as a planet, at which a single force may be considered to act. The center of gravity of a body in a uniform gravitational field conincides with the body's center of mass. Strictly speaking, the moon has no center of gravity, although the resultant force of Earth's gravitational attraction always passes within a few meters of the center of mass.

center of mass the barycenter, center of inertia, or the average location of mass. The point in a body or system at which we consider all the mass to be located. When a body (planet) has a center of gravity, which it does in a uniform gravitational field, the center of gravity coincides with the center of mass. Two bodies moving under the influence of their mutual gravitation will orbit around their center of mass, which lies on the line between them. See BARYCENTER.

central force a centripetal force, a force on a moving body that is directed toward a fixed point or toward a point moving according to known laws. The gravitational attraction between the sun and a planet is an example.

centrifugal force centrifugal acceleration, an inertial force that a moving body has due to its mass, which acts on the object to make it tend to continue moving in its straight path. This force is a reaction to centripetal force, acting away from the center of a circle and opposed to that force. See CENTRIPETAL FORCE.

centripetal force **1.** a force acting toward the center around which an object travels in a circular path;

2. a force, such as gravity, that causes a body to deviate from straight line motion to one along a curved path. See CENTRAL FORCE.

Cepheid variable or **cepheid**, a pulsating star with regular light variations.

Cepheid variables a large group of very luminous yellow or orange supergiants that are pulsating variable stars. These stars are so called because the first variable of this type was named Delta Cephei. They pulsate in a regular manner. Over 700 are currently known in the MILKY WAY, and several thousand in the LOCAL GROUP of galaxies.

Cepheus (Cep) the King, a constellation located in the Northern Hemisphere, near Cassiopeia. Adjoining Ursa Minor, the constellation is far to the north and is not very distinctive. Its brightest star is Alderamin (right arm). Others include Alrai (Errai, or the shepherd) and Alphirk (the flock). The constellation contains several pulsating variable stars, including the prototype Cepheid variable Delta Cephei and the red irregular variable Mu Cephei, or Garnet star.

In mythology Cepheus was the father of Andromeda and husband of Cassiopeia, with whom he ruled ancient Ethiopia. Although some people can see a man in the constellation Cepheus, most refer to it as a *lopsided house*.

Cerenkov radiation light produced by high-energy charged particles passing through a medium at a speed greater than that of light passing through the medium. When cosmic rays enter Earth's atmosphere, they produce Cerenkov radiation. It was discovered in 1934 by the Russian physicist Pavel A. Cerenkov, winner of the Nobel Prize in Physics in 1958.

Ceres the first minor planet (asteroid) discovered. It was observed in 1801 by Italian astronomer Giuseppe Piazzi (1746–1826). Later, English astronomer William Herschel (1738–1822) deduced that Ceres was a new type of body, which he called an *asteroid*. With a diameter of 636 miles, Ceres is the largest of the minor planets that orbit the sun in the asteroid belt. This dark asteroid is nearly spheroidal, and its mass makes up nearly 30% of the mass of the main asteroid belt. Radar observations show a loose powdery surface on the asteroid. Ceres is the pre-Roman goddess of agriculture.

Cetus (Cet) the Whale, an extensive but not very bright equatorial constellation located near Orion. Its brightest stars include Diphda and Menkar. Its most famous star is Mira (Omicron Ceti), a prototype long-period variable. Tau Ceti is one of the two closest stars to bear any real resemblance to the sun. It contains the spiral galaxy M77 (NGC 1068), which is visible with binoculars as a hazy spot, 16 million parsecs from Earth. The other is Epsilon Eridani. Other stars in the constellation include Menkar (Alpha Ceti, the nose); Deneb Kaitos (Beta Ceti, the tail of the whale); and Kaffaljidhma (Gamma Ceti, the head of the whale). Cetus is the sea monster of the Andromeda legend. Modern artists have drawn it as a whale, but a whale is too tame a creature for the myth.

Challenger disaster The Orbiter Challenger lifted off from Pad B, Launch Complex 39, Kennedy Space Center, at 11:37 AM on January 28, 1986. At just under 74 seconds into the flight, an explosion occurred that caused loss of the vehicle and its crew. The crew members were Francis R. Scobee, commander; Michael J. Smith, pilot; Judith A. Resnik, Ellison Onizuka, and Ronald E. McNair, mission specialists; and S. Christa McAuliffe, a New Hampshire schoolteacher, and Gregory B. Jarvis, of Hughes Aircraft, payload specialists.

The primary cargo item was the second Tracking and Data Relay Satellite (TDRS), with an attached Inertial Upper Stage (IUS) booster for the planned transfer to geosynchronous orbit. Also aboard was the Spartan, a free-flying module designed to operate independently of the orbiter and observe Halley's Comet by means of two ultraviolet spectrometers and two cameras. Several small experiments were carried in the pressurized crew compartment, including a set of lessons planned for live TV transmission by teacher Christa McAuliffe, selected as the first passenger-observer in the history of the US manned space program.

When the accident—covered live by nationwide television—occurred in view of millions of spectators, including all the students in the teacher's school back home, the entire nation was shocked, particularly because of the death of Christa, as she was known to everyone. See SPACE SHUTTLE.

Challis, James (1803–1882) English astronomer who is chiefly remembered for his part in the search for Neptune. In July 1846, he initiated a rigorous search for the planet and actually found it on August 4, though he failed to recognize its character. By the time he did, a German astronomer named Johann Galle (1812–1910) had already made the discovery, on September 23.

Chamaeleon (Cha) the Chameleon, a small inconspicuous constellation near Crux, in the southern hemisphere and very close to the south celestial pole. This constellation was noticed by 16th-century navigators, and it was first depicted by the German astronomer Johann Bayer (1572–1625) in his atlas of 1603 to fill in the far southern sky. The Chameleon, as one might expect, is sometimes depicted eating MUSCA, the Fly.

Chandler wobble the wandering of the poles, a small, continuous variation in the location of the geographic poles on Earth's surface.

Chandrasekhar limit the maximum possible mass for a white dwarf star: 1.44 solar masses. A star of greater mass will become a neutron star or a black hole, because of the force of gravity. The Chandrasekhar limit is named after its formulator, the American astrophysicist Subrahmanyan Chandrasekhar (1910–).

channels winding Martian valleys that are the result of stream erosion. They are not associated with the so-called Martian canals. Although now dry, these channels indicate that water once flowed on the planet's surface. See CANALS.

Chao Meng-Fu the south polar crater of Mercury. It has a diameter of 93 miles.

Charioteer the common name for the constellation Auriga. See AURIGA.

Charon the only known satellite of the planet Pluto, discovered in June of 1978 and named by American astronomer James W. Christy. He found Charon to have an orbital period of revolution of 6.4 Earth days at a distance of only 12,000 miles from the center of Pluto. Its diameter is about 750 miles. Charon is the most massive satellite relative to its primary planet in the solar system. It greatly exceeds the Earth-moon system ratio. Both Charon and Pluto have the appearance of large icebergs, composed mainly of water ice, with crusts of frozen methane.

We know Charon in mythology as the ferryman who carried the souls of the dead across the river Styx, but James Christy is said to have chosen the name because his wife Charlene is familiarly known as Char.

Chebyshev a crater on the far side of the moon.

Chekhov a crater north of Schubert Crater on the planet Mercury, at latitude -36° and longitude 62°, that has an inner mountain ring. Chekhov has a diameter of 112 miles.

chemical compound the combination of atoms of different elements.

chemosphere an alternative name for the *atmospheric layers* at altitudes between about 25 and 200 kilometers above Earth. Reactions involving solar radiation and atmospheric atoms and molecules occur in the chemosphere.

Chiron (Asteroid 2960) an outer minor planet, one of those discovered in 1977—another is Hidalgo—by American astronomer Charles T. Kowal. Its 50.68-year orbit lies almost entirely within the orbits of Saturn and Uranus. Chiron is comparatively large, with a diameter of 300 km. It is possible that Chiron is one of the brighter members of a distant swarm of minor planets, and it has been suggested that Chiron was once a satellite of Satrun or Uranus.

chondrite a type of stony meteorite. Chondrites are spherical bodies ranging from less than 1mm to more than 1cm. Most are completely crystalline and tough.

chromatic aberration in optics, **1.** often called a *colored halo*, the inability of a lens to bring all colors in white light to an exact point of focus; **2.** the appearance of colors in a black and white image produced by a lens.

chromosphere the layer of hot gas surrounding the photosphere of the sun. The chromosphere is visible under natural circumstances only when the photosphere is totally eclipsed by the moon. It is then seen in profile at the sun's limb. See SUN.

Chryse Planitia a vast plain region, 840 km in diameter, on Mars, located just north of the Martian equator, at latitude 19° to 30° and longitude 51° to 37°. This relatively smooth plain is 2.5 km below the average planetary surface (on Earth, below sea level). It was chosen as a landing site for the 1976 Viking I probe. The surface feature of Mars looks like a lunar MARE region. A large number of large channels converge on the Chryse Pianitia. See MADLER LAND.

cinder cone a steep-sided volcano formed by violent eruptions of lava fragments.

Circe (Asteroid 34) an asteroid having a diameter of 69 miles and a period of 4.4 years.

Circinus (Cir) the Dividers or Compass, a southern constellation near the front part of the Centaur. First figured by French astronomer Nicolas Lacaille (1713–1762), this fanciful so-called tool was to be used by Sculptor with Norma (the Square) and Caelum (the Chisel). Circinus contains no bright stars.

circular dispersion in rocketry or spacecraft, the diameter of a circle within which occur 75% of the events under study. Circular dispersion is most often used as a measure of error of the accuracy with which rockets or spacecraft reach their intended target.

circumference the distance around the curve of a circle. It is equal to *pi* times the diameter of the circle.

circumpolar constellations see CIRCUMPOLAR STAR.

circumpolar star any of a group of stars that are permanently above the-horizon—they never set. The circumpolar stars visible from mid-northern latitudes are found around Polaris, the polestar. In the northern latitudes, circumpolar stars are found in the constellations of Cassiopeia, Cepheus, Draco, Big Dipper, and Little Dipper.

cirrus high, fair weather clouds composed of ice crystals.

cislunar the region of space between Earth and our moon.

civil time clock time or mean solar time, commonly divided into two 12-hour periods.

Clavius one of the largest lunar craters, at -59° S and -15° W in the Southern Highland of the moon's south polar region. Clavius has a diameter of 140 miles.

Cleomedes a walled plain in the 3rd quadrant of the moon, broken by the crater Tralles. Cleomedes has a diameter of 78 miles.

climate the average of local temperature, precipitation, and wind conditions over a period of years.

closed ecological system a system that provides for the maintenance of life in an isolated living chamber, for example, a spacecraft cabin, by means of a cycle wherein exhaled carbon dioxide and other matter are converted chemically or by photosynthesis into oxygen, water, etc.

cluster a physical grouping of a dozen or more stars in one area of the sky. There are three types of star clusters. An *open cluster* may contain several hundred stars, usually together with gas and dust. There is no shape particular to an open cluster. One example is M6 (NGC 6405), an open cluster in Scorpius. A *globular cluster* contains thousands of stars and is regular in shape. Globular clusters are very remote, lying near the edge of the Milky Way Galaxy. One example is M2 (NGC 7089), a globular cluster in Aquarius. A *loose cluster*, also known as a *moving cluster*, is relatively nearby and is made up of widely separated stars moving through space in the same general direction. For example, 5 of the 7 bright stars in the Great Bear are members of the same loose cluster. Another example is M41 (NGC 2287), a loose cluster in Canis Major.

cluster variable see RR LYRAE STAR.

clutter atmospheric noise, extraneous signals, and the like that tend to obscure the reception of a desired signal in a radio receiver.

Coalsack the Southern Coalsack, a dark cloud in the southern constellation Crux; more properly, an opaque patch of nebulosity about 170 parsecs away. Like other clouds of dust-laden gas, the Coalsack is only seen in silhouette against the background of the Milky Way. On a dark night the Coalsack appears to be the darkest spot in the entire sky.

coaltitude another word for zenith distance, the angular distance from the zenith, that is, the arc of a vertical circle between the zenith and a point on the celestial sphere, measured from the zenith through 90°, for bodies above the horizon.

Cocoon Nebula (IC 5146) a nebula resembling a cocoon located in the northern constellation Cygnus.

Coggia's Comet (1874 III) a bright naked-eye comet with a period of 13,700, seen in 1874 and—not unexpectedly—not seen since.

coherent light light in which all the waves are vibrating in a single plane. Coherent light is the type of light produced by a laser.

colored halo see CHROMATIC ABERRATION.

Collins, Michael (1930–) an astronaut who flew on Gemini 10 and walked in space for an hour and a half during that flight. He also flew on Apollo 11, remaining in lunar orbit aboard the command module while Neil Armstrong and Buzz Aldrin took their famous walk on the moon.

Columba (Col) the Dove, a southern constellation near Canis Major and Carina. Columba's two brightest stars are Phakt and Wazn (or Wezn). The German astronomer Johann Bayer (1572–1625), in his depiction of the stars, traced Columba as a dove, an allusion to the dove that Noah sent from the Ark to find dry land.

In ancient times another constellation was called a dove, but its location is unknown today. Some mapmakers thought Argo Navis was the Ark, and so depicted Columba sitting on the stern, Puppis.

coma a luminous, spherical cloud of gas and dust around a the nucleus of a comet. Most comae are so transparent that even faint stars shine through. See COMET.

Coma Berenices or **Berenice's Hair** (Com) a dim constellation in the Northern Hemisphere near Boötes. In this direction lies the galactic north pole, and because the absorbing dust is thin we can see through it and beyond our galaxy into great depths of space. Coma Berenices consists entirely of a single open star cluster. The cluster is a group of more than 1,000 galaxies at a distance of some 368 million light-years from Earth.

The brightest star in Coma Berenices is Diadem, named for a jewel worn in Berenice's hair (see below). It is a dwarf white star, 57 light-years from Earth and of magnitude 4.32. The Black-eye Nebula (M64) is located near this region. It is a spiral galaxy 12 million light-years from Earth.

Legend has it that Berenice, daughter of the king of Cyrene, married Ptolemy Euergetes, a pharaoh of Egypt in the 3rd century BC. Her hair was famed for its beauty, so in the same century the Greek astronomer Eratosthenes called this star group *Ariadne's hair*. In Tycho's time it became a separate constellation.

Coma cluster or **Berenice's cluster** a very large group of galaxies that emit x-rays. The Coma cluster is about 350 million light-years from Earth.

Comas Sola a comet whose orbit was disturbed in 1912, when it came within 0.19 AU of Jupiter.

comet an independent mass of cosmic dust and ice that orbits the sun. A minor member of the solar system, a comet travels around the sun in an orbit that is much more eccentric than the orbit of a planet. A typical comet—often called a dirty snowball—has three parts: a nucleus, coma, and tail. More than 700 comets have been observed so far, and about six new comets are discovered each year. HALLEY'S COMET and KOHOUTEK are widely known examples.

The name *comet* derives from the Latin *cometes*, which was derived—in an allusion to a comet's tail—from the Greek *kométes* (let one's hair grow). See Appendix F for further information on comets.

cometary group a group of comets that orbit our solar system.

cometary nebulae glowing gas clouds cometlike in appearance but not related to comets. A cometary nebula is associated with a star and shines by reflecting light from that star. Two well-known cometary nebulae are the Egg Nebula and the Red Rectangle.

comet tail a stream of gas and dust that points away from the cometary nucleus and appears only when a comet is near the sun. Not all comets have tails. See COMET.

companion or **companion star** a visual binary star. See BINARY.

compression see FLATTENING.

computer today a complex, programmable electronic device used to solve problems through mathematical operations.

conjunction the position of two or more celestial bodies that reach the same celestial longitude when they make their closest approach in the sky. See Fig. 14. See also INFERIOR CONJUNCTION, PLANETARY CONJUNCTION, and SUPERIOR CONJUNCTION.

constellation 1. originally a name for a group of stars that seemed to form a configuration in the sky;

2. today the 88 recognized constellations that fill the sky. Their boundaries were established in 1928 by the International Astronomical Union. Constellations still bear the names of mythological heroes, for example, Hercules, Perseus, and Orion; of animals, for example, Draco the Dragon, Cygnus the Swan, and Leo the Lion; and of objects, for example, Libra the Scales and Corona the Crown. The movement of Earth in its orbit causes the sun, in the course of a year, to appear to move in a circle through the heavens. The 12 constellations in this apparent path (called the ecliptic) are known as the zodiacal constellations.

convection the movement of heat and matter because of differences in density, usually resulting from differences in temperature.

coordinate system a system by which the direction of a celestial body or a point in the sky can be defined and determined by two spherical coordinates. There are four main coordinate systems: the *equatorial*,

Fig. 14. **Conjunction.** Two or more planets so aligned and so close together in the sky that they are seen as one are said to be in *conjunction*.

horizontal, *ecliptic*, and *galactic* coordinate systems. They are all centered on Earth. See Fig. 15.

Copernican System a sun-centered concept of the solar system advanced by Polish astronomer Nicolas Copernicus (1473–1543). In the Copernican System the planets are considered to move in orbits around the sun. See Fig. 16.

Copernicus[1] a lunar crater famous for its bright rays. The 90-km crater, located at +10 N and -20° W, lies south of MARE IMBRIUM.

Copernicus[2] the Orbiting Astronomical Satellite OAO-3, which was used to study stellar ultraviolet radiation and x-rays. The satellite observed Cygnus X-1, a possible black hole.

Fig. 15. **Coordinate system.** See entry.

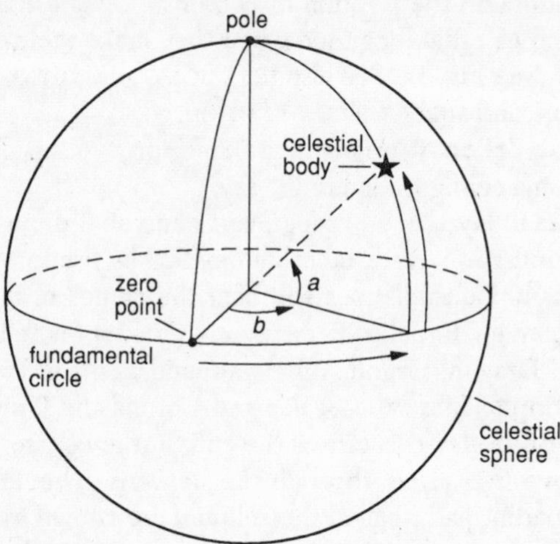

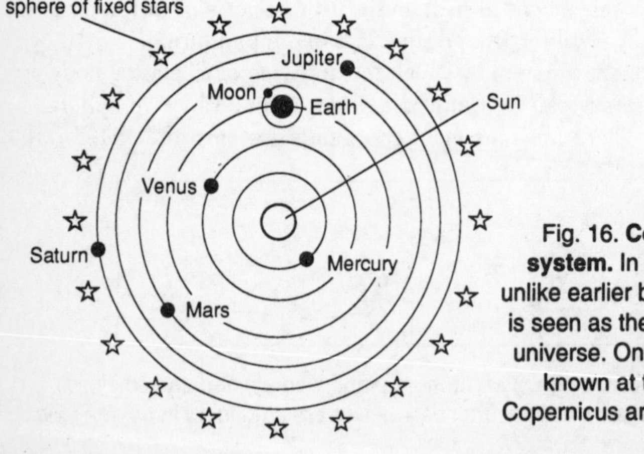

Fig. 16. **Copernican system.** In this system, unlike earlier beliefs, the sun is seen as the center of the universe. Only the planets known at the time of Copernicus are shown here.

Copernicus, Nicolas (1473–1543) Polish astronomer who described the sun as the center of a great system, with Earth and the other planets revolving about it. Modern astronomy was built on the foundation of the Copernican System.

Coprates Catena a crater-chain on Mars.

Cor Caroli also known as Alpha Canum Venaticorum, a bluish-white star—a famous magnetic variable—the brightest star in the constellation Canes Venatici. It was named Cor Caroli (heart of Charles) in honor of Charles II of England. It is a visual binary, the brighter component being the prototype of the spectrum variable stars.

core 1. the inner part of the sun, where fusion occurs;
2. the innermost part of any planet, moon, or star.

coriolis force or **coriolis effect** the deflection seen in the paths of objects moving with respect to Earth that can be attributed to the rotation of Earth.

corona the outermost layer of the sun's atmosphere. See Fig. 17.

Corona Australids a minor meteor shower that appears to radiate from the southern constellation Corona Australis and maximizes on or about March 16.

Corona Australis (CrA) also known as the Southern Crown and Corona Austrinus, a small constellation in the Southern Hemisphere, near Scorpius, but noticeable owing to its distinctive shape—a little curved line of stars. Although it contains no star above magnitude 4, its shape makes it easy to identify. The constellation contains the just-visible globular cluster NGC 6541.

In many legends Corona Australis was a crown, but Ptolemy called it a wreath, perhaps the laurel wreath worn by champions in the Greek games.

Corona Borealis (CrB) also known as the Northern Crown, a small constellation seen in the Northern Hemisphere as a semicircle of stars near Ursa Major and just east of Boötes. In Greek legend, the semicir-

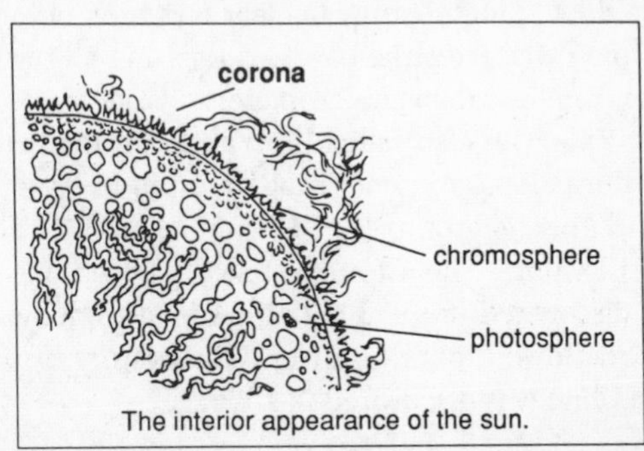

Fig. 17. **Corona.** A representation in cross section of part of the interior appearance of the sun.

cle was the legendary crown of Ariadne, daughter of King Minos of Crete, builder of the labyrinth guarded by the fearsome Minotaur. To the Arabs the semicircle was a dish or bowl; to the Native Americans, a formation of dancing girls.

The brightest star is 2nd magnitude Gemma, the *gem* in the crown. An older name is Alphecca, (meaning the bright one of the dish). Second brightest is Nusakan, a giant A8 star, 102 light-years from Earth.

coronal holes cool low-density areas of the sun's corona. They are also dark regions around the limb—the edge of the disk of the sun—during solar eclipses. They are thought to be the primary source of the enduring high-speed streams in the solar wind.

coronal lines of emission the bright emission lines observed in the spectrum of the sun's corona, consisting pf relatively slow-moving ions.

Cor Serpentis Alpha Serpentis, a K0 type star with an apparent magnitude of 2.7, in the equatorial constellation Serpens, the Serpent. The star is also known as Unuk El Haia, meaning the serpent's neck. Cor Serpentis lies 71 light-years from Earth.

Corvus (Crv) the Crow, a southern constellation, adjoining Hydra and near the star Spica. Sailors sometimes refer to the four brightest stars of Corvus, which form a quadrilateral, as the Sail. Alpha Corvi is known as Alchiba (the tent). It is a main-sequence F2 star, 63 light-years from Earth. Gamma Corvi is known as Gienah (the right wing of the raven), 450 light-years from Earth. Delta Corvi is sometimes called Algorab.

One Greek legend relates how the god Apollo sent a crow to fetch water in the god's cup. The crow delayed and, when questioned by Apollo, lied to Apollo. The angry god then placed the crow in the sky as Corvus, and next to him put the cup as Crater, from which the crow is forever forbidden to drink. Another legend says the crow was placed in the sky for telling tales.

COS-B a satellite launched by the European Space Agency in 1975 to investigate celestial objects emitting gamma rays.

cosmic dust **1.** high-energy nuclear rays from outer space;

2. fine extraterrestrial particles found in all regions of space, ranging in size from less than a micrometer to large meteoritic pieces.

cosmic Fab Four also called the Fab Four, four asteroids designated by the International Astronomical Union in honor of the members of the Beatles musical group: 4147 Lennon, 4148 McCartney, 4149 Harrison, and 4150 Starr. The asteroids, each between five and ten miles across, were discovered in 1983 and 1984 by astronomers Brian A. Skiff and Edward Bowell, of the Lowell Observatory, in Flagstaff, Arizona, at which Pluto was discovered in 1930.

cosmic rays highly charged particles, mainly protons, that travel through space at nearly the speed of light. They bombard Earth's upper atmosphere. They were discovered in 1912 by the Austrian-born American physicist Victor Francis Hess (1883–1964) during a balloon flight. With American physicist Carl Anderson (1905–), Hess won the Nobel Prize in Physics in 1936 for studies of cosmic radiation.

cosmic year the time it takes—about 225 million years—for one complete revolution of the sun around the center of the Milky Way.

cosmology the study of the origin, evolution, and structure of the universe. See UNIVERSE.

Cosmos a long series of Soviet satellites launched into orbit around Earth. The first was launched in March 1962 and the last in March 1978.

counterglow see GEGENSCHEIN.

Coxa Theta Leonis, also called Chort and Chertan, an A0 type star with an apparent magnitude of 3.4. The star is 90 light-years from Earth. Spiral galaxies M65, M66, and NGC 3628 are found just to the southeast of Theta Leonis.

Crab the common name for the CANCER constellation.

Crab Nebula a bright nebula in the northern constellation Taurus 5000 light-years away. It is considered to be a remnant of a supernova seen by Chinese and Japanese astronomers in 1054 and was visible in daylight for weeks. Chinese astronomers recorded the so-called *guest star*, or temporarily visible star, in what is now the constellation Taurus. The star whose explosion produced the Crab Nebula is now an optical pulsar (the Crab pulsar, NP 0532). The Crab pulsar is the radio source for the Crab Nebula.

Crab Pulsar see CRAB NEBULA.

crater a circular rocky formation—one of many—observed on the moon and other bodies in the solar system. There are two kinds of craters: *volcanic* and *impact* (meteorite). See IMPACT CRATER. See also Fig. 18.

Crater (Crt) a constellation known also as the Cup or the Goblet. This inconspicuous constellation is located in the Southern Hemisphere near Leo, west of Corvus and north of Hydra. Its brightest star is Alpha Crateris (Alkes or the shallow basin), a Kl type star of magnitude 4.2 that is 163 light-years from Earth.

Crepe Ring another name for Saturn's Ring C. See RINGS.

crescent phase any moon in its first or last quarter, when it appears to have one concave edge and one convex edge.

Crisium, Mare a lava-filled basin at +18° N and +58° E, close to the moon's eastern LIMB. Soil from Mare Crisium was returned by the Luna 24 spacecraft. See LUNA.

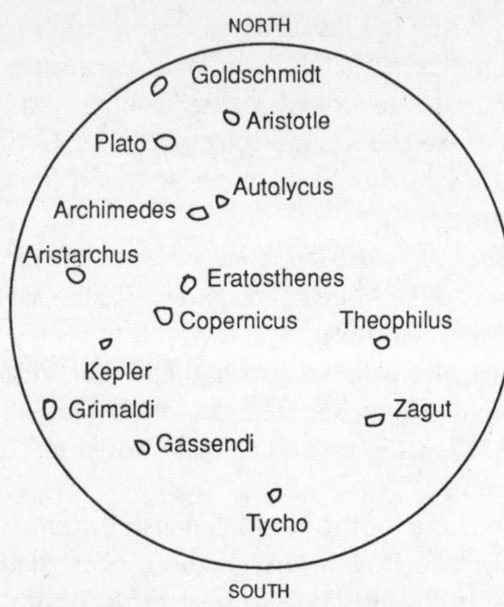

Fig. 18. **Craters on the near side of the moon.** Shown are the principal named craters that can be seen from Earth at all times.

cross-staff an ancient instrument for measuring angular distances. The instrument had two parts: a long calibrated staff and a shorter, sliding staff at right angles to it.

Crumlin meteorite a meteorite of the chondrite variety that fell in 1902 in the village of Crumlin, in County Antrim, Ireland.

Crux or **Crux Australis** also known as the Southern Cross, a small constellation located between Centaurus and Musca. Ursa Major and Crux are considered by many to be the most famous constellations. The upright part of the cross points to the south celestial pole.

While Crux is the smallest constellation in the sky, it is also one of the richest. It is noted for the Jewel Box star cluster Kappa Crucis, which is almost surrounded by Centaurus and the dark nebula of the Coal Sack. Acrux (Alpha Crucis) is its brightest star. Another well-known star in the constellation is Gacrux (Gamma Crucis), a giant M311 star of magnitude 1.64.

C stars see CARBON STARS.

culmination or **transit** the passage of a smaller body across the disk of a larger celestial body. A star will reach its greatest altitude above the horizon at upper, or superior, culmination. The other meridian passage is the lower, or inferior, culmination, when the altitude above or below the horizon will be at a minimum.

Cursa Beta Eridani, a yellow white A3 type star with an apparent magnitude of 2.9. Cursa lies 78 light-years from Earth, in the meandering southern constellation Eridanus, the River.

cusp the horn of an inferior planet when it is in the crescent phase.

CV Serpentis an eclipsing star associated with nebula E41.

Cydonia a region 890 km in diameter in the upper northern hemisphere of Mars, at latitude 30° to 43° and longitude 8° to 20°.

Cygnids a minor meteor shower that appears to originate in the Cygnus constellation and maximizes on or about August 20.

Cygnus (Cyg) often called the Swan or the Northern Cross, a constellation southwest of Draco that is one of the best-known northern constellations. The three brightest stars are Deneb (Alpha Cygni: the tail, or top, of the Northern Cross, a very luminous supergiant); Albireo (Beta Cygni: a glorious double with a golden-yellow primary and a blue companion); and Sadr (Gamma Cygni: called the hen's breast). The star also contains the red Mira variable Chi. Gienah, Epsilon Cygni, is also worthy of note. Gienah, called the wing, must not be confused with Gamma Crv, which is also called Gienah. The star 61 Cygni was the first to have its distance measured. Cygnus contains M39 (NGC 7092), an open star cluster; NGC 7000, the North American Nebula; and the nebula NGC 6992.

In Roman mythology Cygnus was the swan (Jupiter in disguise) that wooed Leda. Their offspring were Castor and Pollux, Clytemnestra, and Helen of Troy. Arabian astronomers saw these stars as forming an eagle.

Cygnus A an extragalactic radio source in the constellation Cygnus.

Cygnus Loop also known as the Veil Nebula, an emission nebula in the northern constellation Cygnus.

Cygnus X-l an intense x-ray source, considered to contain a black hole. See BLACK HOLE.

Cyrillus an apparently old lunar crater 60 miles in diameter, at -13° S and +24° E, just southwest of Theophilus Crater. The highest point on the crater wall is 8200 feet.

Cytherean **1.** in astronomy, referring to the planet Venus; preferred to *Venusian*;

2. in mythology, of or pertaining to Cytherea, or Aphrodite. Cytherea was so named because she was born in the sea near Cythera, an island in the Mediterranean.

D

Dabih Beta Capricorni, in the equatorial region of the southern hemisphere of Capricornus constellation, a G0 type, yellow star with an apparent magnitude of 3.2.

Daedalus a large crater located on the far side of the moon.

dark halo crater a small lunar crater produced when an impacting meteorite excavates dark surface materials, yielding a dark, shadowed residue area ringing the crater.

dark matter the undetected matter that some astronomers believe makes up the missing mass of the universe.

dark nebula or **absorption nebula**, a dense cloud of interstellar gas and dust that silhouettes objects lying behind it. Examples are COALSACK, HORSEHEAD NEBULA (Rho Ophiuchi), and the Great Rift, in the Milky Way between Cygnus and Sagittarius.

D'Arrest, Heinrich Louis (1822–1875) German astronomer who worked with Galle in 1846. D'Arrest discovered three comets and one asteroid.

D'Arrest's Comet the faint comet discovered in 1851 by German astronomer Heinrich Louis D'Arrest, discoverer of numerous comets and nebulas. D'Arrest's Comet, with a period of 6.4 years, has been seen at 14 returns, including that of 1892, the year in which American astronomer Edward E. Barnard discovered Amalthea, Saturn's fifth moon. When D'Arrest's Comet appeared in 1976, it made a close approach to Earth and could be observed with the naked eye.

data acquisition the receiving and recording of basic parameters, which are telemetered from a space vehicle while in flight.

Davida (Asteroid 511) the seventh largest asteroid of the regular asteroid swarm, with a diameter of 200 miles. It has a magnitude at opposition of 10.5 and a revolution period of 5.7 years. It was discovered in 1903.

Davy Chain a prominent crater chain at -12° S and -8° W on the moon.

day the period (duration) of a planet's rotation on its axis. Earth has a day measuring 23 hours, 56 minutes, and 4 seconds. Jupiter's day is 9 hours and 56 minutes.

De Cheseaux's Comet a brilliant multitailed comet seen in 1744. It was discovered by two astronomers, on December 9 by Klinkenberg, on December 13 by de Cheseaux. The comet reached apparent magnitude -7.

declination a coordinate used on the celestial sphere in the same manner that latitude is used on Earth. An object's declination is measured from the celestial equator, positive to the north and negative to the south.

Deep Space Network (DSN) a communications network managed by the Jet Propulsion Laboratory, at Goldstone, California, for command and control of all planetary flights.

deferent in Ptolemaic astronomy a circle with Earth as its center, around which moves the center of a smaller circle, which is the orbit of a planet. The smaller circle is called an *epicycle*. See Fig. 19.

deflection of starlight 1. the bending of light as it passes close to a massive object;

2. any bending due to gravity.

degenerate matter extremely high-density matter in which, due to quantum mechanical effects, pressure no longer depends on temperature.

degenerate star a star composed mainly of degenerate matter. Two examples are a white dwarf and a neutron star.

Deimos a satellite (moon) of Mars that orbits farther from Mars than its companion moon Phobos. It is an irregular body measuring 11 × 12 × 15 km, and is locked into a synchronous rotation above Mars' equator at a distance of 23,490 km from the center of the planet in a period of 1.26 days. As a result, the moon would appear almost stationary to an observer standing on the surface of Mars. The dark surface, which is composed of carbonaceous chondritic material similar to some asteroids, has two large craters, Voltaire and Swift, which measure only about 2 km across.

Delambre a 32-mile diameter lunar crater located at -2° S and +18° E, in the area of Mare Tranquillitatis, the landing site of Apollo 11 in 1969.

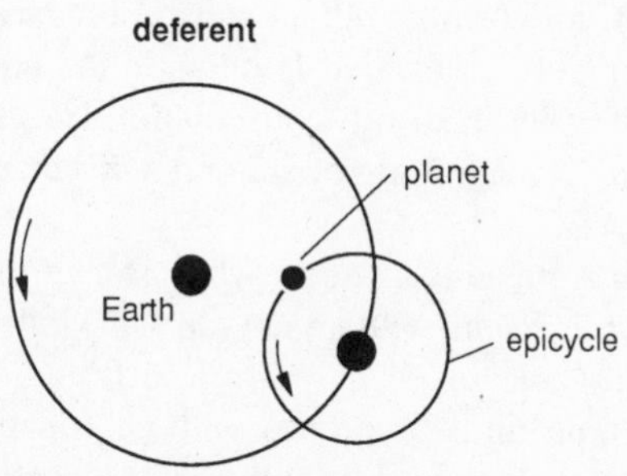

Fig. 19. **Deferent.** See entry.

de la Rue, Warren (1815–1889) British astronomer and physicist who studied the sun, mainly its sunspots and prominences. He invented the photoheliograph and pioneered celestial photography.

Delphinus (Del) the Dolphin, a small constellation in the Northern Hemisphere, between Aquila and Pegasus, near Cygnus. In Greek legend, Delphinus saved the life of the poet-minstrel Arion, who had leaped overboard from a ship to escape ruffian-sailors. Alpha Delphini (Sualocin) and Beta Delphini (Rotanev) were named in 1814 by whimsical astronomers at Italy's Palermo Observatory.

The names Sualocin and Rotanev—the reverse of Nicolaus and Venator—were formed by first rendering the name of one of the astronomers in Latin and then reversing the letters. The astronomer's name, Niccolo Cacciatore, was Latinized as Nicolaus Venator, since the Italian word *cacciatore* and the Latin word *venator* mean hunter. This complicated procedure yielded the common names Sualocin and Rotanev for the stars Alpha Delphini and Beta Delphini. See ROTANEV.

Delta a NASA rocket used for launching intermediate-size spacecraft into Earth orbit.

Delta Aquarids an annual meteor shower seen near the constellation Aquarius, in the equatorial region of the Southern Hemisphere. The shower has a maximum of 30 to 40 meteors seen per hour on or about July 27.

Delta Scuti stars a class of PULSATING VARIABLES.

Demon Star see ALGOL.

Deneb Alpha Cygni, also known as Arided, a brilliant white supergiant of the A2 star type. It is the brightest star in the constellation Cygnus and lies at one end of the long arm of the Northern Cross. Deneb is 540 light-years from Earth and has an apparent magnitude of 1.3.

Deneb Algedi Delta Capricorni, also known as Scheddi, a white star in the constellation Capricornus, with an apparent magnitude of 3.0.

Deneb Kaitos Beta Ceti, also called Diphda, in the equatorial region of the southern hemisphere, in the constellation Cetus. It is an orange star with an apparent magnitude of 2.2 and a distance of 57 light-years from Earth.

Deneb Okab Delta Aquilae is a yellow white star in the tail of the constellation Aquila, the Eagle, with an apparent magnitude of 3.4. Deneb Okab means eagle's tail.

Denebola Beta Leonis, an A2-type star with an apparent magnitude of 2.2. This white star is the third-brightest in the northern constellation Leo, the Lion. Denebola, which means lion's tail, lies at a distance of 43 light-years from Earth.

density the mass per unit of volume of a body of material.

density wave theory a theory proposed to account for spiral arms as compressions of the interstellar medium in the accretion disk of the galaxy.

deployment the process of removing a payload from a stowed or berthed position in a cargo bay and releasing the payload to a position free of the spacecraft (shuttle or orbiter).

depressed lowlands a topographic feature of the surface of Venus lying below the planet's average plain, which covers about 27% of the surface. The most extensive lowland region, Atalanta Planitia, is about as large as the Gulf of Mexico, on Earth.

depressed pole the celestial pole below the horizon.

Descartes a lunar crater, -12° S and +17 E, 31 miles in diameter. Descartes lies in a heavily cratered area southwest of Mare Tranquillitatis.

descending node the orbital point at which a celestial body crosses to the south of the ecliptic.

Diadem the brightest star in the northern constellation Coma Berenices. It is a yellow white star with an apparent magnitude of 5.2. See COMA BERENICES.

diameter a straight line passing through the center of a circle or sphere, going from one side to the other.

diamond ring effect during a total solar eclipse the momentary appearance of a spot of photosphere at the edge of the moon, producing a brilliant glare set in the silvery ring of the corona.

Diana Chasma the fracture on Venus, at -15° S and 150° E, in the Aphrodite Terra region of the southern hemisphere. The lowest point on the planet, Diana Chasma extends 2000 km (6600 feet) below the average surface of Venus.

dichotomy the half-phase of the moon point or of an inferior planet. See INFERIOR PLANET.

differential rotation the rotation of a celestial body in which different parts of the body have different periods of rotation. This is true of the sun, the Jovian planets (moons of Jupiter), and the disk of our galaxy.

differentiation the separation of planetary material according to density.

diffraction the spreading of light as it passes an object or passes through a small opening.

diffraction grating a system of finely ruled lines that diffract light and, by interference, produce a spectrum.

diffuse nebula 1. a bright or dark nebula of irregular shape but not of the planetary form;

2. any luminous cloud of gas in space.

Dione a satellite (moon) of Saturn that looks similar to RHEA. Its icy surface is covered with craters and a system of valleys. Dione, 696 miles across, is 234,500 miles from Saturn. It has a density of 1.4 g/cm^3, which is greater than the densities of all the other moons of Saturn except Titan and Phoebe. Dione was discovered in 1684 by French astronomer César François Cassini (1714–1784), who served as director of the Paris Observatory.

Dione was photographed during the Voyager flybys of 1980 and 1981. The encounter revealed evidence of craters in the range of 18–25 miles and some large craters 100 miles in diameter. Dione's most striking feature is a white spot named Amata, a crater 150 miles across.

Dionsysius a brilliant lunar crater located at +3° N and +17° E, on the edge of the MARE TRANQUILLITATIS, the landing site of Apollo 11 in 1969. The crater has a diameter of 12 miles.

Diphda see DENEB KAITOS.

direct motion the typical west-to-east motion of a planet as seen from Earth against the background of stars.

dirty snowball theory the theory holding that the nuclei of comets are kilometer-sized chunks of ice with embedded silicates traveling in long elliptical orbits around the sun. See WHIPPLE.

Discoverer a series of unmanned United States Air Force polar-orbiting satellites that employed Thor-Agena rockets to place research payloads into orbit. Once in orbit, the payload ejects a small capsule that can be snatched by an aircraft while the payload parachutes down after reentering Earth's atmosphere. Since Discoverer launches were made in secret from Vandenberg Air Force Base, details are no longer issued. It is known, however, that Discoverer 13 in 1960 ejected a 300-pound capsule over the Pacific Ocean, which became the first manufactured object ever recovered from space.

Discovery Rupes a mountain ridge on Mercury at latitude -54° and longitude 38°, south of Schubert Crater in the southern hemisphere.

disk 1. the round shape of a planet as seen in a telescope;

2. the flattened portion of a spiral galaxy, for example, the Milky Way, hence the disk's spiral arms.

distance indicator any object in space whose luminosity or diameter is known and thus can be used to find the distance to a star cluster or galaxy.

distance modulus 1. the measure of the distance to an object;

2. the difference between apparent magnitude and absolute magnitude of a star or galaxy.

diurnal having a period of, occurring in, or related to a day.

diurnal circle the apparent path of an object in the sky during one day, due to Earth's rotation.

diurnal motion the daily apparent motion of all celestial objects, due to Earth's rotation.

Di Vico-Swift Comet a short-period comet that was discovered in 1844 by Italian astronomer Francisco Di Vico (1805–1848).

docking a procedure for the locking together of two spacecraft in space following their rendezvous.

dogleg a directional turn made in a launch trajectory to produce a more favorable orbital inclination than was originally set.

Dog Star the common name for Sirius, which is the brightest star in the sky. It lies in the southern constellation Canis Major, the Great Dog, in the mouth of the Dog, near Puppis and Lepus.

Dolphin the common name for DELPHINUS.

dome any small, low, rounded protuberance on the lunar surface.

Donati, Giambattista (1826–1873) Italian astronomer, director of the observatory of Florence, who discovered 5 comets and, in 1864, recognized that the tails of comets consisted of gases. See DONATI'S COMET.

Donati's Comet a comet first located by Giambattista Donati on June 2, 1858. The comet is famous for its multiple haloes. While orbiting the sun—it is called a sun-grazer because at perihelion it approaches within 0.578 AU of the sun—it developed a long curved tail and a bright nucleus.

Doppler, Christian Johann (1803–1853) Austrian physicist who described in 1842 the priniciple now called the DOPPLER EFFECT.

Doppler effect or **Doppler shift** the change in observed wavelength of sound, radio, or light, due to the motion of the source, the observer, or both.

Dorado (Dor) the Swordfish, a small southern constellation lying between Pictor and Reticulum. The system contains part of the Large Cloud of Magellan (a satellite galaxy of the Milky Way) and the magnificent Tarantula Nebula (Great Looped Nebula). *Dorado* is Spanish for fish dolphin. See LARGE MAGELLANIC CLOUD.

double galaxy method a method of finding the masses of galaxies from orbiting pairs of galaxies.

double-lobed radio galaxy a galaxy that emits radio energy from two regions (lobes) located on opposite sides of the galaxy.

double star a star system that is composed of two stars, each influenced by the other's gravitational field. The dual nature of a double star is revealed by telescopic or spectroscopic observation. See BINARY.

DQ Herculis a remnant of Nova Herculis, which rose to first magnitude in 1934. This 14th-magnitude variable star, 1200 light-years from Earth, is classified as an ECLIPSING BINARY.

Draco (Dra) the Dragon, a north celestial pole constellation recalling the dragon slain by Cadmus. Draco lies between Ursa Major and Ursa Minor. Its head is near Vega in Lyra. Draco is the radiant point for the Draconid meteor showers. Alpha Draconis, also called Thuban, used to be the north pole star in ancient times (1750 BC). Beta Draconis, also called Rastaban, is called the *dragon's head*. Gamma Draconis, also called Eltanin and also known as the dragon's head, is the brightest star in the constellation, magnitude 2.22. Delta Draconis, also called Nodus II, is identified as the second *knot*, or *loop*, of the dragon's body. Zeta Draconis, or Nodus I, is the first knot, or loop. Lambda Draconis, or Giansar, means *central one*. Mu Draconis, or Arrakis, means the *danger*.

Legend has it that during the war between the gods and the Titans, the goddess Minerva fought a dragon and hurled it into the sky, where the dragon became wrapped around the north celestial pole.

Draconid meteor shower an October meteor shower that tends to be insignificant, in most years occurring rarely and lasting only a few hours. The Head of Draco is the radiant point for the shower, which occurs on or about October 10. Also known as Giacobinid meteors, this shower is associated with the GIACOBINI-ZINNER COMET.

D ring the innermost part of Saturn's ring system. See SATURN'S RING SYSTEM.

Dschubba Delta Scorpii, a blue white star with an apparent magnitude of 2.5, in the southern constellation Scorpion. This star lies at a distance of 590 light-years from Earth.

Dubhe Alpha Ursae Majoris, an orange yellow giant found in the top of the northern constellation Ursa Major, the Great Bear. The brighter of the POINTERS to the pole star, Dubhe has an apparent magnitude of 1.9 and is 105 light-years distant from Earth.

Dumbbell nebula Messier 27 and M27 in the northern constellation Vulpecula. The planetary nebula was so named by Irish astronomer William Parsons, third Earl of Rosse (1800–1867), who first observed its dumbbell or hourglass shape. Parsons in 1845 built the most powerful and fully steerable telescope of his time. The instrument was sometimes referred to as the Leviathan.

Dundrum meteorite a four-pound meteorite that fell in Dundrum Bay, Ireland, in 1865.

Dunham, Theodore (1897–1984) American astronomer who, in 1932, first made spectroscopic detections of carbon dioxide in the atmosphere of Venus and detected methane and ammonia in Saturn's atmosphere.

dust clouds clouds of interstellar dust. See DARK NEBULAE.

dwarf see DWARF STAR.

dwarf galaxy a small galaxy, such as the Magellanic clouds.

dwarf star a star of less than average mass and luminosity. Dwarf stars are the most common stars in our galaxy.

dynamo effect the theory that Earth's magnetic field is generated in the conducting material of its molten core.

Dziban Psi Draconis, a yellow white star with an apparent magnitude of 4.9, found in the northern constellation Draco, the Dragon.

E

Eagle the common name for AQUILA.

Eagle Nebula (M16) a large emission nebula located 2.5 kiloparsecs from Earth, within the constellation Serpens. The Eagle Nebula contains some hot young stars that are part of an open cluster.

Earth the third planet of the solar system. Earth is the largest of the four terrestrial planets and has the moon as its satellite. The planet lies an average of 93 million miles from the sun, around which it circles in 365.25 days, speeding along its orbital path at more than 67,000 miles an hour. It rotates—makes a complete spin on its axis—every 24 hours. Earth's axis is tilted 23.5248° with respect to the plane of its orbit around the sun.

earthcrossers see EARTHGRAZERS.

earth current a large-scale surge of electric charge within Earth's crust, associated with a disturbance of the ionosphere. Current patterns are closely related to solar-induced variations in the extreme upper atmosphere.

earthgrazers or **earthcrossers** the Earth-crossing asteroids, including Adonis, Atan, Hermes, and Icarus. All have orbits that can bring them within about 0.1 AU (15 million kilometers) of Earth. See Fig. 20.

earthlight see EARTHSHINE.

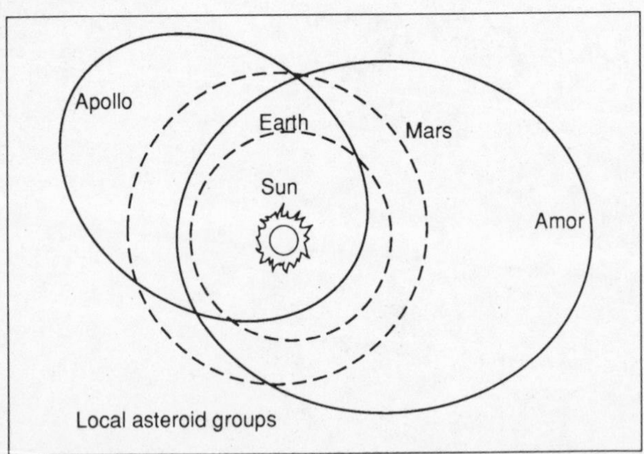

Fig. 20. **Earthgrazers.** The idea that minor planets can be characterized as earthgrazers when they are really quite far from Earth is an effective reminder of how vast astronomical space truly is.

earthquake or **quake** a release of stresses that have been stored within Earth's crust, the release producing a movement of the crust.

earth satellite a body that orbits about Earth, specifically, an artificial satellite.

earthshine or **earthlight** light that is reflected by Earth's atmosphere and which illuminates the dark portion of the moon.

eccentric a point within a circle, but off-center.

eccentricity a measure of the elongation of an ellipse. It is computed by dividing the distance between the foci of an ellipse by the length of its major axis.

Echo an early type of United States passive communications satellite. It was essentially a huge inflatable balloon that reflected radio waves from one ground station to another. Echo I was launched in 1964; Echo II, in 1964.

eclipse 1. the total or partial obscuration of light from a celestial body;
2. a reduction in visibility or disappearance of a nonluminous body by passing into the shadow cast by another nonluminous body;
3. a solar or lunar eclipse. See Fig. 21.

eclipse path the path on Earth's surface swept out by the shadow of the moon during a total eclipse of the sun.

eclipsing binary a binary-star system in which the plane of revolution of the two stars is seen almost edge-on. The light of each star is periodically diminished by passage of the other star in front of it.

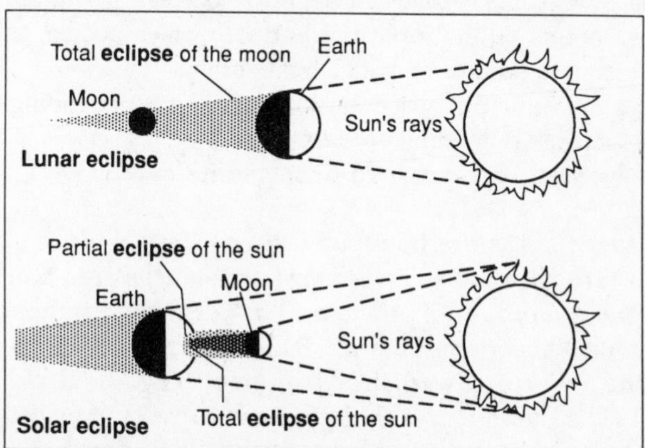

Fig. 21. **Eclipse.** Because the moon is much smaller than Earth, only a portion of Earth's surface, rather than all of it, is affected at any time during a solar eclipse. For the same reason, during a lunar eclipse, the entire moon is obscured at the height of the eclipse.

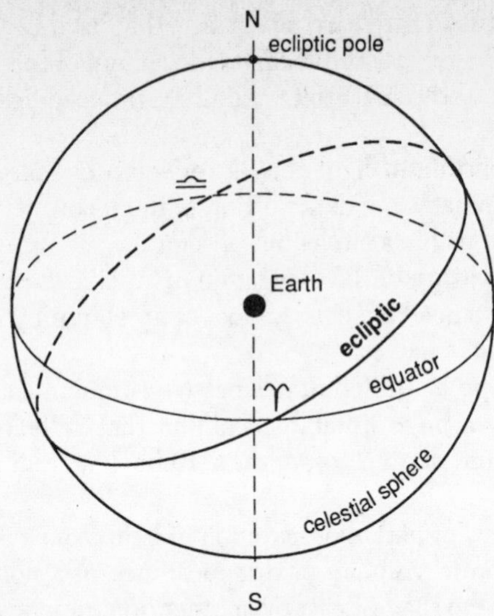

Fig. 22. **Ecliptic.** The ecliptic is the great circle formed by the intersection of the plane of Earth's orbit with the celestial sphere.

ecliptic 1. the plane of Earth's orbit projected onto the sky. See Fig. 22. **2.** the apparent path of the sun among the stars.

ecological system a habitable environment, either (a) created artificially, as in a manned space vehicle, or (b) occurring naturally, such as the environment on the surface of Earth, in which people, animals, or other organisms can live in mutual relationship.

ecosphere the volume of space surrounding the sun, extending from the orbit of Venus past the orbit of Mars.

ejecta pulverized rock scattered by meteorite impacts on a planetary surface.

Ekman layer the layer of transition between Earth's surface boundary layer, where shearing stress is constant, and the free atmosphere, where the atmosphere is treated as an ideal fluid in approximate geostrophic equilibrium. Both the Ekman layer and the Ekman spiral were the work of Swedish astronomer Vagn Walfrid Ekman (1874–1954), known for his work on ocean currents produced by wind friction. See EKMAN SPIRAL and GEOSTROPHIC WIND LEVEL.

Ekman spiral an idealized mathematical description of the wind distribution in the planetary boundary layer of Earth's atmosphere, within which Earth's surface has an appreciable effect on air motion. See EKMAN LAYER.

Elara a small satellite (moon) of Jupiter, discovered in 1905 by American astronomer Charles Dillon Perrine (1878–1951), who discovered several comets and Jupiter's moon Nimalia. He also published a star catalog.

Electra the common name for the star 17 Tau, apparent magnitude 3.8, found in the northern constellation Taurus. Electra is one of the PLEIADES.

electromagnetic radiation 1. a flow of energy;

2. a disturbance that is transmitted from its source to the observer by means of changing electrical and magnetic fields. Light is the most familiar form of such radiation; other forms include radio, TV, infrared, ultriviolet, x-rays, cosmic, gamma rays, and alpha rays.

electromagnetic spectrum the full array of electromagnetic disturbances—radio, infrared, visible light, ultraviolet, x-rays, gamma rays, etc. See Fig. 23.

electron a subatomic particle that carries a negative charge and is thought to move about the nucleus of an atom.

electrostatic engine see ION ENGINE.

elements of an orbit or **orbital elements**, the particular quantities that describe the size, shape, and orientation of the orbit of a body in space. Such quantities are used to determine the location of the body at any given time.

elevated pole the celestial pole above the observer's horizon.

Elliot, James the American astronomer who led the research team that discovered the rings of Uranus in 1977. His group, flying aboard a specially modified NASA aircraft, the KAO (Kuiper Airborne Observatory), observed an occultation of a faint star by the planet Uranus. This

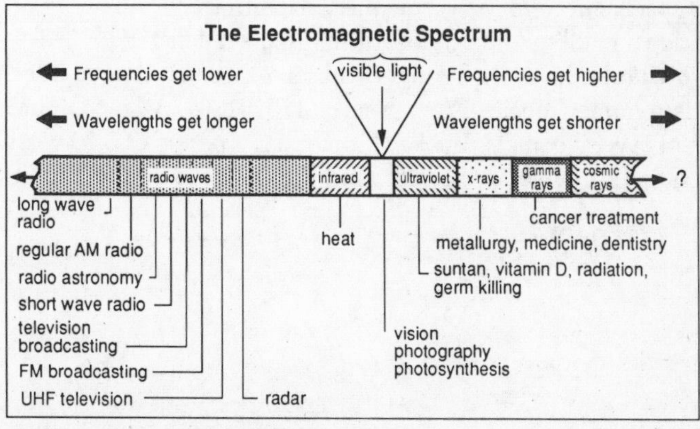

Fig. 23. **Electromagnetic spectrum.** See entry.

led to the realization that the rings of Uranus were temporarily cutting off the light of the faint star.

ellipse 1. a closed curve obtained by passing a plane completely through a circular cone;

2. a curve (elliptical orbit) that describes the orbits of bodies in space.

ellipsoid see SPHEROID.

ellipsoid of revolution see SPHEROID.

elliptical galaxy a galaxy whose visible shape forms an ellipse. A galaxy that is round or elliptical in outline contains little gas and dust, no disk or spiral arms, and few hot, bright stars. Examples of elliptical galaxies are M49 (NGC 4472) in Virgo, M59 (NGC 4621) in Virgo, and M105 (NGC 3379) in Leo.

elongation the apparent angle, measured at the Earth observer's eye, between the sun and a specified object. The elongation of Mercury is 14° when it appears in the sky 14° from the sun. See Fig. 24.

Eltanin another name for the orange star Gamma Draconis, also called the *dragon's head*. Eltanin is the brightest star in the Draco constellation. It is of magnitude 2.22 at 117 light-years from Earth.

Elysium Planitia a center of volcanic activity, at latitude -10° to 30° and longitude 180° to 260°, on an elevated Martian plain about 2000 km in diameter. Its main volcano is Elysium Mons, which is 15 km high.

emission nebula a bright cloud of gas that has been excited and is producing its own light. Some examples are the Orion Nebula, Crab Nebula, Ring Nebula, and the Cygnus Loop. See NEBULA.

EMU *abbreviation for e*xtravehicular *m*obility *u*nit, a suit worn by United States Space Shuttle astronauts while performing an extravehicular activity. An EMU includes all the equipment needed for working outside a spacecraft or for exploring the lunar surface.

Enceladus a satellite (moon) of Saturn, discovered in 1789.

Encke's Comet the most frequently observed comet, named after German astronomer Johann Franz Encke (1791–1865), who computed the orbits of several comets. Encke's Comet has a period of 3.30 years, one of the shortest cometary periods, and is thought to be the parent body

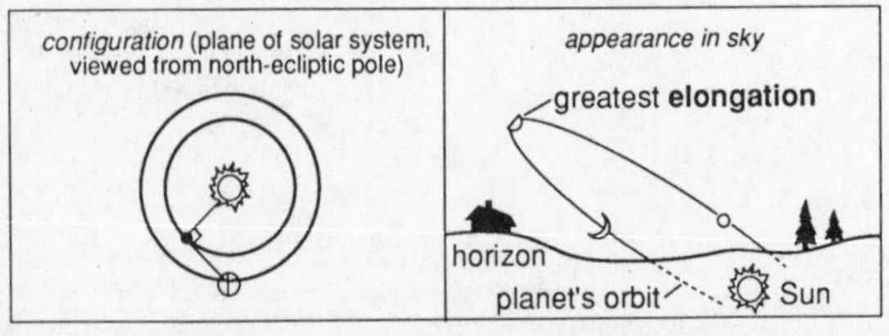

Fig. 24. **Elongation.** See entry.

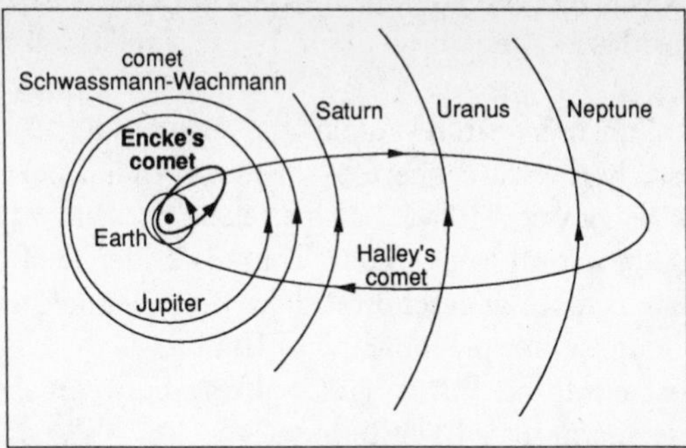

Fig. 25. **Encke's Comet.** The orbits of several comets are shown here to illustrate the shortness of the period of Encke's Comet, which intersects Earth's orbit, but not the orbits of other planets.

of the Taurid meteor stream. Encke is one of the prime candidates for a spacecraft investigation of a comet. See Fig. 25.

endocrater any craterlike depression attributed to a force other than that of impact.

energy the ability to do work, for changing the state of another body or system.

energy transport the flow of energy from hot regions to cooler regions by conduction, convection, or radiation.

Enif a common name, meaning the nose, for the orange red supergiant star Epsilon Pegasus. Enif has a magnitude of 2.38 and lies 780 light-years from Earth.

eon see AEON.

ephemeris **1.** a table showing the positions of a celestial body on various dates in a regular sequence;

2. an astronomical almanac containing such tables.

epicycle in the Ptolemaic system, a small circle, the center of which moves along the deferent. Since a planet moves on the epicycle, the motion of the planet may be described as a circle moving on a circle. See DEFERENT.

epoch **1.** an arbitrarily fixed instant of time that is used as a fixed reference datum, especially for stellar coordinates and orbital elements;

2. the mean longitude of a planet as seen from the sun at a fixed instant of time.

Epsilon Aurigae an eclipsing binary star. It consists of an extremely luminous white supergiant about 30 times the mass of our sun and an invisible secondary star. The variability of Epsilon Aurigae was first observed in 1821, by German astronomer J. Fritsch. The invisible secondary is considered likely to be identified as a collapsed star, possibly a black hole.

Epsilon Eridani an orange red double star, magnitude 3.73, one of the nearest—possibly the third-nearest—of the so-called naked-eye stars, stars that can be viewed without using a telescope. Only Alpha Centauris and Sirius are known to be closer. There is evidence of one or more associated planets, but the exact orbits have not been determined.

epsilon ring the most conspicuous ring of Uranus.

equator a great circle on Earth lying halfway between the poles. All points on the equator have 0° latitude.

equatorial bulge the excess of Earth's equatorial diameter compared with the polar diameter. See Fig. 26.

equatorial satellite a satellite whose orbital plane coincides, or almost coincides, with Earth's equatorial plane.

equinox either of the two intersection points of the celestial equator and the ecliptic, occurring at the two times of the year when day and night are of equal length throughout the world. Equinoxes occur in the Northern Hemisphere when the sun lies exactly above the equator: in spring (the vernal equinox) on or about March 21, and in autumn (the autumnal equinox) on or about September 23. See Fig. 27.

Equuleus (Equ) the Colt, a small northern constellation between Delphinus and Aquarius. This group of stars is associated with Celeris, the brother of Pegasus.

Erakis the common name for the star Mu Cephei, in the northern consteallion Cepheus. Erakis is an M2 type variable star.

Eratosthenes (275?–195? BC) Greek geographer, astronomer, and mathematician living in ancient Egypt who first gave proof of Earth's size.

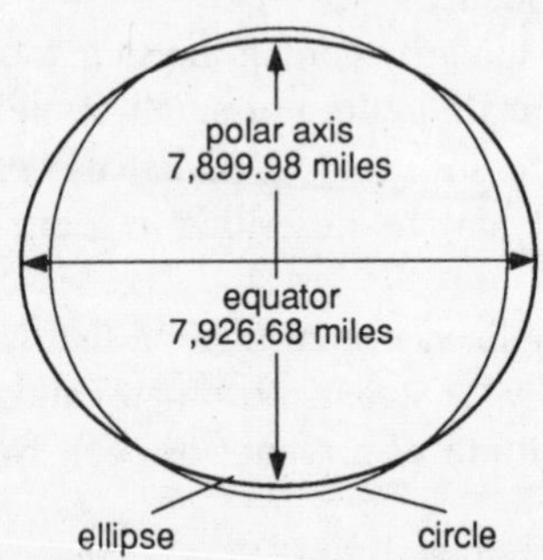

Fig. 26. **Equatorial bulge.** This figure shows that Earth does not form a perfect sphere.

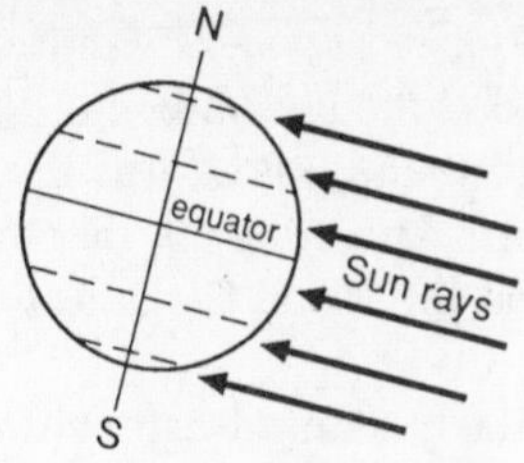

Fig. 27. **Equinox.** The apparent path traced out by the sun on the celestial sphere is known as the *ecliptic.* It is inclined 23° 27' with Earth's (or the celestial) equator. The points of intersection of the two orbits are called *equinoxes.*

By careful observations and simple arithmetic, Eratosthenes computed the circumference of Earth. See Fig. 28.

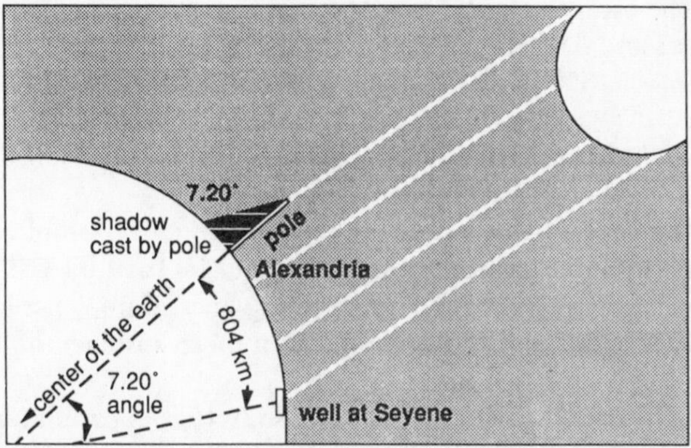

Fig. 28. **Eratosthenes' method.** Eratosthenes was told that at noon at the summer solstice, the sun had cast no shadow at the site of a well in Syene, far south from Alexandria. At the same time, he observed from the shadow cast by a pole that the sun was 7.2° from the zenith in Alexandria. This meant that Earth curved between the well and the pole. Since Eratosthenes knew the distance between Syene and Alexandria, he was able to compute how far it would take the curvature of Earth to continue all the way around Earth. The distance turned out to be 25,000 miles, giving him the circumference of Earth.

Eridanus (Eri) the River, also called Eridani, a large river-like constellation in the Southern Hemisphere—Achernar is its brightest star—meandering from the foot of Orion to near Tucana.

Early writers appear to have looked upon Eridanus as a river, flowing into the ocean that surrounded the known world. Virgil called Eridanus "the king of rivers." Eratosthenes said it was the Nile, "the only river that runs from south to north," pointing out that the star Canopus lay at the end of Eridanus, just as the island Canopus lies at the mouth of the Nile.

Eros (Asteroid 433) an irregularly shaped asteroid discovered by astronomer G. Witt, working in Berlin, Germany, in August of 1898. At that time there were proposals to discontinue further attention to the rapidly growing number of asteroid discoveries brought about by the introduction of photography. Eros is a member of the Amor group. The asteroid, 22 miles long, passes near Earth every 44 years. In 1975 it came within 23.5 million kilometers of Earth.

ESA see EUROPEAN SPACE AGENCY.

escape orbit see OPEN ORBIT.

escape velocity or **escape speed** the minimum velocity required for an object such as a spacecraft to leave a celestial body, such as a planet or moon. The escape velocities of all planets and moons vary according to their mass and diameter. The escape velocity for Earth is 25,000 mph; for the moon, 5300 mph; for Jupiter, 140,000 mph. See VELOCITY OF ESCAPE.

Etamin another name for Eltanin, a star in the Draco constellation. See ELTANIN.

Europa the second and largest of Jupiter's moons, one of the four Galilean satellites. Europa was discovered in 1610 by Galileo. Its smooth surface is crisscrossed with fracture lines. Europa has a diameter of 1942 miles and orbits Jupiter at a mean distance of 420,000 miles.

European Space Agency (ESA) the body that coordinates space research in Europe. One of its main projects is Spacelab, a manned laboratory that is carried into space by an orbiting United States space shuttle.

EVA *abbreviation for e*xtra*v*ehicular *a*ctivity—all actions performed outside a spacecraft. Spacewalk is an example. The first EVA was completed on March 18, 1965, by a Russian cosmonaut, Alexei Leonov, just before astronaut Edward White performed the first EVA by an American.

evening star 1. any planet visible in the sky just after sunset;

2. the common name for Venus when it is the most brilliant object in the western sky after sunset;

3. loosely, Mercury or other planets when visible at night.

event horizon the boundary of the region of a black hole, from which no radiation can escape. No event that occurs within the event horizon is visible to a distant observer.

exobiology 1. the study of life that may exist on planets other than Earth;

2. collectively, theories concerning living systems that may exist on other planets or their satellites in the solar system or on planetary systems of others stars. The probability of extraterrestrial life occurring at some time on some planetary system of some star is considered fairly high.

exosphere or **fringe region**, the outermost part of Earth's atmosphere—beyond the IONOSPHERE—starting above 500 km altitude.

expandable space structure a structure that can be packaged in a small volume for launch into space and then erected to its full size and shape outside Earth's atmosphere.

Explorers a large group of United States scientific satellites. Explorer missions included exploration of the atmosphere, ionosphere, magnetosphere, and regions of interplanetary space. Explorer 1, the first artificial satellite launched by the United States, discovered the Van Allen radiation belts in 1958. See Fig. 29.

extragalactic outside the Milky Way galaxy.

extraterrestrial existing beyond Earth.

extraterrestrial intelligence hypothetical beings—*extraterrestrials*—thought by some to exist elsewhere in the universe.

extravehicular activity see EVA.

extravehicular mobility unit see EMU.

extrusive rocks volcanic rocks, formed from magma that has poured out or been ejected onto a planet's surface. Lava is an extrusive rock.

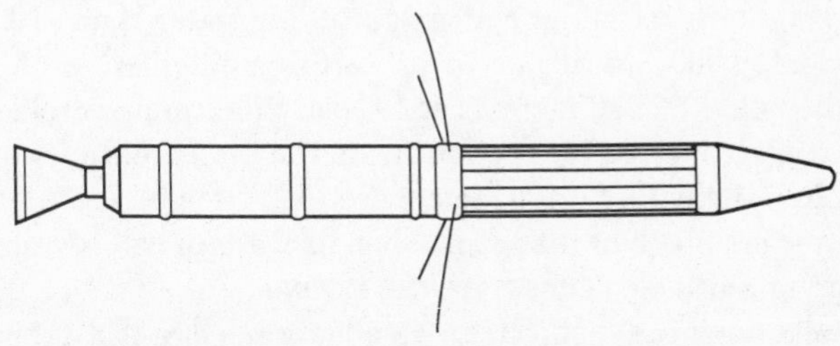

Fig. 29. **Explorer 1.** See entry for Explorers.

F

Fab Four see COSMIC FAB FOUR.

faculae the large patches of bright material forming a veined network in the vicinity of sunspots.

fail-safe system a system designed to minimize risk in case of a malfunction.

fall 1. of a spacecraft or spatial body, to drop toward another spatial body under the influence of the latter's gravity;

2. a meteorite that is seen to fall to Earth and is subsequently recovered. See FIND.

False Cross a star pattern in the Southern Hemisphere composed of Iota and Epsilon Carinae, and Kappa and Delta Velorum. It is often mistaken for the Southern Cross.

Fermi a large crater on the moon's far side.

F, G, and K subdwarfs F, G, and K blue dwarf stars located below the main sequence. See SUBDWARF STAR.

field stars background stars in the same region of the sky as, but not physically associated with, an astronomical object being observed.

filament 1. a dark region snaking across the sun;

2. a prominence seen in projection against the solar disk.

find a meteorite that is not seen to fall to Earth but is recognized on the surface of Earth some time after its arrival. See FALL.

Finlay's Comet a dim comet discovered by W.H. Finlay in 1886 while the astronomer was working at Cape Town, South Africa. He also noted the comet's return in 1893. The comet has a period of 6.85 years and an average distance from the sun of 3.6 AU. Its perihelion is 1.07 AU.

fireball 1. a bright meteor with a luminosity that equals or exceeds that of the brightest planets and usually leaves a briefly glowing trail;

2. a bright visual meteor of magnitude greater than -10. About 50,000 to 100,000 fireballs occur in Earth's atmosphere each year. It should be noted that all meteors are visual. When a meteoroid collides with Earth's atmosphere, friction heats the meteoroid to white hot, causing it to shine briefly as a meteor. See TETON FIREBALL.

first quarter the phase of the moon when its western half is visible to an observer on Earth. See PHASES OF THE MOON.

fixed satellite or **geosynchronous satellite** a satellite that orbits Earth from west to east at such a speed as to remain fixed over a given location on Earth's equator. Thus, its period of 23 hours, 56 minutes, and 4.1 seconds is equal to the Earth's period of rotation on its axis.

fixed star any star that appears to retain the same position in the sky in relation to other stars. One example is Polaris, the Pole Star, but any star in a given constellation that retains its relative position in the star system may be considered a fixed star.

Flamsteed number the number assigned to a star in a given constellation, in order of right ascension, in the 1725 catalog of English astronomer John Flamsteed (1646–1719). He supplied the observations by means of which Isaac Newton verified his lunar theory, and his 1725 catalog was the first trustworthy enumeration of the fixed stars. Examples of Flamsteed numbers:

Star	Flamsteed number
Algol	26 Per
Aldebaran	87 Tau
Castor	66 Gem
Spica	67 Vir

flare or **solar flare** **1.** a bright eruption from the sun's chromosphere;
2. a sudden shortlived brightening on a small area of the sun. Flares are related to radio fadeouts and terrestrial magnetic disturbances. They emit high-energy protons, which present a serious hazard to people in unshielded spacecraft.

flattening or **compression** of Earth or any other celestial body, the ratio of the difference between the equatorial radius and the polar radius to the equatorial radius, expressed as $f = (a - b)/a$.

flickering the rapid variations in brightness—occurring in minutes—in many close binary stars, chiefly novas and dwarf novas.

flight **1.** the movement of an object through the atmosphere or through space;
2. the portion of a space mission encompassing the period from launch to landing of the active life of the spacecraft. The term Shuttle flight means a single round trip of the Shuttle—its launch, orbital activity, and return to Earth. It is important to note that a flight may deliver more than one payload.

flightpath **1.** the path made or followed in the atmosphere or in space by a rocket;
2. the path of the center of gravity of a moving body, relative to Earth or other fixed reference.

flocculi (singular *flocculus*) **1.** the various masses of gases appearing as bright or dark mottle patches on the sun's surface, usually just above sunspots and visible only in a spectroheliogram—a photograph of the sun. Bright flocculi, in older literature called *plages*, are composed of calcium; dark flocculi, in older literature called *filaments*, are composed of hydrogen;

2. bright mottles in the solar chromosphere. See PLACE and FILAMENT.

Flora (Asteroid 8) an asteroid with a diameter of 151 kilometers, a magnitude of 8.7, perihelion 1.86 AU, and aphelion 2.55 AU. Flora was discovered in 1847 by English astronomer John R. Hind (1823–1895), who discovered 10 asteroids.

fluid parcel or **parcel** an imaginary portion of any fluid that, for theoretical studies, may be considered to have all the basic dynamic and thermodynamic properties of the fluid but is small enough so that its motion with respect to the surrounding fluid or space does not induce marked compensatory movements.

flux a measure of energy, the number of particles emitted from or passing through a surface per unit of time.

flyby a deep space mission in which the spacecraft collects data while passing close to a planet or moon but not impacting or going into orbit. Voyager, Mariner, and Pioneer are examples.

focus 1. one of the two points (foci) on which an ellipse is based. For example, the sun is located at one focus of the orbit of each of its planets;

2. the point at which a fault motion occurs during an earthquake.

Fomalhaut Alpha Piscis Austrini, a dwarf white star that is the brightest star in the southern constellation Piscis Austrinus. Fomalhaut has a visual magnitude of 1.2 at a distance of seven parsecs. In addition, it has a protoplanetary system around it. The name *Fomalhaut* is from a Spanish Arabic expression meaning mouth of the fish, so-called because of Fomalhaut's position in Piscis Austrinus, the Southern Fish. See PROTOPLANET.

Forbush decrease or **Forbush effect** a sudden observed decrease in cosmic ray activity in Earth's atmosphere about a day after a solar flare. The decrease is an effect of a magnetic storm. The phenomenon was named for United States physicist Scott E. Forbush (1904–).

Fornax (For) the Furnace, a small southern constellation south of Eridanus and Cetus. It contains no bright stars.

Foucault, Jean B.L. (1819–1868) French physicist known best for his attempt to demonstrate with the use of a pendulum that Earth rotates on its axis. See FOUCAULT PENDULUM.

Foucault pendulum a simple pendulum suspended so that the plane of motion is not fixed. When the pendulum is set in motion along a meridian in the Northern Hemisphere, the pendulum appears to turn clockwise; when the same demonstration is conducted in the Southern Hemisphere, it appears to turn counterclockwise. The phenomenon is taken to demonstrate the axial rotation of Earth.

Fox the common name for the Vulpecula constellation.

Fracastor see FRACASTORIUS.

Fracastorius or **Fracastor**, a lunar bay 97 km across, at -21° S and +34° E, leading off Mare Nectaris.

Fra Mauro a low-walled crater at -6° S and -17° W on the moon, in the Mare Nubium. Apollo 14 landed on Fra Mauro in 1971.

frame of reference a set of coordinate axes to which position, motion, etc. in a star system can be referred and by means of which celestial objects and their parameters can be measured.

free fall 1. a fall or drop of a rocket—unguided, not under thrust, and with no braking device;

2. the motion of a body in a gravitational field when no resistance is offered to the acceleration due to gravity.

free flight 1. unassisted flight, as by a rocket after consumption of its propellant or after engine shutoff.

2. flight of an unguided projectile or spacecraft.

frequency channel 1. a specific band of frequencies that must be used in a carrier system to transmit a specified amount of information;

2. the band of radio frequencies within which a station must maintain its modulated carrier frequency to prevent interference with stations in adjacent channels.

fretted channels wide, steep-walled Martian channels that have smooth, flat floors.

Freyja Montes a section of mountain on the northern flank of Ishtar Terra, on Venus. See ISHTAR TERRA.

Friendship 7 the first orbital manned United States spacecraft, launched on February 20, 1962, using a Mercury-Atlas 6 launch vehicle. Astronaut John Glenn (1921–), the sole crew member, became the first American to orbit Earth as Friendship 7 made three orbits of Earth.

F ring a ring outside the A ring in Saturn's system. It has two shepherd satellites, Pandora and Prometheus. See Fig. 30. and A RING.

fringe region the upper portion of the EXOSPHERE.

full moon 1. the moon when it is in opposition to the sun, when the nearside of the moon is completely illuminated;

2. the phase of the moon at this time.

fundamental star one of 1535 standard comparison stars whose right ascensions and declinations are known so they can be used to identify

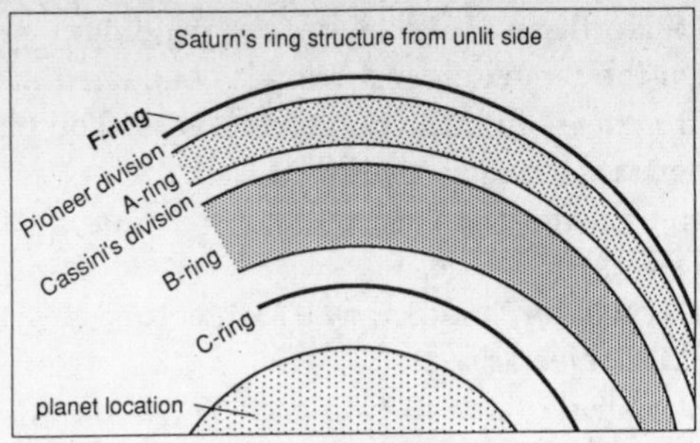

Fig. 30. **Ring structure of Saturn.** The rings are shown from the unlit side of the planet.

the positions of other stars.

Furnace the common name for the constellation Fornax.

Furnerius a crater of diameter 129 km, at 36° S and 60° E, on the near side of the moon, southeast of Mare Nectaris in the Petavius chain.

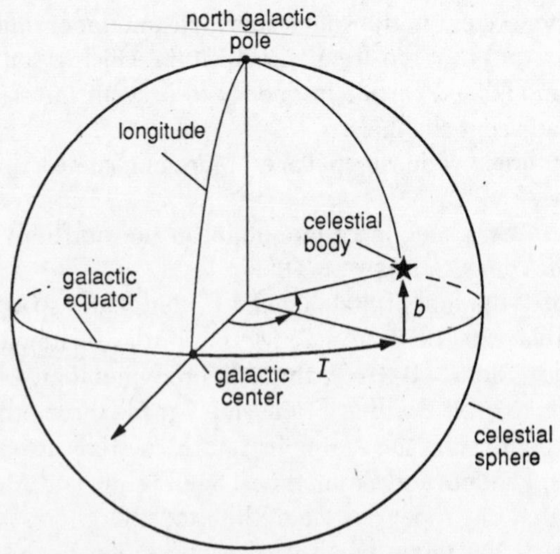

Fig. 31. **Galactic coordinate system.** The galactic center is the point around which a galaxy rotates. The galactic center of our own Milky Way is Sagittarius A. The densest collection of old stars lies in this region of intense radio wave emission.

G

G or **g** a unit of acceleration equal to the acceleration of gravity at Earth's surface, about 32.2 feet per second per second.

Gagarin, Yuri (1934–1968) Russian cosmonaut, the first human being in space. He orbited Earth in the spacecraft Vostok I on April 12, 1961. He died in a 1968 plane accident while he was in training.

gain a measure of the amplification of an electronic device.

galactic pertaining to a galaxy; in our case, to the Milky Way.

galactic center 1. the point around which a given galaxy rotates; **2.** Sagittarius A, the very center of our Milky Way galaxy. The densest collection of old stars lies in this region of intense radio wave emission. See GALACTIC COORDINATE SYSTEM.

galactic cluster see OPEN STAR CLUSTER.

galactic coordinate system an astronomical coordinate system using north and south latitude and longitude (or right ascension) as coordinate points. The galactic latitude (b) of a celestial body is its angular distance (from 0° to 90°) north or south (counted negative= -45°) of the galactic equator. The galactic longitude (l) of a celestial body is its angular distance (0° to 360°) from the galactic center measured eastward along the galactic equator to the intersection of the great circle passing through the body. For example, the galactic longitude of the north celestial pole is 123°. See Fig. 31.

galactic equator a great circle on the celestial sphere that indicates the plane of the galaxy. The galactic equator is equidistant from the galactic poles, lying about 1° north of the Milky Way center line and is inclined approximately 62° to the celestial equator. See GALACTIC COORDINATE SYSTEM.

galactic halo a distribution of old stars and globular clusters that surround the nucleus of the galaxy. See GALAXY.

galaxy a giant assembly of stars, gas, and dust held together by mutual gravitation, and in which most of the visible matter in the universe is concentrated. Galaxies are separated one from another by vast regions of space and are classified by their configurations, such as elliptical, spiral, and irregular galaxies.

Galaxy the Milky Way, the giant star system to which the sun belongs. It appears to be a spiral structure and contains about 100 billion stars. See Fig. 32 and MILKY WAY.

Galilean satellites the four large moons of Jupiter, called the Galilean satellites because they were discovered by Galileo. The discovery date was January 7, 1610; on the next night the moons were independently discovered by the German astronomer Marius, who named them Io, Europa, Ganymede, and Callisto (in order outward from Jupiter) after associates and paramours of Zeus, the Greek version of the Roman god Jupiter. Jupiter's moons are also labeled with numerals: J1, J2, J3, and J4 in the order given above. The moons are bright enough to be seen from Earth with the aid of binoculars.

Galileo 1. Italian astronomer, physicist, and natural philosopher (1564–1642), full name Galileo Galilei. He is noted for his many inventions and scientific discoveries and for his pioneering telescopic observations of the heavens, especially his studies that convinced him of the validity of the Copernican system of the universe. See GALILEAN SATELLITES;

2. the orbiter/atmospheric probe that is the next step in explorations of Jupiter. Originally scheduled for launch aboard a Space Shuttle in the early 1980s, the launch of Galileo was delayed several times, most notably as a result of the Challenger disaster, before it was finally launched by Space Shuttle Atlantis on October 18, 1989. Because, for

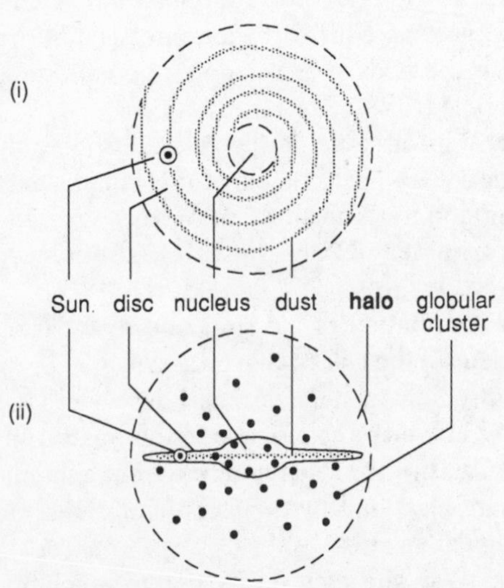

Fig. 32. **Galaxy.** Schematic views of our galaxy, the Milky Way, shown from above (i) and from the side (ii).

safety reasons, the Shuttle was not able to carry a rocket large enough to boost Galileo directly to Jupiter, a complex mission using three gravity-assist encounters is being used. If all continues to go well, Galileo will travel toward a December 1995 encounter with Jupiter. At that time the craft will go into orbit around Jupiter and observe it for a period of at least two years. An atmospheric probe will be sent into the clouds of Jupiter and will transmit information about conditions it encounters until it is crushed by the enormous atmospheric pressure. See CHALLENGER DISASTER and SPACE SHUTTLE CHALLENGER.

Galileo Regio the largest area—about 1700 km wide—of dark, cratered terrain on Jupiter's satellite Ganymede. Galileo Regio was photographed by Voyager 2 in 1979.

gamma the third letter of the Greek alphabet; in stellar terminology (as Gamma) designating the third-brightest star in a constellation.

gamma ray a high-energy, extremely short wavelength form of electromagnetic radiation.

gamma-ray astronomy the study of celestial objects by analysis of their radiation.

Gamma Velorum the brightest of the WC-type stars. Located in the southern constellation Vela, it is 3800 times as luminous as our own sun but unstable. Gamma Velorum is 520 light-years from Earth.

Gamma Virginis a double star in the equatorial constellation Virgo. Gamma Virginis is also known as Arich and as Porrima, a minor goddess of justice. The yellow stars of Gamma Virginis together have a magnitude of 2.76 and lie at a distance of 32 light-years from Earth.

Gan De the Chinese astronomer who recorded a naked-eye observation (365 BC) of Jupiter's brightest moon, Ganymede.

Ganges Catena 1. a crater chain on Mars, at latitude -2° to -3° S and longitude 67° to 71° S, diameter 233 km;

2. the name Ganges was also given to one of the so-called CANALS OF MARS.

Ganymede 1. (Asteroid 1036) an asteroid of the Amor group. It was discovered in 1924 by astronomer Walter Baade (1893–1960). The asteroid has a diameter of 35 km and is the largest close-approach asteroid to Earth. See AMOR GROUP OF ASTEROIDS;

2. the third and brightest of the Galilean satellites of Jupiter. Ganymede, with a diameter of 5100 km, is larger than the planet Mercury. Photos taken by Voyager I show that the surface is heavily cratered and covered with ridges and grooves.

Garnet star (Mu Cephei) a very red supergiant in the northern constellation Cepheus.

gaseous nebula or **emission nebula** any nebula whose light is generated by the gas component rather than by the dust of the cloud.

gas tail the puffs of ionized gas trailing a comet.

gegenschein or **counterglow** (its meaning in English) a faint patch of light that can be seen on a clear moonless night in the direction opposite from the sun's position. Gegenschein, caused by reflection of dust particles in space, is part of the ZODIACAL LIGHT.

Gemini 1. (Gem) the Twins, a northern constellation near Orion. In 1787 a small bright nebula (NGC 2392; Eskimo Nebula or Clown-Face Nebula) was discovered in Gemini by the British astronomer William Herschel (1738–1822), who was born in Germany. The brightest stars of Gemini are Pollux (Boxer or Pugilist), first magnitude; and Castor (The Horseman), second magnitude.

Since antiquity, Pollux and Castor have suggested the concept of Heavenly Twins. In Greek legend they were the sons of Leda and Zeus, and are referred to variously as the *Twin Laconian Stars*, the *Spartan Twins*, the *Ledaean Lights*, or the *Geminum Astrum*. The Roman poet Manilius calls them *Phoebi Sidus*, alluding to the legend that the Twins were under the protection of the god Apollo. The Twins are depicted frequently on coins of the ancient Greeks and Romans. In the Greek world, Castor and Pollux were venerated by mariners and were invoked for protection against storms and the perils of the seas. Shelley's "Hymn to Castor and Pollux" refers to the Twins of Jove. St. Elmo's fire, the electrical glow sometimes seen in a ship's rigging in stormy weather, was in classical times associated with the guiding spirit of the Twins, and called the Ledaean Lights. However, Arabian astronomers called them *Al Tau'aman*, the Twins, and some medieval Arabian maps show them as peacocks;

2. a two-person United States spacecraft designed for orbital rendezvous and docking in the Gemini Program, see 3. below;

3. a program of space missions (1965–1966) that extended the knowledge gained from the Mercury project and preceded the Apollo program. Gemini demonstrated that people could function effectively over long periods of weightlessness, both inside and outside a spacecraft, and that two spacecraft could be made to rendezvous and dock while in orbit. Gemini 3, the first manned flight, was launched in 1965 with two astronauts on board. America's first space walk was made in June of that year by astronaut Edward White III (1930–1967) in Gemini 4.

Geminids a major winter meteor shower with a zenithal hourly rate (ZHR) of 60 meters per hour that is visible during December—it maximizes about December 13. Associated with Phaeton (Asteroid 3200), the shower radiates from the Gemini constellation.

Geminus a lunar crater at +34° N and +57° E, in the Crisium area. It has broad terraced walls and a central elevation. Its diameter is 90 km.

geodesy the study and measurement of the size, shape, and gravitational field of Earth, in modern times using the observations of artificial satellites, such as the GEOS satellites. See GEOS.

geomagnetic storm see MAGNETIC STORM.

geomagnetism 1. Earth's magnetic field and the phenomena associated with it;

2. the study of Earth's magnetic field and its phenomena. See Fig. 33.

geomagnetic storm or **magnetic storm** the sudden alteration in a planet's magnetic field due to the effects of solar flares.

geometric position see TRUE POSITION.

geostationary orbit see GEOSYNCHRONOUS ORBIT.

GEOS *G*eodetic *E*arth *O*rbit *S*atellite, a satellite placed in GEOSYNCHRONOUS ORBIT. The satellite's mission was to study Earth's magnetosphere. GEOS-1 was launched in April of 1977 but failed to reach a geosynchronous orbit and was eventually placed in an elliptical orbit. GEOS-2 was launched successfully in July 1978 and carried 7 experi-

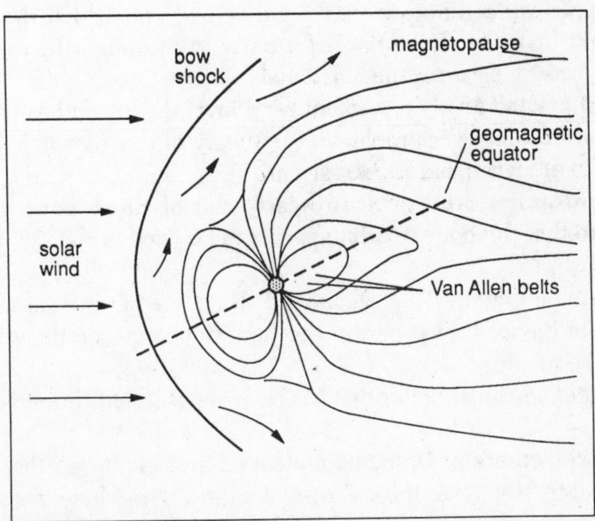

Fig. 33. **Geomagnetism.** This diagram shows Earth and the various geomagnetic phenomena associated with it.

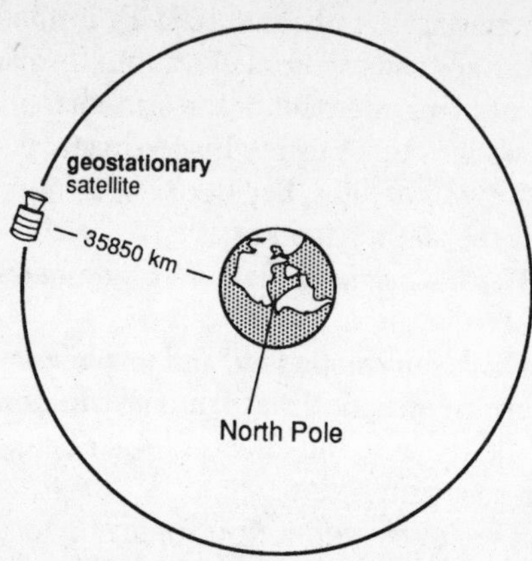

Fig. 34. **Geosynchronous orbit.** A communication satellite is usually placed into geosynchronous (or geostationary) orbit. High above Earth, the satellite can relay messages over great distances.

ments that studied atmospheric radiation particles. Both GEOS satellites were built by the European Space Agency (ESA).

geostrophic wind the horizontal wind velocity for which the coriolis acceleration—the deflection of a body in motion with respect to Earth—exactly balances the horizontal pressure force.

geostrophic wind level or **gradient wind level** the lowest level at which the wind becomes geostrophic in the theory of the Ekman spiral. See GEOSTROPHIC WIND and EKMAN SPIRAL.

geosynchronous orbit a west-to-east orbit of Earth once every 24 hours, so that the body in orbit appears to be fixed in the sky. See Fig. 34.

Gerard a lunar crater at +44° N and -78° W, in the Sinus Roris area, also called the Bay of Dews, west of the Jura Mountains, on the northwest rim of the moon.

ghost crater any lunar crater that has been almost totally buried by mare lavas.

Giacobinid meteors or **Draconid meteors** a meteor shower that is associated with the Giacobini-Zinner Comet. The shower seems to emanate from a radiant near the head of Draco. See DRACONID METEOR SHOWER.

Giacobini-Zinner Comet a small comet first observed by French astronomer Giacobini on December 20, 1900; its period is 6.5 years. On September 11, 1985, the United States International Cometary Explorer flew through the tail of the comet. This was the first comet intercept in history. When it flew through the gas tail of the comet, it found the magnetic field from the outward-flowing solar wind draped over the nucleus of the comet like seaweed over a fishhook. The International Cometary Explorer studied the basic structure of the comet.

In 1946, it must be pointed out, this small comet passed within 131,000 miles of the point Earth occupied eight days later, a near miss in terms of galactic distances.

Gianfar or **Giansar** common names for the orange giant star Lambda Draconis. Of magnitude 3.84, Gianfar is at 188 light-years from Earth. It can be seen in Draco, half way between Polaris and the Pointers, in the tip of the Dragon's Tail.

giant or **giant star** a star that is larger and brighter than the main sequence stars of the same color. A giant's magnitude is brighter than zero. Capella and Arcturus are examples of giant stars.

giant planets the planets Jupiter, Saturn, Uranus, and Neptune, which have diameters between 3.8 and 11.2 times that of Earth. They all have low densities and are composed largely of hydrogen, helium, ammonia, and methane. All have ring and satellite systems.

giant star see GIANT.

gibbous referring to a phase, often called a *gibbous phase*, of the moon when it is between quarter full and half full, or to any illuminated heavenly body when it is convex at both edges.

Gienah the Wing or Epsilon Cygni, in the northern constellation Cygnus, the Swan. This orange star of 2.46 magnitude at a distance of 74 light-years from Earth should not be confused with Y Crv, which is also called Gienah.

Gill, David (1843–1914) Scottish astronomer who served as director from 1879 to 1907 of the Cape Observatory, in South Africa. He founded the Astrographic Catalogue. His photograph of the Great Comet of 1882 had led him to propose photography as the best method of preparing star catalogs.

Gioja the north polar crater of the moon, at +89° N and -9° W, with a diameter of 35 kilometers.

Giotto a spacecraft of the European Space Agency (ESA), launched from French Guiana on July 2, 1985. After an eight-month interplanetary journey, Giotto made a flyby of Halley's comet. The spacecraft was named for the Italian painter Giotto (c.1266–1337), who depicted Halley's comet as the Star of Bethlehem in a fresco he painted in 1304.

Giraffe the common name for the northern constellation Camelopardalis, near Ursa Major and Cassiopeia. See CAMELOPARDALIS.

Glenn, John [Herschel] (1921–) a United States Marine who clearly had the right stuff. He became an astronaut in 1959 and was the first to orbit Earth. He made a three-orbit flight on February 20, 1962, in Friendship 7, a Mercury 6 spacecraft. He later entered politics and was elected to the U.S. Senate in 1975, where he still serves.

glide path 1. the flight path of a space vehicle in a glide as seen from the side;

2. the path used by a spacecraft in the approach procedure and which is generated by an instrument-landing system.

glitch 1. a sudden change in the period of a pulsar;

2. a slang word for any machine malfunction or defect.

globular cluster a compact, comparatively old, spherically symmetrical cluster of stars (held together by mutual gravitational forces) and containing from tens of thousands to a million stars in a sphere about 75 light-years in diameter. Some examples are the Great Cluster in Hercules and the Globular Galaxy in Virgo. See CLUSTER, OPEN CLUSTER, and STELLAR ASSOCIATION.

globule a dense compact dust cloud in space.

gnomon an ancient astronomical instrument used to measure the elevation of the sun. The device indicates the hour of the day by the direction and length of its shadow. In its simplest form it consists of an upright rod. The sun's elevation is easily found from the length of the rod and the length of its shadow. The arm of a sundial is still known as a gnomon.

Goddard, Robert Hutchings (1882–1945) American physicist and rocket pioneer. In 1926 he launched the first liquid-propellant rocket, with 9 pounds of thrust, and in the next year one with 200 pounds of thrust. He invented many devices and techniques that proved useful in rocket technology, including jet vanes and gyroscopic control.

Goethe a crater on Mercury, at latitude +80° and longitude 44°, near the edge of the Planitia Borealis, with a diameter of 340 kilometers.

Gomeisa the common name for Beta Canis Minoris, a blue-white dwarf star, magnitude 2.91. Beta Canis Minoris, in the constellation Canis Minor, the Smaller Dog, in the equatorial region of the southern hemisphere, is 210 light-years from Earth.

gossamer ring a faint component of Jupiter's ring system. It extends outward beyond the main ring.

Gould's Belt a band of gas and stars inclined to the plane of the galaxy by 20°. The brightest stars are not scattered uniformly over the sky, but tend to lie along a band that has been named Gould's Belt. It was discovered by English astronomer John Herschel (1782–1871) and was studied in 1879 by American astronomer Benjamin Apthorp Gould (1824–1896), founder of the *Astronomical Journal* and director of the Dudley Observatory, Albany, New York, who catalogued the southern stars.

Gould's Belt is close to but not identical with the Milky Way. In the northern sky the bright stars concentrate in Orion and Taurus and are off to one side of the Milky Way. In the southern sky the Lupus and Centaurus constellations lie off to the other side of the Milky Way. Observers in either hemisphere can see the belt with their own eyes. According to the late Australian astronomer Colin Gum, Gould's Belt represents a fin projecting from the nearest spiral arm of our galaxy, stuck out from the plane of the Milky Way at an angle.

graben or **rift valley 1.** on the crust of Earth, the moon, or other planets and their moons, a long and narrow region between faults that has subsided. See RIFT VALLEY.

2. the sunken areas between lunar faults.

gradient wind level see GEOSTROPHIC WIND LEVEL.

Grafias the common name for Zeta Scorpius, with an apparent magnitude of 3.8. Grafias is located in the lower right portion of the equatorial constellation Scorpion, 15° below Antares, Alpha Scorpius, which is called the red heart and is the brightest star of the constellation.

grand tour 1. any interplanetary exploration aided by so-called *gravity assists*, which are provided by the planets themselves—the gravitational pull of each planet gives the spacecraft a boost in velocity as it encounters the planet, enabling a spacecraft such as Voyager to travel great distances at high speed. For example, in 1989, only twelve years after launch, Voyager 2 passed Neptune. Without gravity assist, a direct flight from Earth to Neptune would have required 30 years;

2. the Tour Mission launch to Jupiter and Saturn by Voyager 1, on September 5, 1977, and similar launches to Jupiter, Saturn, Uranus, and Neptune on August 20, 1977. Voyager 2 completed the Tour Mission with its August 1989 flyby of Neptune.

granulation the mottled appearance of the sun's photosphere resulting from convection cells that bring thermal energy to the surface.

gravitation the force of attraction between any two material bodies. This mutual attraction was first expressed by Isaac Newton. See GRAVITY and NEWTON.

gravitational collapse the contraction of a celestial body that is caused by the gravitational pulls of its constituents, the final stage of stellar evolution. Gravitational collapse usually refers to the sudden collapse of the core of a massive star at the end of nuclear burning, when its internal gas pressure can no longer support its weight. The collapse may initially result in a supernova explosion. See SUPERNOVA.

gravitational interlock the control by gravitational attraction that is exercised by one body, such as a planet, on the orbit or rotation of another body, such as a moon.

gravitational lensing the creation of a distorted image of a distant quasar or galaxy when its light is focused by the gravity of a galaxy located between the observer on Earth and the body under observation.

gravitational radiation see GRAVITATIONAL WAVE.

gravitational redshift 1. a red shift caused by light emitted from a region of very high gravity, such as a neutron star;

2. a displacement of spectral lines toward the red when the gravitational potential of the observer of the light is greater than the gravitational potential at the source of the light;

3. the lengthening of the wavelength of a photon due to its escape from a gravitational field.

gravitational wave or **gravitational radiation** a gravity field produced by some change in the distribution of matter. It travels at the speed of light, exerting forces on masses in its path.

gravity 1. another name for gravitation, the force of attraction that Earth exerts on a given object;

2. the weight of an object.

Great Bear the common name for the northern constellation Ursa Major. Its seven main stars compose the Plow, or Big Dipper.

Great Dark Spot an atmospheric storm of Neptune that is similar to Jupiter's Great Red Spot, a long-lasting feature that is larger than Earth. The weather activity that is the Great Dark Spot is exceeded only by the Great Red Spot. In 1989, Voyager 2 discovered the Great Dark Spot atmospheric marking primarily in Neptune's southern hemisphere. The cloud feature is located at 20° south latitude. It measures 12,000 km by 8000 km in size and has a rotational period of 18.3 hours.

South of the Great Dark Spot, at 33° south latitude, is a white feature called the *bright companion*. This feature appears to be 50 km higher in the atmosphere than the Great Dark Spot. Neptune's white clouds are believed to be located this high above the remainder of the methane cloud deck, because winds around dark features such as the Great Dark Spot cause atmospheric gases to rise high enough that the temperature drops below the freezing point of methane. In this respect, the white clouds are similar to the high cirrus clouds of Earth's atmosphere.

Great Dog the common name for the southern constellation Canis Major.

greatest elongation the largest angle of separation between the sun and either Mercury or Venus.

Great Nebula of Orion see ORION NEBULA.

Great Red Spot or **Red Spot** an immense oval feature in Jupiter's atmosphere, a huge anticyclonically rotating storm or eddy that is 24,000 km long and 11,000 km wide. It has been observed for centuries. See GREAT DARK SPOT.

Gredi a common name for Alpha Capricornus, also called the Goat. See CAPRICORNUS.

greenhouse effect an atmospheric heating phenomenon causing a planetary environment to be heated by trapping infrared radiation within the atmosphere. The sun's radiation passing through the translucent roof of a greenhouse creates heat waves inside the greenhouse. Escape of the heat waves is blocked by the roof, thus heating the greenhouse. In a similar way, light waves passing through layers of Earth's atmosphere create heat waves when they strike the ground. Escape of these heat waves is blocked by Earth's atmosphere, causing the air surrounding Earth to warm. The atmosphere of Venus provides a striking example of what can happen to a planet that experiences the greenhouse effect. The temperature on Venus is nearly 900° F, more than four times higher than the temperature of boiling water on Earth. The carbon dioxide and water vapor in the air of Venus let in sunlight, but they trap the heat and do not let it escape. Because of this greenhouse effect, the planet gets hotter and hotter.

Greenwich time see UNIVERSAL TIME.

Grigg-Mellish Comet (1907 II) a long-period comet once thought to have a period of 164 years, but now believed to be much longer than that. It was discovered by New Zealand amateur astronomer John Grigg (1838–1920), who discovered several comets.

Grimaldi a walled plain on the moon at -6° S and -68° W, west of Oceanus Procellarum. Grimaldi, the darkest point on the moon, is never well seen from Earth.

G ring a ring in Saturn's system, lying between the orbits of the moons Janus and Mimas. Only the E Ring is farther from the planet.

Groombridge 1830 a G8 yellow star of the northern constellation Ursa Major. It has a visual magnitude of 6.5, slightly underluminous for its spectral class and, therefore, is defined as a subdwarf. Its actual luminosity is about 1/7 that of the sun. Groombridge 1830, 16° due south of Gamma Ursae Majoris, has a faint companion star and is noted for its exceptionally large angular motion. It was discovered in 1830 by English astronomer Stephen Groombridge (1755–1832). Its companion star was discovered in 1968.

grooved terrain regions of the surface of Ganymede (Jupiter's moon) consisting of parallel grooves. The terrain is believed to have formed by repeated fracture and refreezing of Ganymede's icy crust.

ground-controlled approach (GCA) a ground radar system that provides information by means of which spacecraft approaches can be directed via radio communications.

ground-effect machine a vehicle that hovers or moves just above the ground by creating a cushion of supporting air between the vehicle and the ground surface and by varying the thrust vector and magnitude to regulate direction and rate of motion.

ground-elapsed time the number of hours, minutes, and seconds after a rocket liftoff.

Grumium or **Grummium** the common name for Zeta Draconis. This star is computed to be about 600 light-years from Earth. Its luminosity is 1500 times greater than that of our sun. Grumium is the base of the dragon's head in the Draco constellation. See DRACO.

Grus (Gru) the Crane, a southern constellation between Phoenix and Indus and the most distinctive of the so-called Southern Birds. The Crane constellation was the first figured in Bayer's star atlas of 1603. This identification seems fitting, because in ancient Egypt a crane was the symbol for a star-watcher. Early Arabian astronomers, however, considered the stars of Grus to be part of the constellation Piscis Austrinus, just above Grus. Two of the brightest stars of Grus are Alpha Gruis (Al Nair, the bright one) and Gamma Gruis, the eye of the crane. See SOUTHERN BIRDS.

guardian satellite any of the small moons that orbit just inside or outside the edge of a planetary ring. The gravity of these moons causes the edges of the ring to be sharp and distinct. See SHEPHERD SATELLITE.

guidance the process of directing the movements of a spacecraft with reference to the selection of a flight path.

guest star a translation of the ancient Chinese term for stars that are temporarily visible. Fourteen supernovas ranging back 2000 years have been identified from ancient records. The three most famous guest stars are the Crab Nebula explosion, Tycho's star, and Kepler's star. See NOVA and SUPERNOVA.

guided missile see MISSILE, GUIDED.

Gum Nebula a large nebula in the sky of the Southern Hemisphere, formed by a supernova explosion about 9000 BC.

gyroscope an instrument consisting essentially of a wheel with weighted rim designed to rotate at high speed within a universal mounting. The gyroscope, which is used in aerospace guidance systems, retains its initial orientation in space regardless of external forces applied to it. Thus, the gyroscope on an aircraft or spacecraft can maintain a fixed direction even though Earth is moving.

H

habitable zone the area of space around a star in which a planet will have surface temperature conditions that will enable liquid water to exist.

Hadriaca Patera a volcano on the northern rim of the Hellas basin in the southern hemisphere of Mars, at latitude -31° and longitude 267°. Its central caldera is 60 km in diameter.

Hagaromo a lunar probe launched by the Japanese that went into orbit around the moon in March of 1990. Because its transmitter failed, the lunar probe became untrackable.

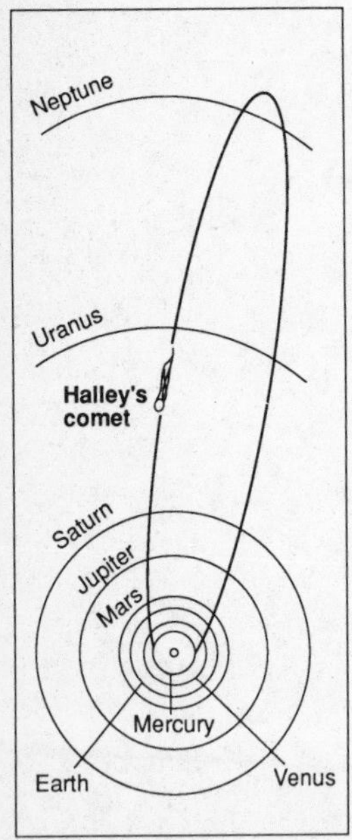

Fig. 35. **Halley's comet.** The comet known best by interested stargazers on Earth. While in its most recent return it failed to live up to its advance billing, astronomers learned much from it.

half moon the lunar first-quarter or third-quarter phase, when half the visible side of the moon is illuminated.

Hall an impact crater on Phobos, the larger of the two Martian moons.

Hall, Asaph (1829–1907) American astronomer who was on the staff of the United States Naval Observatory. In 1877 he discovered and named Deimos and Phobos, the two moons of Mars.

Halley, Edmond (1656–1742) English astronomer amd mathematician, sometimes called the father of geophysics, who devised a method of determining the sun's distance from transits of Venus. He showed that comets travel in elliptical orbits about the sun and made the first scientific prediction of a comet's reappearance—it was the 1758 return of Halley's comet.

Halley's comet the brightest of the predictable comets, first recorded in 240 BC and first noted by Chinese astronomers in 1059. It has a period of 76 years, and one return coincided with the Battle of Hastings, in 1066. The comet—called a sungrazer because its orbit at perihelion takes it close to the sun, 0.59 AU—was named after English astronomer Edmond Halley because he was the first person to calculate its path around the sun. The comet, which has had 28 returns, was seen most recently in early spring of 1986. Halley's next return will be in 2061. See Fig. 35.

halo 1. the portion of Jupiter's ring system located closer to the planet than the main ring plane;

2. a huge cloud of gas atoms surrounding the head of a comet;

3. a system of globular clusters, stars, and gas that surrounds the nucleus of our galaxy.

Hamal Alpha Arietis, Arabic for sheep, the brightest star in the northern constellation Aries, the Ram. Its distance from Earth is 22 parsecs.

hangfire 1. a faulty condition in the ignition system of a rocket engine;

2. a delay in detonation of gunpowder etc.

Hansen a lunar crater at +14° N and +74 W, in the Crisium area, close to the moon's eastern limb. Its diameter is 36 kilometers.

Harbinger Mountains clumps of highlands at +27° N and -42° W, in the Imbrium area of the 2nd quadrant of the moon.

Harding, Karl L. (1765–1834) German astronomer who discovered the minor planet (asteroid) Juno in 1804 while working at the Lilienthal Observatory, near Bremen, Germany. He observed nebulae and variable stars and was the author of a star atlas containing about 60,000 stars. It was one of the first prepared according to scientific principles. Harding also discovered three comets.

hard radiation radiation of high penetrating power. A 10-cm thickness of lead is usually used as the criterion on which to judge the relative penetrating power of the various types of radiation.

Haris a common name for Gamma Boötes, sometimes called Seginus, and situated in the left shoulder of Boötes. Its magnitude is 3.05, and its distance from Earth is 118 light-years.

harmonic law Kepler's third law of planetary motion: The cubes of the semimajor axes of the planetary orbits compare in the same way as the squares of the periods of the planets.

Harpalus a deep lunar crater at +53° N and -43° W, in Sinus Roris, the Bay of Dew, near the southwest boundary of Mare Frigoris, the Sea of Cold. The diameter of Harpalus is 52 kilometers.

Harriot, Thomas (c.1560–1621) English mathematician and scientist who began making telescopic observations in the same year as Galileo. Harriot developed the earliest moon maps, studied Jupiter's satellites, and derived the sun's rotation period. He also observed the return of Halley's comet in 1607.

Hartmann, Johannes Franz (1865–1936) German astronomer who was an authority in the field of spectroscopy.

harvest moon the full moon at or about the time of the autumn equinox.

Hasseleh a common name for Iota Aurigae. This star in the Auriga constellation has an apparent magnitude of 2.9 at a distance of 330 parsecs.

Hathor (Asteroid 2340) an asteroid discovered in 1976. It has a period of .76 year and is only a few kilometers in diameter.

Hatsya a common name for Iota Orionis. This star in the Orion constellation lies at a distance of 2,000 parsecs from Earth.

Hay Moon or **Thunder Moon** July's full moon. It was known to colonial Americans. Some Native American names for it include (in translation): Moon When the Cherries Are Ripe, Killer Whale Moon, Red Salmon Time, Corn Tassle Moon, Sun House Moon, and Rain Moon.

Haystack Vallis a valley on the planet Mercury. It is at 4° N and 46° W, close to the equatorial crater Homer.

HDE 226868 a blue supergiant star in Cygnus, an x-ray source.

head the coma and nucleus of a comet when seen together. See COMA.

heading the horizontal direction in which a spacecraft in flight is pointed.

heat barrier or **thermal barrier** a temperature effect that tends to limit the maximum speed of a missile (spacecraft) through the atmosphere.

heat pulse the sudden rise and fall in the temperature of a space vehicle during reentry.

heat shield 1. any device that protects something from heat;
2. the protective structure necessary to protect a reentry body from aerodynamic heating.

heavily cratered terrain a type of landscape found on Mercury and on Saturn's satellite Dione. Heavily cratered terrain resembles the terrain of the lunar highlands.

heavy elements all the elements heavier than hydrogen and helium. The cosmic abundance of the heavy elements is much less than that of hydrogen and helium, the two most abundant elements in the universe.

Hebe Asteroid 6, diameter 195 km. It was discovered by Karl Hencke in 1837, who also discovered the asteroid Astraea, in 1845.

Hecates Tholus a prominent SHIELD VOLCANO on Mars.

Hector a large, dumbbell-shaped asteroid of the TROJAN GROUP, near Jupiter. Its perihelion is 5.0 AU, its aphelion is 5.3 AU, and its diameter is 190 kilometers.

Heemskerck Rupes a mountain ridge at latitude +27° and longitude 125°, southwest of the Degas Crater on Mercury.

Heka a common name for the star Lambda Orionis.

Helene (1980 S6) a small moon of Saturn that co-orbits with Dione. It was discovered by Lacques and Lecacheux in 1980.

heliacal occurring near the sun, especially applied to the visible rising and setting of a star that most nearly coincide with the rising, called *heliacal rising*, and the setting of the sun.

heliocentric relative to the sun as a center, as in *heliocentric orbit*.

heliocentric parallax the parallax of a celestial body that results from the change in the position of a point of observation during Earth's annual revolution around the sun. Nearby stars are seen to be displaced in position relative to the more remote background stars. See PARALLAX.

heliocentric universe a model of the universe with the sun at the center, such as the *Copernican universe*.

heliographic referring to positions on the sun measured in latitude from the sun's equator and in longitude from a reference meridian.

heliopause the outer boundary of the heliosphere. See HELIOSPHERE.

Helio probes two interplanetary spacecraft designed to observe the sun and the solar wind. They were launched on December 10, 1974, and January 15, 1976, using a Titan-Centaur launch vehicle. See HELIOS.

Helios a joint project of the United States and West Germany in the 1970s to investigate interplanetary space and explore the near-solar region. The two probes that were launched carried instruments closer to the sun than any previous spacecraft. They made their way to within the outer edge of the corona, 45 million km (28 million miles) from the sun.

heliosphere the vast region of space in which the solar wind is found.

helium flash the explosive ignition of helium that occurs in some giant stars.

Helix nebula (NGC 7293) a luminous nebula in the constellation Aquarius, 450 light-years from Earth.

Hellas **1.** a circular impact basin in the southern hemisphere of Mars, at 300° W and 40° S. Images from Mariner 9 revealed it to be the largest of Mars' impact basins, diameter 1800 km. It is also one of the oldest of Mars' three volcanic provinces and one of the largest features of the planet;
2. the identification name for the southern hemisphere Martian quadrant MC-28.

Hellas Planitia the large crater floor of Hellas, containing large volcanic plains and wind-blown deposits. Hellas Planitia is sometimes shortened to Hellas.

Hemmungspunkt see STOPPING POINT.

Henbury craters twelve meteorite craters located in Central America, formed by a body that fragmented just before impact.

Hephaistos (Asteroid 2212) an asteroid discovered in 1978. It has a period of 3.17 years.

Herbig-Haro objects or **HH objects 1.** small nebulae, varying irregularly in brightness, made of concentrations of interstellar gas and dust. Some of these objects, particularly those in the Orion Nebula, have changed in the last 50 years;

2. dust clouds in space that reflect the light coming from hidden young stars. They were discovered in the 1950s by astronomers G. Herbig and G. Haro.

Hercules an inconspicuous northern constellation between Lyra and Corona Borealis, named after the great hero of mythology. Its brightest star is Rasalgethi (also Ras Algethi), an irregular variable star that is reddish in color. The name is derived from an Arabic phrase meaning the Head of the Kneeler, though the star was also known as the Shepherd's Dog. Other names for this star include the Kneeling One and the Phantom. The second brightest star is Kornephoros, the club-bearer.

Also found in this constellation is Nova Herculis 1934, one of the brightest novas of the 20th century. It was first noticed by British amateur J.P. Prentice on the night of December 13, 1934. The Great Cluster in Hercules, discovered in 1714 by Edmond Halley, is also of importance. Designated M13 or NGC 6205, it is the finest of its type in the northern sky.

Hercules crater a lunar crater 67 km in diameter and 3 km deep. It is located at +47° N and +40° E, east of the Caucasus Mountains, in the northeast section of the face of the moon.

Hercules X-1 an x-ray binary star—after Centaurus X-3, the second so identified based on observations by the Uhuru satellite. Hercules X-1, in the Hercules constellation, was the first x-ray binary star to be optically identified. The primary of an x-ray binary star is an x-ray pulsar; the secondary is a visible, or optical, star, for example, HZ Hercules. See UHURU.

Herculina (Asteroid 532) a binary asteroid with a companion asteroid some 1000 km away. This was established when Herculina occulted a star on June 7, 1978.

Hermes (Asteroid 1937B) a small asteroid discovered by K. Reinmuth in 1937, then within 0.006 AU (780,000 km) of Earth, closer than any other known earthgrazer. Hermes, with a diameter of a few kilometers, is a member of the Apollo group. See EARTHGRAZER.

Herodotus a lunar crater at 23° N and 50° S, 37 km in diameter, that marks the start of the great winding Schroter Valley.

Herschel an impact crater—130 km across—on the leading hemisphere of Saturn's satellite Mimas. Since the width of the crater is about a third as large as the diameter of the satellite, it is thought that Mimas could not have withstood impact by a body larger than the one that created Herschel. The crater, nearly 10 km deep, has a central peak almost 6 km high and was photographed by Voyager 1.

Herschel, John (1792–1871) an English astronomer who continued the studies of double stars and nebulas conducted by his father, William Herschel. He also contributed to knowledge of the Milky Way, the brightness and color of stars, and the Magellanic Clouds.

Herschel, William (1738–1822) British astronomer, born in Germany, a pioneer of stellar astronomy. In 1781 he discovered Uranus and, later, two of its satellites as well as two satellites of Saturn—one of them was Mimas, see the entry above. Herschel built the largest telescopes of his time, which he used to study planetary nebulae and variable stars.

hertz the SI unit of frequency.

Hertzsprung-Russell (H-R) diagram a plot of a group of stars according to their absolute magnitude and spectral class (temperature). See Fig. 36.

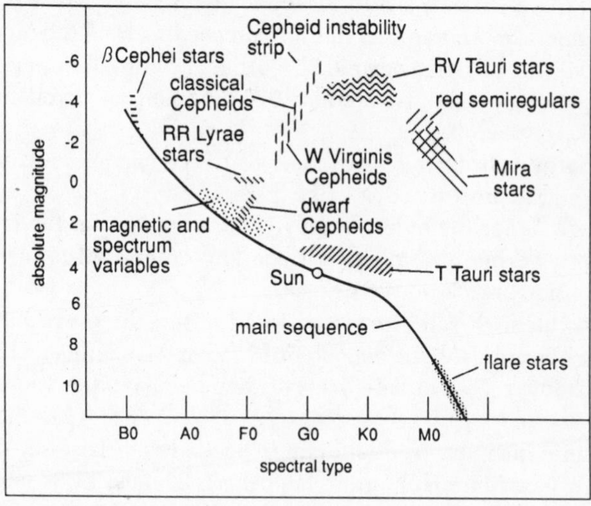

Fig. 36. **Hertzsprung-Russell diagram.** Cepheid variable stars are positioned in the upper right of the main sequence. The Cepheid instability strip represents stars that are undergoing the first transition stage of instability—they are experiencing cycles of expansion and contraction, and of luminosity—after leaving the main sequence.

Hesiodus a lunar crater at 29° S and 16° W, south of the Mare Nubium. A companion of Pitatus, Hesiodus has a diameter of 45 km.

Hesperus the Greek name for Venus when it was visible as an evening star; also called Phosphorus.

Hevelius a lunar walled plain 122 km in length, at 2° N and 65° W, of the Grimaldi chain.

Hevelius, Johannes (1611–1687) German astronomer who constructed his instruments himself and used them to chart the lunar surface. He catalogued many stars, observed sunspots, studied the phases of Saturn, and discovered 4 comets. Hevelius was one of the first to observe the transit of Mercury. See SEXTANS.

Heze a common name for the star Zeta Virginis, in the Virgo constellation.

HH objects see HERBIG-HARO OBJECTS.

hibernating spacecraft a spacecraft maintaining an orbit without using propellant power and without maintaining orientation within the orbit, but with inherent power capability.

Hidalgo (Asteroid 944) a visible asteroid 18 miles in diameter that travels in a cometlike orbit around the sun, proceeding from the inner edge of the asteroid belt out beyond the orbit of Saturn. Its period is 14.2 years. Hidalgo was discovered in 1920 by American astronomer Walter Baade (1893–1960).

high-energy astrophysics the study of x-rays, gamma rays, and cosmic rays, and the processes that make them.

highlands, lunar the older, heavily cratered portion of the crust of the moon, covering 83% of its surface and composed in large part of anorthositic breccia, a type of rock.

Himalia the sixth satellite (moon) of Jupiter; discovered in 1904 by Charles Perrine, it has a diameter of 185 km. See ELARA and PERRINE.

Hind's Nebula (NGC 1554–5) a reflection nebula in the Taurus constellation.

Hippalus a lunar bay—an old crater flooded with lava—at -25° S and -32° W, near Mare Humorum. Hippalus is 33 miles by 37 miles in area, and its southwest wall is missing.

Hipparchus a flat-floored lunar crater at -6° S and +6° E, near the center of the moon's nearside; its diameter is 84 miles (135 kilometers).

Hipparchus (of Nicaea) (fl.160–125 BC) Greek astronomer who determined the lengths of the four seasons, measured the length of the solar year to within 6.5 minutes, and derived a mathematical theory to express the motions of the sun and moon. He also estimated the sizes and distances of the sun and moon. Hipparchus is most noted for his discovery of the precession of the equinoxes.

Hirayama families various asteroids clustered into families or groups with similar orbital properties. The first families recognized were Themis, Eos, Koronis, Maria, and Flora. In all, more than 40 families are recognized. The Japanese astronomer Kiyotsugu Hirayama (1874–1943) discovered the first nine families in 1928. It is believed that each family represents debris resulting from a collision between larger asteroids.

Hoba meteorite the largest single meteorite ever discovered. It was found in 1920 near Grootfontein, Namibia. This iron meteorite weighs 60 tons and measures 2.7 × 2.7 × 1 meter. Its impact did not result in a crater.

Hodr crater a crater on Jupiter's satellite Callisto.

Hoedus I a common name for the star Zeta Aurigae. See AURIGA.

hold a halt during a space launch countdown. The procedure at *hold* calls for launch personnel to stop counting and wait until an impediment has been removed so that the countdown can be resumed, as in the familiar "T minus 40 and holding...."

Homan a common name for the star Zeta Pegasi, also called the lucky star. This star, of magnitude 3.4, is 210 light years from Earth. See PEGASUS.

Homer a crater at 1° S and 37° W, on the equator of the planet Mercury. Homan has a 320-km diameter.

Homunculus Nebula a cloud of gas and dust thrown out in 1843, when the star Eta Carina flared up.

horizon 1. the great circle of the celestial sphere midway between its zenith and nadir;

2. a line resembling such a circle.

horizontal system a system by which the location of an object is specified in terms of its angle above the horizon (altitude) and the angle it makes relative to due north (azimuth).

Horologium (Hor) the Clock, a faint southern constellation lying near Eridanus. Horologium is one of the constellations introduced by French astronomer Nicolas Louis de Lacaille (1713–1762). Alpha is its only star brighter than magnitude 4.

Horsehead Nebula (NGC 2024) a dark nebula located near the star Zeta Orionis, in the constellation Orion.

Hubble, Edwin Powell (1889–1953) American astronomer who studied the shift in spectral lines, the speed of galaxies, Cepheids, and other variable stars. He also produced a classification system for galaxies. The Hubble Space Telescope is named in his honor.

Hubble's constant (H_0) the ratio that expresses the apparent relationship between the distance to the galaxy and its speed of recession. The currently accepted value for the expansion rate of the galaxies is 50 to 80 km/megaparsecs.

Hubble's Law the linear relation between the velocity of recession of a distant object and its distance from us.

Hubble Space Telescope (HST) a large telescope with a main mirror 2.4 meters (94 inches) in diameter, designed to be put in orbit by the Space Shuttle and to work for 15 years. It was placed in orbit in May of 1990 at an altitude of 512 km. The advantages of putting a telescope in space are based on the fact that above the atmosphere, starlight should be concentrated, there should be less distortion, it is easier to detect faint celestial objects because the sky is dark and, with no atmosphere above the telescope, HST should be able to detect ultraviolet and infrared rays.

A serious limitation was discovered two months after launch: the telescope had no single good point of focus. All the images of stars were too large. Apparently, one of the mirrors was not made to the proper shape, causing spherical aberration, or distortion. It was as though the telescope was nearsighted. It could not differentiate between a single star and a binary star system. A corrective lens camera is being constructed to correct the defect.

In the meantime there is plenty for the HST to do with its unique ultraviolet capability, and in observing celestial objects within the solar system. Resolution of images of Mars, Jupiter, and Saturn in photographs taken with Hubble while in orbit have been comparable to those taken by Mariner and Voyager, and Hubble photographs are better than any taken to date by Earth-based telescopes.

Hubble's Variable Nebula (NGC 2261) a peculiar gaseous nebula, also called *Hubble's Nebula,* enveloping the variable star R Monocerotis. Discovered by William Herschel in 1783, the nebula is rather cometlike in shape, with the star R Monocerotis located near the southern tip and the tail of the nebula extending northward. Hubble's Nebula was the first celestial object photographed with the 200-inch reflecting telescope at Palomar Observatory, January 26, 1949. See R MONOCEROTIS.

Hun Kal a 1.5-km diameter crater, at latitude -06° and longitude 20°, close to the Homer crater on Mercury. See HOMER.

hunter's moon the full moon following the harvest moon; it usually occurs in October in the Northern Hemisphere.

Huygens, Christiaan (1629–1695) Dutch astronomer who was the first person to explain adequately the phenomenon of Saturn's rings.

Galileo had described the planet as having what he called *handles* and thought that Saturn was perhaps accompanied by two large nearby satellies. Huygens was the first to see that Saturn was circled by a ring system. In the three centuries since then, improved telescopes and spacecraft visits have given us increasingly clear views of Saturn's rings. Titan was the first Saturnian satellite discovered—by Huygens, in 1655—and prior to the space age it was considered to be the largest satellite in the solar system.

Hyades an open cluster of over 200 stars about 46 parsecs from Earth, in the northern constellation Taurus, near Orion.

Hydra (Hya) the Water Serpent, the largest constellation in the Southern Hemisphere, and considered the longest of all constellations, extending through 90° of the sky. Its stars are rather faint, but the west end of this long, south-equatorial group is distinctively marked by the yellow star Alphard, which shines in the empty sky south of Leo's paws. Hydra is sometimes called the Sea Serpent or Monster, representing the 9-headed monster killed by Hercules.

Hydrus (Hyi) the Water Snake or Little Snake, a small constellation near the south celestial pole, between the Large and Small Magellanic clouds (galaxies). Beta Hydri, a 3rd-magnitude star, is the constellation's brightest star.

Hygieia (Asteroid 10) a minor planet, discovered in 1849 by the Italian astronomer de Gasparis. Hygieia has a radius of 160 km, a rotational period of 18 hours, and a revolution period of 5.59 years. Its mean distance from the sun is 3.151 AU.

hyperbolic velocity a velocity sufficient to allow escape from the solar system.

Hyperion (S VII) a satellite of Saturn discovered in 1848 by astronomers William Boyd (1789–1859) and William Lassell (1799–1880), working independently. Hyperion, which has a diameter of 400 km, orbits Saturn in 21.28 days and is at a mean distance of 1,481,000 kilometers from the planet.

hypersonic pertaining to speeds of mach 5 or greater. See MACH.

hypersonic glider an unpowered vehicle, specifically a reentry vehicle, designed to fly at hypersonic speeds.

I

Iapetus the third largest moon (satellite) of Saturn discovered in 1671 by CASSINI. It is 1440 km in diameter and has a heavily cratered water-ice surface.

Icarus (Asteroid 1566) a minor planet discovered in 1949 and belonging to the Apollo group of asteroids. Its orbit crosses Mercury's orbit. Icarus passed only 0.04 AU from Earth in 1968. See APOLLO GROUP.

ICE the International Cometary Explorer, also known as ISEE-3. This spacecraft was launched in 1978 and on September 11, 1985, became the first to fly through the tail of the Giacobini-Zinner comet. This was the first known comet intercept in history. ICE passed through Halley's comet in 1986.

ice frost a thickness of ice that gathers on the outside of a rocket over surfaces supercooled, as by liquid oxygen inside the vehicle.

icy planets planets or satellites that are composed of ice, but usually have a rocky interior. The planet Pluto is one example.

Igaluk a crater on Jupiter's moon Callisto.

ignition delay or **ignition lag** the time lapse between the instance of an igniting action of a fuel and the onset of a specified burning reaction.

Ikeya-Seki Comet a brilliant comet observed in 1965. It was perhaps the brightest of the 20th century.

ILS *abbreviation for* instrument landing system.

immersion the entry of a celestial body into a condition of invisibility during an eclipse.

impact area the area in which a meteor or other object, such as a rocket, strikes the surface of Earth or other celestial body.

impact basin a crater or other feature that has been formed by impact of a meteorite, sometimes called an *impact formation*.

impact crater a roughly circular depression of any size (microscopic to greater than 1000 km) caused by a meteorite impact. See ARIZONA METEORITE CRATER.

implosion a rapid inward collapsing of the walls of a vacuum system or device as the result of failure of the walls to sustain the ambient pressure.

incidence of multiplicity among stars, the fraction of systems containing more than one star. It is believed that probably 50% to 70% of systems have companion stars, many of them having more than one companion.

inclination magnetic dip, the angle between the orbital plane of a planet and the plane of the ecliptic. See Fig. 37.

Index Catalogue (IC) a listing of star clusters, nebulae, and galaxies that supplements the New General Catalogue (NGC).

Indus (Ind) the Indian, a small constellation in the Southern Hemisphere, between Grus and Pavo. Indus is found by locating Pavo and then looking just to the east.

Inertia the tendency of a mass to resist a change in motion. Thus, a body at rest tends to remain at rest, and a body moving uniformly in a straight line tends to continue movement uniformly along that line. To effect a change in movement of a mass, an external force is required. See Fig. 38.

Inertial orbit the type of orbit described by all celestial bodies, in conformance with Kepler's laws of celestial motion. This applies to all satellites and to spacecraft, providing the spacecraft are not under any type of propulsive power.

Inferior conjunction the passage of an inferior planet (Mercury or Venus) and a few asteroids and comets between the sun and Earth.

Inferior planets the planets Mercury and Venus, which are between the sun and Earth.

Infrared an electromagnetic radiation of wavelength just longer than that of red light.

Infrared Astronomical Satellite see IRAS.

Infrared outburst a sudden brightening of an object at infrared wavelengths.

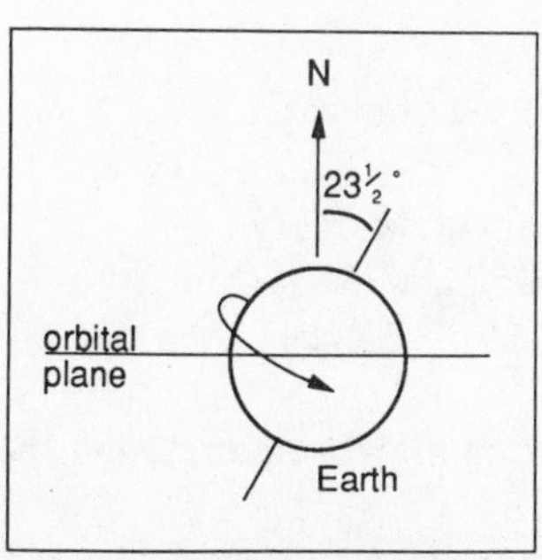

Fig. 37. **Inclination.** See entry.

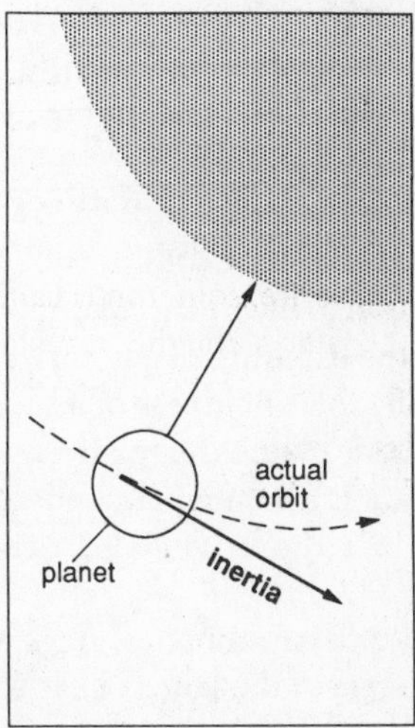

Fig. 38. **Inertia.** See entry.

Infrared star a star detected primarily by infrared light.

Injection insertion, the process of boosting a spacecraft into a particular orbit or trajectory.

Inner planets the terrestrial planets, the four planets nearest the sun: Mercury, Venus, Earth, and Mars. They lie closer to the sun than the asteroid belt and are occasionally called the inner solar system.

Innes, Robert Thorburn (1861–1933) Scottish astronomer who held the post of secretary of the Cape Observatory, in South Africa. While there, he continued his double-star observations and compiled a catalog of southern double stars. At the Transvaal Observatory, also in South Africa, he became the first astronomer to place double-star research on a sound modern footing. He was a pioneer in the use of the blink microscope in astronomy to examine telescope sky photographs. With this instrument, he made his celebrated discovery of Proxima Centauri. (In 1977, astronomer Charles Kowel, using a blink microscope, discovered Pluto's moon Charon.)

When Innes discovered the manikin-shaped Eta Carinae's Homunculus nebula in 1909, he thought he saw several companion stars within it. The star Eta Carinae, which is one of the most luminous in the galaxy, now lies shrouded within Homunculus. Since the discovery of Homunculus, it has been growing larger. Today, Homunculus has a rich orange center and a yellow-white surround. See CHARON.

Innes's star Proxima Centauri, discovered by R.T. Innes in 1915, a double star. Proxima Centauri is 2° away from its companion, Alpha Centauri. With a distance of 1.31 parsecs, slightly closer than Alpha Centauri, Proxima is the nearest known star to our solar system. It is a dwarf star with a magnitude of 13.1; it is also a flare star, brightening to twelfth magnitude.

Insertion the process of putting an artificial satellite or spacecraft into orbit. See INJECTION.

Insolation **1.** incoming solar radiation;

2. the exposure of any surface or body to solar radiation.

Intensity the brightness of a source of light.

Intercrater plains the relatively smooth terrain on Mercury.

Interface **1.** a common boundary between two parts of a system;

2. in a rocket vehicle, a common boundary between two components.

Interferometer an optical device used in astronomy for determining the diameters of the largest nearby stars.

Intergalactic globular cluster a globular star cluster or a small galaxy resembling such a cluster, found in intergalactic space.

intergalactic matter the matter that exists in the space between galaxies.

International Sun-Earth Explorer see ISEE.

International Ultraviolet Explorer see IUE.

interplanetary dust a cloud of dust and electrons surrounding the sun.

interplanetary medium As viewed from Earth, the space between planets is empty. This space is actually filled with gas, mostly hydrogen, and with dust particles (charged protons).

interstellar dust the microscopic dustlike grains that exist in the space between stars.

interstellar matter the gas and dust in the space between the stars.

interstellar medium the interstellar gas, dust, and cosmic rays.

interstellar obscuration the absorption of starlight by interstellar dust, causing distant objects to appear fainter.

interstellar reddening the process by which dust scatters blue light out of starlight and makes stars look redder.

interstellar wind see SOLAR WIND.

intramercurial planet Vulcan, a hypothetical major planet, thought during the 19th century to orbit the sun within the orbit of Mercury. A small planet was discovered in that location in the spring of 1986. In 1859 the astronomer Lescarbault observed a dark spot moving across the sun. It may have been the same small planet discovered in 1986.

intrinsic brightness **1.** the amount of energy (usually light) that an object gives off;

2. true brightness, independent of the effects of distance or dimming by intervening material.

inverse square law a rule holding that the strength of an effect (such as gravity) decreases proportionally as the distance squared increases.

Io Jupiter I, a satellite of Jupiter, discovered by Galileo, orbiting at a mean distance of 421,800 km. Io is the innermost of the four large Galilean satellites (moons) of Jupiter. It is yellow-brown in color and has extensive surface deposits resembling those of the Utah salt flats. A sodium cloud is seen in Io's orbit, and the surface of Io lacks impact craters. Intense volcanic action was observed by the Voyager I probe, and Io gives off bursts of electrical discharges that emit radio waves detectable on Earth.

Io flux tube a region of magnetic lines and electric currents connecting Io and Jupiter.

ion column a trail of ionized gases seen in the trajectory of a meteoroid when it enters the upper atmosphere.

ion engine or **electrostatic engine**, a reaction engine in which ions, accelerated in an electrostatic field, are used as propellant.

Ionized hydrogen hydrogen that has lost its electron.

Ionized hydrogen gas gas with free protons and free electrons, commonly found in stars and nebulae.

Ionosphere the atmospheric shell; characterized by a high ion density. Its base is about 70 km above Earth, and the ionosphere extends to an indefinite height.

Ionospheric storm a disturbance of the ionosphere, resulting in anomalous variations in its characteristics and in its effects on radio communication.

Ion tail see COMET TAIL.

Iota Aquarids a minor meteor stream in the southern sky that is active in August.

IRAS the Infrared Astronomical Satellite, the first satellite-borne infrared telescope, launched in 1981. The orbiting infrared telescope operates unhampered by the atmosphere, thus providing the first deep-sky survey.

Iris (Asteroid 7) a minor planet discovered in 1847 by English astronomer John R. Hind (1823–1895). With a diameter of 209 km, Iris has a magnitude of 7.8. Only three other asteroids are brighter: Vesta, Ceres, and Pallas.

IRIS-1 a satellite (*I*nternational *R*adiation *I*nvestigation *S*atellite) that measured radiation from the sun and cosmic rays, including x-rays, solar and Van Allen belt protons, and high-energy electrons.

Iron meteorites meteorites composed of iron-nickel metal. Most of the rest are nickel. The Cape York and Arizona craters are examples of iron meteorites.

Irregular galaxy a galaxy of relatively low mass and no specific shape, neither spiral nor elliptical.

Irregular variables pulsating variable stars, such as red giants, with flares in their outer layers. See VARIABLE STAR.

Ishtar Terra or **Ishtar** one of the main highland regions in the northern hemisphere of Venus. Located west of Maxwell Montes, the largest volcano on Venus (11 km in elevation), Ishtar is the highest surface point of Venus (2.5 km above datum) and is approximately the size of Australia.

Isidis Planitia a low-lying Martian plain, 15° N and 170° W, that is west of Olympus Mons Volcano.

Island universe the name once given to galaxies. See GALAXY.

Ismenia Fossa or **Ismenius Lacus** a shallow depression 37 to 42° S and 315 to 337° W on Mars. It lies north of Hellas.

ISEE International Sun-Earth Explorer, a series of three satellites launched in 1977 and 1978 to study Earth's magnetosphere and its interaction with solar phenomena.

IUE International Ultraviolet Explorer, the main satellite used for ultraviolet astronomy until the launching of the Hubble Space Telescope.

Ius Chasma a canyon in the equatorial region of the southern hemisphere of Mars, at latitude -10° to -14° and longitude 77° to 92°, that forms the western portion of Valley Marineris.

Ivar (Asteroid 1627) a part of the Amor asteroid group. Ivar has a diameter of 7 km.

Izar the common name for the triple star Epsilon Boötes, in the Northern Hemisphere, near Virgo. Izar, also called the Girdle, is 103 light-years from Earth.

J

jansky (Jy) a unit of flux density for electromagnetic radiation, used in radio astronomy; named for Karl Jansky.

Jansky, Karl Guthe (1905–1950) American engineer and pioneer in radio astronomy. He developed the first radio telescope and, in 1931, became the first person to detect radio waves from the Milky Way.

jansky noise another name for *cosmic noise*.

Janssen a low lunar walled plain at -47° S and +43° E, broken by the Fabricius crater. Janssen is 170 km in diameter.

Janus the tenth and innermost satellite (moon) of Saturn. It was discovered in 1966, when Saturn's rings were edge-on to Earth. Janus, which is 200 km in diameter, orbits Saturn in 0.75 days.

jet propulsion the propulsion of a rocket or other craft by employing its reaction to a force ejecting a gas or liquid from it.

Jet Propulsion Laboratory (JPL) an observatory at Goldstone, California, the site of NASA's Deep Space Communications Complex.

jets intergalactic gaseous streamers composed of highly excited electrons that are noted for their luminosity and radio emission. Jet sources include quasars and protostars.

Jewel Box (NGC 4755) a brilliant open star cluster in the southern constellation Crux. The cluster is named from the remark by John Herschel that NGC 4755 resembled a superb piece of jewelry. It is about 8 parsecs across and 2400 parsecs away. See HERSCHEL, JOHN.

Jodrell Bank the site of a large radio astronomy observatory, located near Manchester, England.

Johnson Space Center the headquarters for United States manned space missions, located at Houston, Texas.

Jolly balance an apparatus used to measure the mass of Earth.

joule (J) the unit of work or energy in the SI metric system.

Jovian planet a term applied to the giant planets: Jupiter, Saturn, Uranus, and Neptune.

Jovian satellites Jupiter's moons. See Fig. 39.

Julian calendar a calendar based on the apparent motions of the sun, introduced by Julius Caesar in 46 BC. It provides a year of 365 days, except for every fourth year, which has 366 days.

jumbled terrain the strangely disturbed regions of the moon opposite the locations of the Imbrium Basin and Mare Oriental.

June Lyrids a minor meteor shower maximizing on or about June 16.

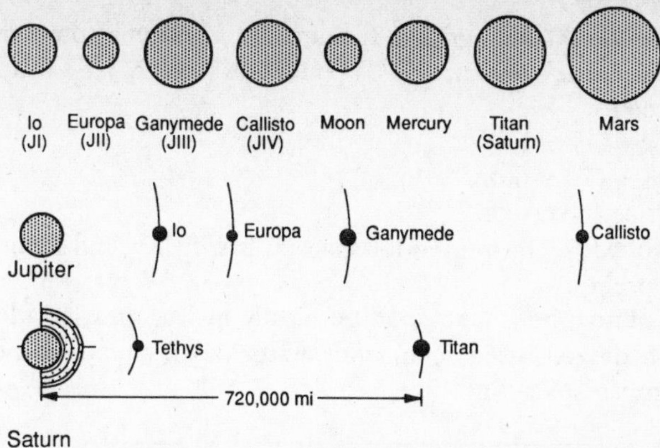

Fig. 39. **Jovian satellites.** Io, Europa, Ganymede, and Callisto—the four largest moons of Jupiter—are shown in their order and distance from Jupiter. Other celestial bodies are shown for purposes of comparison.

June solstice another name for the summer solstice, which occurs on June 22 in the Northern Hemisphere and on December 22 in the Southern Hemisphere.

Juno the third minor planet (asteroid) to be discovered, found by German astronomer Ludwig Harding (1765–1834) in 1804. Juno, the fourth largest and one of the four brightest asteroids, has a diameter of 247 km. See HARDING.

Jupiter the fifth planet from the sun and the largest in the solar system. Jupiter's equatorial diameter is 142,800 km, and its rotation period is less than 10 hours, shorter than that of any other planet. Jupiter has 16 moons as well as a ring system. This planet is bigger and heavier than all of the other planets and their moons combined. It gives off about twice as much heat as it receives from the sun—its core temperature may be 53,000° F or more. Jupiter also emits off radio signals and x-rays.

Jupiter's atmosphere is made up mostly of hydrogen, with some helium. In its clouds are traces of colorless methane, ammonia, water vapor, and other gases. Countless tiny particles and large rocks whiz around Jupiter. The rings they form, which reflect sunlight, extend some 34,000 miles outward from Jupiter's cloud tops. Jupiter shines more brightly than any other planet except Venus. With a telescope, an observer on Earth can see Jupiter's Great Red Spot, stripes of clouds, and Jupiter's four largest moons: Io, Europa, Ganymede, and Callisto.

Four United States spacecraft have flown by Jupiter. In 1973 and 1974, Pioneer 10 and 11 sent the first close-up photographs of Jupiter back to Earth. In 1979 Voyager 1 and 2 returned important data and more than 33,000 photographs. Incidentally, a person who weighs 1000 pounds on Earth would weigh 234 pounds on Jupiter. See VOYAGER.

Jupiter I see IO.

Jupiter II see EUROPA.

Jupiter III see GANYMEDE.

Jupiter IV see CALLISTO.

Jupiter probes the term used for spaceprobes, flybys, and Pioneer and Voyager probes.

Jupiter's atmospheric composition mostly hydrogen, with additional helium, hydrogen-based compounds, water vapor, ammonia, methane, and other gases. See Fig. 40.

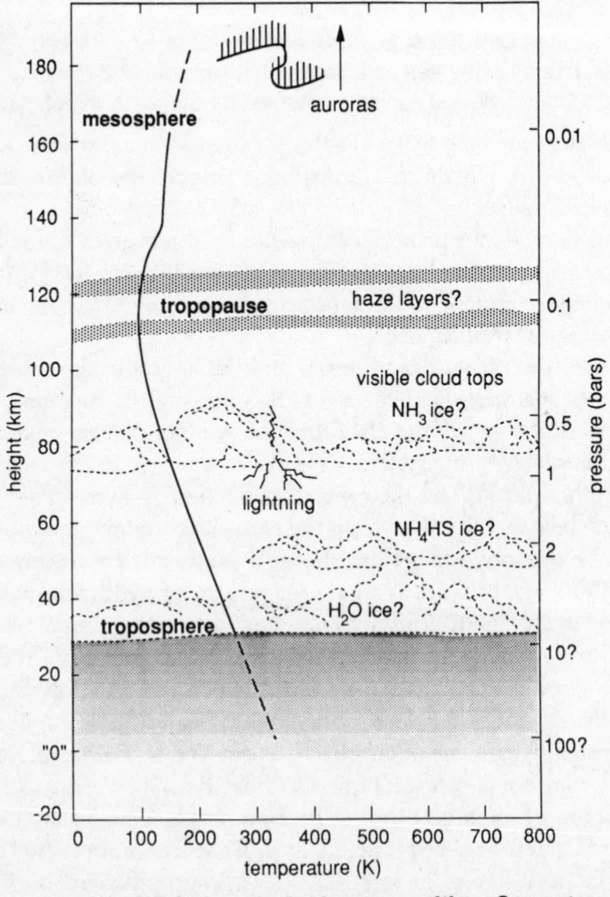

Fig. 40. **Jupiter's atmospheric composition.** See entry.

Jupiter's belts the dark cloud bands in Jupiter's atmosphere that parallel the planet's equator. They are permanent enough to be given names, such as North Polar Region and North Temperate Belt.

Jupiter's comet family a comet family whose distribution of aphelion distances (the comets' farthest points from the sun) correlates with the mean distance of the planet Jupiter. The family includes about 70 members. See Hector and Achilles.

Jupiter's infrared thermal radiation the infrared radiation from Jupiter resulting from slow contraction of its interior and exceeding the incoming solar radiation.

Jupiter's interior a mostly liquid volume with a small rocky core, temperature 53,000° F, and a deep (70,000-km) hydrogen-rich atmosphere, as confirmed by the Pioneer spacecraft. See Fig. 41.

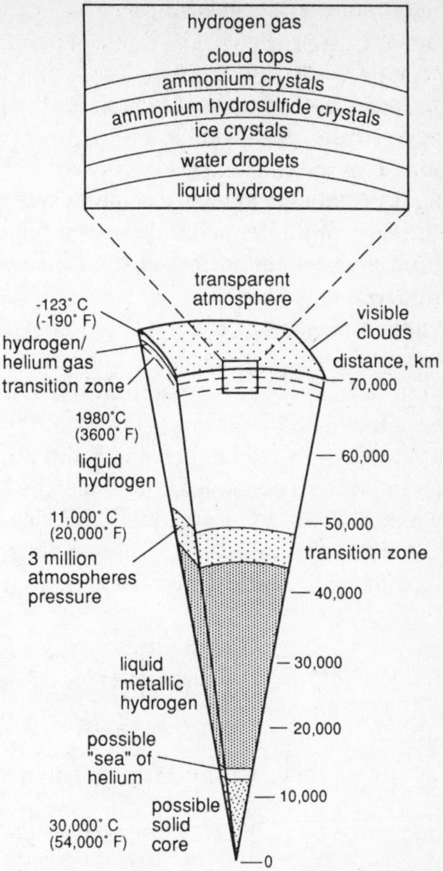

Fig. 41. **Jupiter's Interior.** A three-dimensional representation of the planet in cross section.

Jupiter's (or **Jovian**) **magnetosphere** the large cavity within which Jupiter's magnetic field dominates the interplanetary magnetic field. Jupiter's magnetosphere, one of the largest in the solar system, is among the most dramatic features of the planet. It is actually much larger than the sun and completely envelops the innermost satellites of Jupiter. If we could view the magnetosphere in the sky, it would be the size of Earth's moon. See Fig. 41.

Jupiter's radiation belts the belts of particles trapped in the Jovian magnetic field. The satellites sweep up many of these charged particles. See Fig. 42.

Jupiter's rings nine rings around Jupiter that are probably composed of fine rocky particles. Voyager 1, in its flyby of Jupiter in March 1979 discovered the rings, fainter and narrower than the famous rings of Saturn. They extend 57,000 km outward from Jupiter's cloud tops.

Jupiter's satellite system a complex system of at least 16 moons outside the rings of Jupiter and somewhat resembling a small solar system. The four large moons are called the *Galilean satellites* because they were discovered by Galileo.

Jupiter's temperature about -200° F measured at and above the cloud tops in Jupiter's atmosphere, but increasing below the clouds to values approaching room temperature (on Earth) and even warmer. In the core the temperature could be 53,000° F or higher. See Fig. 43.

Jupiter's zones the bright cloud bands in the atmosphere that run parallel to Jupiter's equator, for example, the North Temperate Zone, North Tropical Zone, and Equatorial Zone. See JUPITER'S BELTS.

Jura Mountains a 155-mile diameter lunar crater, at +46° N and -38° W, that forms the northwest border of Sinus Iridum, a lava-flooded lunar bay.

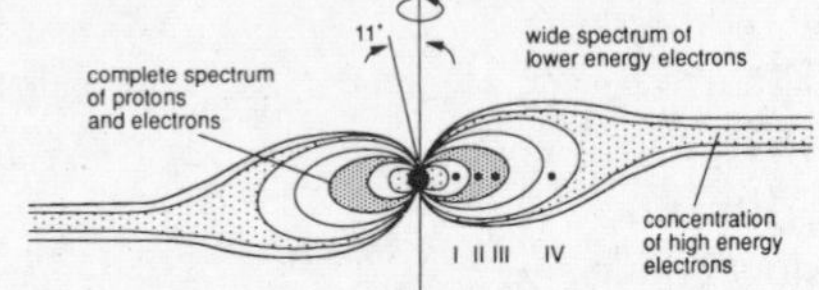

Fig. 42. **Jupiter's radiation belts.** See entry.

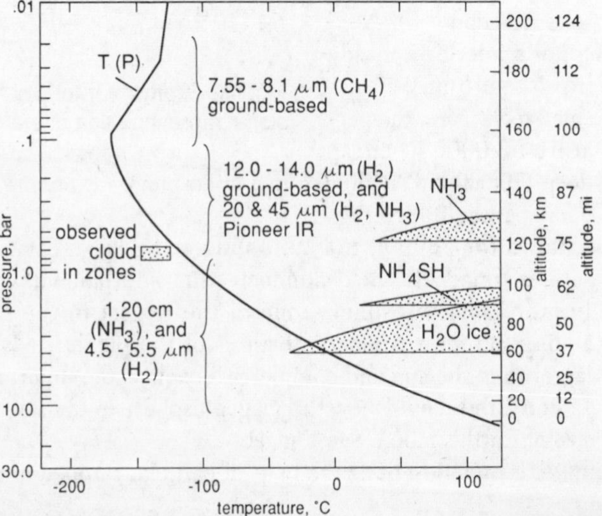

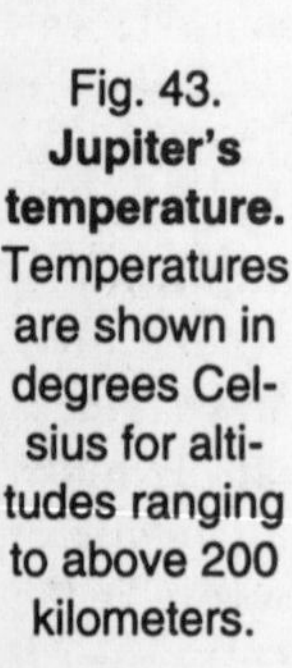

Fig. 43. **Jupiter's temperature.** Temperatures are shown in degrees Celsius for altitudes ranging to above 200 kilometers.

K

Kaalijarv see OESEL CRATER.

Kaffaljidhma the common name for the dwarf star Gamma Ceti of the Southern Hemisphere, in the Cetus constellation. Kaffaljidhma, meaning head of the whale, is a double star of 3.48 magnitude and appearing 68 light-years from Earth.

Kaiser, Frederick (1808–1872) Dutch astronomer who specialized in the study of double stars and constructed a map of Mars.

Kajam the common name for the white star Omega Hercules in the Northern Hemisphere, a dim star on the so-called chest of Hercules, just below Pi Hercules.

Kappa Crucis (NGC 4755) also called the Jewel Box, an open cluster of stars in the Crux constellation of the Southern Constellation.

Kappa Cygnid meteors a meteor stream near Kappa Cygni in the Cygnus constellation that peaks on or about August 20. The meteors are usually seen in the Northern Hemisphere as bright, slow-moving fireballs.

Kasei Vallis a major channel on Mars, at latitude 18° to 27° and longitude 56° to 75°, entering the Chryse Plains. The diameter of Kasei Vallis is 1090 kilometers.

Kaus Australis a common name for the star Epsilon Sagittarii, referring to the southern part of the centaur's bow. See SAGITTARIUS.

Kaus Borealis a common name for the orange star Delta Sagittarii, referring to the northern part of the centaur's bow. See SAGITTARIUS.

K-corona that portion of the radiation from the solar corona consisting of the continuous spectrum scattered by electrons.

Keel a common name for Carina, a southern constellation centered between Puppis to the north and Volans to the south.

Keeler, James Edward (1857–1900) American astronomer, at one time director of the Lick Observatory, near San Jose, California. He pioneered in astronomical photography, applying its techniques to spectroscopy. Keeler discovered 120,000 nebulae and conducted other planetary research. In 1895, he determined the composition of Saturn's rings, showing that parts of the rings revolve more slowly than the inner rings. By measuring the Doppler shifts of various parts of the rings, he demonstrated that the rings are composed of small particles.

Kelb Alrai a common name for the orange star Beta Ophiuchi, 124 light-years from Earth. The Ophiuchus constellation is in the equatorial region, near Hercules and Scorpius. Beta Ophiuchi is also called Cebalrai, the heart of the shepherd.

Kelvin scale the absolute temperature scale, with 0 Kelvin equal to absolute zero. A Kelvin degree is the same as a centigrade degree.

Kennedy Space Center formerly called Cape Canaveral, a spaceport in Florida; NASA's location for the Apollo missions and for the space shuttle missions.

Kepler crater a lunar crater, diameter 35 km, on the Oceanus Procellarum. (Procellarum was the landing site for Apollo 12 in 1969.) The Kepler crater has a major ray-center, bright streaks that radiate out from the center of a lunar crater.

Kepler, Johannes (1571–1630) German astronomer who worked in 1600 with Tycho Brahe. In 1604 Kepler observed a supernova, later known as Kepler's Star, and wrote a book about it. It was the second supernova to appear in 32 years and was also seen by Galileo. No other supernova was seen in our galaxy since that time until the appearance of Nova Cygni in 1975 and Supernova 1987A, a bright supernova that flared up in the Large Magellanic Cloud in February of 1987, reaching naked-eye visibility. It was the first supernova to do so since Kepler's Star of 1604.

Kepler was the first to deduce the shapes and relations of planets' elliptical orbits, proposing three fundamental laws of planetary motion: (1) the orbit of each planet is an ellipse with the sun at one focus of the ellipse; (2) known as the law of equal areas and describing the speed with which the planets travel in their orbits: a line joining the sun and a planet sweeps through equal areas in equal periods of time; (3) the square of the period of revolution—the length of time a planet takes to orbit the sun—is proportional to the cube of the semimajor axis of the ellipse. See TYCHO BRAHE.

Keplerian motion orbital motion in accord with Kepler's laws of planetary motion.

Kepler's laws see KEPLER.

Kepler's star a type I supernova that was observed in October 1604 in the constellation Ophiuchus, the Serpent Bearer. Kepler's star was the second supernova observed in the constellation. The first was Tycho's Star, discovered 32 years earlier. Kepler's star, which could be seen with the naked eye for over a year, was studied by astronomers in Europe, China, and Korea. See OPHIUCHUS.

Kerb a common name for the white star Tau Pegasi, in the Northern Hemisphere. It is part of the so-called body of Pegasus, the winged horse.

Kerr black hole a solution to the equations of general relativity that describes the properties of a rotating BLACK HOLE. The Kerr black hole is named for Roy P. Kerr, who in 1963 solved Einstein's equations dealing with black holes.

Keyhole nebula a dust cloud associated with CARINA and named by astronomer John Herschel (1792–1871, son of William HERSCHEL).

Kiffa Australis a common name for the white giant star Alpha Librae, magnitude 2.75, part of the southern constellation Libra and 65 light-years from Earth. This double star is also known as Zubenelgenubi or Zuben El Genubi, which may be translated as the southern claw of the scorpion.

Kiffa Borealis a common name for Beta Librae, 140 light-years from Earth and with an actual luminosity about 145 times that of the sun. There is a classic controversy over a supposed change in brightness that has been said to have occurred since ancient times. It is said that Eratosthenes assigned the star first place among all the stars in Scorpius and Libra. Ptolemy, several centuries later, found the star the equal of Antares, and some astronomers suggest that it may be Antares, rather than Beta Librae, that experiences changes in brightness. Another mystery concerns the fact that this white star has so often been described as *greenish* or *plain emerald*. Olcott refers to Kiffa as the only naked-eye star that is green in color, while T.W. Webb refers to its beautiful plain green color. Modern observers generally agree that the only stars which appear definitely green are the close companions to red stars, such as Antares itself. If Beta Librae truly appears greenish, which observers must decide for themselves, it is the only bright single star that does so. Beta Librae is also known as Zubeneschemali, meaning *northern claw of the scorpion*.

King the common name for Cepheus, a northern constellation.

kiloparsec (kpc) a unit of space distance equal to 1000 PC (parsecs) or 3260 ly (light-years).

kinetic energy energy associated with motion. The kinetic energy of a body is one-half the product of its mass and the square of its velocity.

Kirchhoff's laws statements that describe the formation of continuous spectra, emission spectra, and absorption spectra: (1) a gas at high pressure, a liquid, or a solid, if heated to incandescence, will glow with a continuous spectrum, or continuum; (2) a hot gas under low pressure will produce only certain bright colors, called emission lines; and (3) a cool gas at low pressure, if placed between an observer and a hot continuous-spectrum source, absorbs certain colors, causing absorption lines in the observed spectrum.

Kirkwood, Daniel (1814–1895) American astronomer who first explained, in 1857, the Kirkwoods gaps. He wrote extensively on meteoric astronomy and comets.

Kirkwood's gaps voids in the spacing of particles in the rings of Saturn or in the asteroid belt. The gaps were named after American astronomer Daniel Kirkwood (1814–1895), who first explained the gap phenomenon. See SATURN.

Kocab or **Kochab** the orange dwarf star Beta Ursae Minoris, one of the so-called Guardians of the Pole, also called Kochab. This giant, 104 light-years from Earth, is in the Ursa Minor constellation, near the north celestial pole and just above Pherkad.

Kochab see KOCAB.

Kohoutek (Comet 1973 XII) a comet discovered in March of 1973 by the Czech astronomer Lubos Kohoutek (1935–). The comet traveled a distance of almost 4000 AU in a parabolic orbit and had a period of approximately 80,000 years. On December 28, 1973, it passed within a million kilometers of the sun. Kohoutek was extensively investigated from outside Earth's atmosphere by Skylab 4 in 1973, and astronaut Edward G. Gibson, a crew member, photographed it with an ultraviolet camera. Gibson reported that Kohoutek was orange in color and had an impressive sunward spike. Because of Kohoutek's parabolic orbit, it may be lost until its next predicted return, about 80,000 years from now.

Kopff's Comet a comet first observed in 1906. It passed near Jupiter in 1942 and 1954, apparently so close to the planet's strong gravitational field that the slingshot effect caused a change in the orbit of the comet. The comet's period is 6.4 years. The most recent return was in 1983, but Kopf's Comet has not been seen since.

Korelev a circular crater at 4° S and 167° W on the far side of the moon, near the equator, and more than 400 km in diameter.

Kornephoros the common name for the yellow giant star star Beta Herculis, also called Rutilicus, in the Northern Hemisphere. Beta Hercules is 105 light-years from Earth, next to Rujan (meaning star) in the Hercules constellation. Kornephoros is from a Greek word meaning club-bearer.

Kraz the common name for the yellow giant star Beta Corvi 108 light-years from Earth. Kraz is opposite Alchiba in the southern Corvus constellation, next to the Crater constellation.

KREEP *acronym for* potassium *(K)*, *r*are *e*arth *e*lements *p*hosphorus—all constituents of a type of basaltic rock found on our moon. KREEP samples have been brought up from the moon's interior by impact cratering.

Kruger 60 a binary red dwarf star of the 12th magnitude found in the northern constellation Cepheus. It is 12.8 light-years from Earth.

Kuiper a crater 40 km in diameter, at latitude -11° and longitude 32° on Mercury, named for astronomer Gerard Peter Kuiper. Kuiper was the first crater observed on Mercury during the Mariner 10 approach in 1974.

Kuiper, Gerard Peter (1905–1973) American astronomer, born in The Netherlands, who discovered Miranda, a moon of Uranus, and Nereid, a moon of Neptune—both named for the sea nymphs that served as Poseidon's attendants. In 1950, Kuiper tried to measure Pluto's disk with the newly operational 200-inch telescope on Palomar Mountain and concluded that Pluto was less than 3500 miles in diameter.

Kuiper Airborne Observatory (KAO) the world's largest aircraft-borne observatory, operated by NASA. The host aircraft, which became operational in 1975, is an instrumented Lockheed C-141 transport carrying a 0.9-meter telescope for high-altitude astronomical observations, mainly at infrared wavelengths. Using this telescope, the world's largest airborne instrument of its kind, scientists discovered the rings of Uranus while observing the temporary disappearance of a faint star behind the planet. Five rings were found to lie 18,000 km from the planet's cloud tops. They appear to consist of four thin inner rings that follow nearly circular orbits around Uranus, and one thick outer ring whose orbit may not exactly circular. KAO also enabled scientists to discover the presence of water vapor in the atmosphere of Jupiter and to make a close study of Halley's Comet.

Kuma the common name for the white star Nu Draconis, the faintest of the four stars that form the little quadrangle in the head of Draco. Nu Draconis, a double star of the Draco constellation, is 120 light-years from Earth and one of the easiest pairs to find in the Northern Hemisphere. It is generally visible with the aid of good binoculars.

L

Lacaille, Nicolas Louis de (1713–1762) French astronomer known as the father of southern astronomy for his work at the Cape of Good Hope, where he compiled an extensive catalog of southern stars and became the first observer to measure a South African arc of the meridian. He determined lunar and solar parallax, pioneering the lunar-distance method of finding longitude. In addition, he named 14 new constellations, personally observed 10,000 stars, and determined the coordinates of 2000 others. See LUNAR PARALLAX.

Lacerta (Lac) the Lizard, a faint northern constellation in the Milky Way lying between Cygnus and Andromeda. Lacerta was introduced by Polish astronomer Johannes Hevelius (1611–1687) in his star atlas of 1687. Lacerta's stars are of 4th magnitude and fainter, and have not been named.

lag an interval of time occurring between a change in a condition being monitored and the indication of the change on the monitoring instrument employed.

Lagoon Nebula (NGC 6523) a nebula in Sagittarius, in the Southern Hemisphere. See SAGITTARIUS.

Lagrange, Joseph Louis (1736–1813) French mathematician and astronomer who developed the Turin Academy of Sciences, was president of the French commission on weight and measures, and is particularly remembered for his encouragement of the adoption of the metric system. He and the famous French mathematician Pierre-Simon de Laplace (1749–1827) used Newton's law of gravity to show that if the moon were found to be slightly egg-shaped, gravitational forces would make the moon's longest axis point toward Earth at all times. Space vehicles have confirmed this in the last few decades. One axis of the moon is indeed about 2 or 3 km longer than the others and points steadily toward Earth.

Lagrangian coordinates or **material coordinates**, a system of coordinates by which fluid parcels are identified by assigning them coordinates that do not vary with time. Examples of such coordinates are: (1) the values of any properties of the fluid conserved in motion, and (2) more generally, the positions in space of the parcels at some arbitrarily selected moment. Subsequent positions of the parcels in space are then the dependent variables, functions of time and of the Lagrangian coordinates. See FLUID PARCEL.

Lagrangian points. Joseph Louis Lagrange calculated in 1772 that when the law of gravity is applied to two bodies orbiting one another, such as Jupiter and the sun, there would be two positions along the orbit of Jupiter 60° ahead and 60° behind the planet at which small objects near those sites would oscillate without falling to Jupiter or the sun. Many years later, in 1904, asteroids began to be found as those positions, called the Lagrangian points.

There are, in fact, five Lagrangian points for any two bodies revolving around one another. The three not mentioned so far lie along a line connecting the two celestial bodies. These points are not stable for small objects, because if the objects are disturbed even slightly from their positions by the influence of the sun or another planet, they will wander away and never return. No asteroids have thus far been found at the Lagrangian points in the Earth-moon system, but there have been reports of particles detected at the orbital positions 60° ahead and 60° behind the smaller body. See Fig. 44 and LAGRANGE.

Lakshmi Planum one of two main highlands on Venus, the western part of Ishtar Terra. Height of the highland is 3 kilometers above the standard level. See ISHTAR TERRA.

Lambda Scorpii also known as Shaula, the sting. With a magnitude of 1.63, Lambda Scorpii is the brightest star in the so-called sting of Scorpius. See SCORPIUS.

Lambda Tauri an eclipsing binary star in the Taurus constellation, in the Northern Hemisphere. See TAURUS.

Landau damping damping of a space charge wave by electrons that move at the phase velocity of the wave and gain energy transferred

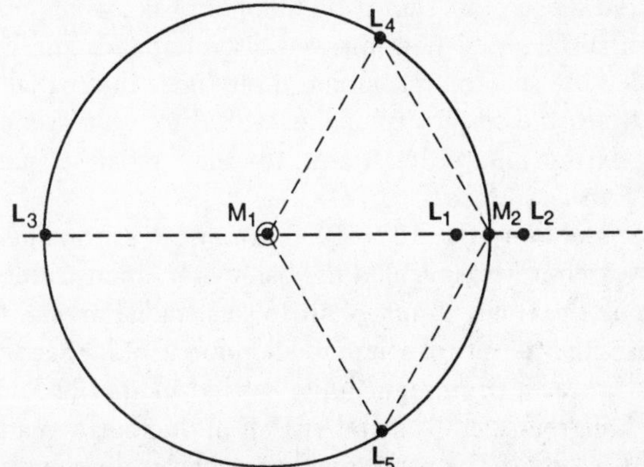

Fig. 44. **Lagrangian points.** The five points discussed in the entry are shown here, marked L, 1 to 5.

from the wave. The phenomenon is named after the Russian physicist Lev Davidovich Landau (1906–1968), winner of the 1962 Nobel Prize for Physics.

Landsat satellites a series of U.S. satellites used to monitor Earth's resources by means of photography and remote sensing techniques. These satellites have greatly increased our ability to monitor and understand the dynamics and character of the features and materials covering the surface of Earth. Because different surface features have different spectral responses, it is possible to monitor such features as forests, crops, pollution, and marine biology. The first three Landsats were placed in high polar orbits and were capable of scanning all of Earth in 18 days. The last two were placed in lower polar orbits, which afforded better resolution. The name Landsat was changed to NOAA when the operation and management of Landsat was transferred to the *N*ational *O*ceanic and *A*tmospheric *A*dministration of the Department of Commerce for use as an operational civil land remote sensing satellite system. Thus, Landsat 5 is not mentioned in the following paragraphs.

Landsat 1 (July 1972), *Landsat 2* (January 1975), and *Landsat 3* (March 1978): Landsats 1 and 2, originally called ERTS, for *E*arth *R*esources *T*echnology *S*atellites, carried an Earth-viewing sensor called the Multispectral Scanner (MSS). This radiometer obtains images of Earth's surface in four discrete spectral bands. While these three Landsats operated—they were retired in 1983—MSS established that it could provide such valuable images as vegetation types, bare soil and rock conditions, and snow cover on a repetitive basis.

Landsat 4 (July 1982) In addition to the MSS, Landsat 4 has a more sophisticated sensor, the Thermatic Mapper (TM), which measures the intensity of surface radiation in seven discrete bands and has approximately twice the spectral resolution, three times the spatial resolution, and four times the sensitivity of the MSS. From a 695-km orbit it is providing extraordinary detail and, for the first time, natural color images of Earth's surface.

Langley, Samuel Pierpont (1834–1906) American astronomer and aeronautics researcher who invented the balometer, an instrument he used to determine the transparency of air to solar radiation and to measure the increases in intensity of solar radiation found at higher altitudes.

Langrenus crater a prominent lunar walled plain 132 kilometers in diameter. Langrenus, at -9° S and +61° E in the fourth quadrant of the face of the moon, has pronounced terraced walls, level floor, and prominent central peak.

large-impact hypothesis the theory that Earth's moon formed from debris ejected during a collision between Earth and a large planetesimal. See PLANETESIMALS.

Large Magellanic Cloud (LMC) a small galaxy that is a close neighbor (satellite) of our own Milky Way galaxy. It appears as a hazy cloud in the Southern Hemisphere in the constellations DORADO and MENSA and can be seen with the naked eye. The Large Magellanic Cloud was first reported, in 1519, by Portuguese navigator Ferdinand Magellan (c.1480–1521).

Larmor orbit the circular motion of a charged particle in a uniform magnetic field, named for British physicist Joseph Larmor (1857–1942).

laser *acronym for* light *a*mplification by the *s*timulated *e*mission of *r*adiation. A laser is a device that emits a beam of light composed of rays all of the same wavelength (COHERENT LIGHT). The uniformity of wavelength of the rays within the beam makes possible an intense concentration of energy at a sharply defined point. The uses of lasers include illumination at lunar distances, signal communication in outer space and, possibly, destruction of spacecraft and artificial satellites.

Lassell, William (1799–1880) English astronomer and pioneer in the reflecting telescope, noted for building two large reflecting telescopes. He discovered 600 nebulae and several planetary satellites, including Triton, a moon of Neptune, and Hyperion, a moon of Saturn. He also discovered Ariel and Umbriel, satellites of Uranus.

latitude angular distance from a primary great circle or plane. *Terrestrial latitude* is defined as angular distance from the equator, measured

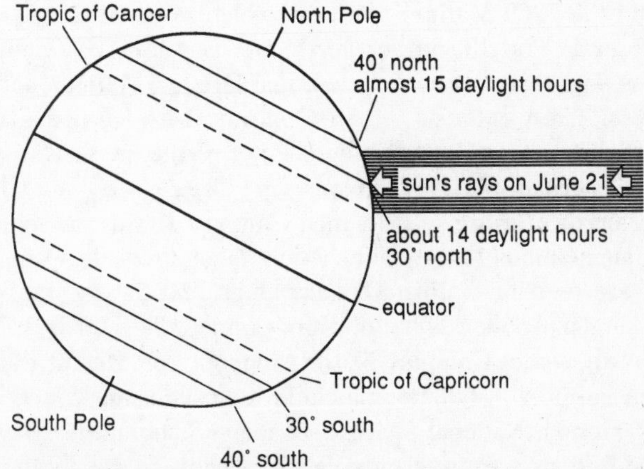

Fig. 45. **Latitude.** Terrestrial latitudes are represented here, along with variations in length of day for Earth's Northern Hemisphere.

northward or southward through 90° and labeled N or S to indicate the direction of measurement. *Astronomical latitude* is defined as angular distance between the direction of gravity and the plane of the equator. See Fig. 45.

launch to send off a rocket vehicle under its own power, as in the case of a space vehicle.

launch azimuth the initial heading of a powered vehicle at launch, commonly applied to launch vehicles.

launch complex the site, facilities, and equipment used to launch a rocket vehicle or space shuttle. NASA operates launch sites at the Eastern Space Missile Center, Florida, and the Western Space and Missile Center, California. It also has access to the San Marco launch complex, owned by Italy, off the east coast of Africa.

About 40 launch complexes have been built at the Kennedy Space Center, Florida, since the area was set aside in 1947 for research and development of guided missiles. A notable one is Launch Complex 39, which is used for manned Saturn 5 vehicles. The complexes, not in strict numerical order, run from south to north along the base. Numbers 5 and 6, now preserved as museums, were used for the first United States spaceflights, the Mercury-Redstone rockets that sent up Alan B. Shepherd and Virgil I. Grissom in 1961. A few miles north is Launch Complex 17, still in use, from which Delta rockets have launched a series of satellites, including Echo, Explorer, and Telstar. Launch Complex 36 is used for Centaur launches. The satellites sent up from here include Surveyor, the Orbiting Astronomical Observatory, and the 1969 Mariner satellites, which revealed secrets of Mars. Complexes 12 and 13, farther north, are used for Atlas/Agena rocket launches, whose successes include Lunar Orbiter, Mariner, and Ranger satellites. Then comes Launch Complex 14, also preserved as a museum. It was from 14 that John Glenn became the first American in orbit on February 20, 1962, followed by three more manned launchings on top of Atlas rockets. Launch Complex 19 was the scene of the 10 two-man Gemini flights, launched by Titan 2 rockets. Complexes 34 and 37 are used for Saturn 1B launchings, and the the first manned Saturn launch, Apollo 7, went up from Complex 34. Finally, still farther to the north, comes Complex 39, the Moonport, on Merritt Island.

NASA support installations include the following: Kennedy Space Center, Florida; National Space Technology Laboratories, Mississippi; Langley Research Center and Wallops Flight Center, both Virginia; NASA Headquarters, Washington, D.C.; Goddard Space Flight Center, Maryland; Lewis Research Center, Ohio; Marshall Space Flight Center,

Alabama; Ames Research Center, Western Test Range, Jet Propulsion Laboratory, and Flight Research Center, all California; White Sands Test Facility, New Mexico; and Johnson Space Center, Texas.

Launch Control Center the area at Kennedy Space Center in Florida from which NASA launch preparations, countdown, and actual launch are controlled. Ten seconds after a rocket has lifted off—the moment when it has traveled vertically a distance exactly equal to the height of the rocket—conduct of the operation is taken over by Mission Control, at the Manned Spacecraft Center, in Houston, Texas, nearly 1000 miles from the Florida site.

Since Gemini 4, the second of the 10 Gemini flights, Mission Control, with a staff of 1000 technicians, has been the centralized control point for all NASA's manned flights, including the space shuttle flights. Teams monitor the progress of each flight continuously. Flight controllers sitting at 117 consoles can check—at the touch of a button—any one of several thousand graphs, tables, and pictures, all constantly updated by computer input.

launch window the precise and very limited period of time during which it is possible to launch a spacecraft for its intended mission. On the Apollo 11 flight, for example, launch had to take place during daylight and under favorable weather conditions, including little sidewind. These requirements were dictated by the need to (a) rescue the astronauts in case of an abort; (b) enable the spacecraft to arrive at the moon at a time when its lunar orbit would be over the selected landing site on the moon and so that touchdown could be made with the sun at a desired angle behind the craft to give the astronauts a good view of the lunar surface; and (c) enable, on return to Earth, a daylight splashdown in the Pacific Ocean.

These requirements mean that a moonlanding launch is possible on three days each month. For Apollo 11, in 1969, it was during a 4-hour, 30-minute period on July 16; a 2-hour, 30-minute period on July 18, or a 2-hour, 15-minute period on July 21. Naturally, as launch time draws near, weather requirements may restrict launch windows further.

On the Apollo 12 flight, because of the requirement to land beside the old Surveyor 3 spacecraft, which had been left on the moon, a launch window of only 3 to 4 hours was available and on only one day a month. (The requirement was successfully met.)

Launch windows for planetary missions are even more constricted—every two years for Mars, but for the GRAND TOUR when Voyager was bounced from Saturn to Uranus to Neptune, the launch window occurred every 180 years.

Launton meteorite the chondrite meteorite that fell in Oxfordshire, England, in 1830. See CHONDRITE.

lava or **magma** molten rock on the surface of a planet. Minerals rarely occur as large, pure samples but are more likely to occur in mixtures, called rocks. These rocks are of three types, according to how the rocks were formed: igneous, metamorphic, and sedimentary.

Igneous rocks are formed by the solidification of hot, molten rock, called magma or lava. These are the most abundant rocks in Earth's crust and presumably in the crusts of the moon and other planets. Igneous rocks are subdivided into two groups. *Extrusive igenous rocks* form when magma cools at the surface of a planet or moon. Their comparatively rapid cooling leaves insufficient time for large crystals to develop, thus giving them a homogeneous appearance. *Intrusive igneous rocks* form beneath the surface of a planet or moon, where surrounding rock acts an insulator, making for slower cooling. Gradual cooling promotes the formation of large crystals that can be seen individually.

Lava or magma also varies in composition, depending primarily on the type of rock melted during its formation. Terrestrial magmas can be divided into acidic and basic varieties. *Acidic magmas* have a comparatively high quartz content, light color, and high viscosity. *Basic magmas* have comparatively low quartz content, dark color, and low viscosity. There are indications that igneous rocks derived from acidic magmas are absent from, or very rare on, other planets. Basic igneous activity, however, has occurred on other bodies of the solar system, including the moon, Mercury, and Mars. The chemical composition of a magma has a significant effect on its behavior when it reaches the surface during a volcanic eruption and also on the types of volcanic structures that will be formed.

law of areas Kepler's second law of planetary motion: A line drawn between any planet and the sun sweeps out equal areas in equal periods of time. See KEPLER'S LAWS.

law of gravitation see LAW OF UNIVERSAL GRAVITATION.

law of the red shift for distant galaxies, the recessional velocities of the galaxies are proportional to their distance from Earth. Their recessional velocities are measured by their red shift; hence, the red shift becomes an indicator of distance. See RED SHIFT.

law of universal gravitation or **law of gravitation** any two objects in space experience a mutual and equal force of attraction. This force is proportional to the product of their masses and inversely proportional to the square of the distance separating the objects. See GRAVITY.

L-corona that portion of the radiation from the solar corona consisting of coronal line emission. See CORONAL LINES OF EMISSION.

leapfrogging the process of phasing, or delaying, the ranging pulse of a tracking radar in order to move, or shift, the target blip on the radarscope presentation past the target blip from another radar tracking station.

Leda a dark rocky satellite of Jupiter about 10 km in diameter. It was discovered in 1974 by astronomer Charles Kowal. Leda has a sidereal period (in which it orbits around Jupiter) of 239 days at a mean distance of 11,110,000 km from Jupiter. Leda lies beyond Jupiter's fourth largest moon.

LEM see LUNAR EXCURSION MODULE.

lenticular galaxies galaxies that appear lens-shaped when seen on edge. The word *lenticular* derives from a Latin word meaning lentil-like.

Leo the Lion, also called Leo Major, a large zodiacal constellation in the Northern Hemisphere near Ursa Major and between Virgo and Cancer. Its brightest stars include the bright star Regulus (meaning the Little King and sometimes called Cor Leonis, the Lion's Heart); Denebola (the Lion's Tail, Serpha, Dafirah, the Changer or the Governor of the Weather); Algeiba (Gamma Leonis or the Lion's Mane); Zozma (Delta Leonis, the Girdle, Duhr, and the Lion's Back, Zubra); and Ras Elased (Epsilon Leonis, or the Southern Star of the Lion's Head). The area of the Leo constellation contains the Mira star R Leonis, the dwarf nova X Leonis, and several galaxies including the spirals M65, M66, M95, and M96.

Leo Minor (LMi) the Little Lion, a small inconspicuous constellation introduced by Polish astronomer Johannes Helvelius in 1687 and located in the Northern Hemisphere between Leo and Ursa Major. In Arab folklore Leo Minor was a gazelle with its young; in China it was part of a dragon. Leo Minor was formed from faint stars that previously were not part of any constellation. Its brightest stars are of only fourth magnitude. Curiously, Leo Minor has no star labeled Alpha, although there is a Beta Leo Minoris. This seems to have been caused by an oversight on the part of the 19th-century English astronomer Francis Baily. Helvelius did not label the stars in any of his newly formed constellations, so Baily did it for him 150 years later. Thus, Baily assigned Beta to the second brightest star in Leo Minor but neglected to assign the label Alpha to the brightest. See LEO.

Leonids the so-called *November swarm*, a periodic meteor shower occurring in the Northern Hemisphere about November 15 and appearing to radiate from a point in the constellation Leo. An associated meteor stream is the dust debris from the comet Tempel-Tuttle. The Leonids produced spectacular displays in 1799, 1866, and 1966. See LEO and TEMPEL-TUTTLE COMET.

Leonov, Alexei Arkhipovich (1934–) Soviet cosmonaut who was the first man to walk in space. When he was aboard the Voskhod 2 spacecraft orbiting Earth on March 18, 1965, he performed the first extravehicular activity (see EVA), walking in space for 10 minutes. Leonov in 1975 participated in the joint US-USSR Apollo-Soyuz space mission. See APOLLO-SOYUZ MISSION.

Leo systems the two members of the Local Group of galaxies, Leo I system and Leo II system. Both these galaxies are approximately 220 kiloparsecs from Earth. See LOCAL GROUP.

Lepus (Lep) the Hare, a constellation in the Southern Hemisphere south of Orion. Its brightest stars include the very luminous remote Arneb (Alpha Leporis or Arsh) and Nihal (Beta Leporis). The constellation is also noted for the Crimson Star, a famous long period pulsating red variable that was first seen, in 1845, by English astronomer John Russell Hind (1823–1895).

Lesath the common name for the star Nu Scorpii, called the Sting.

Le Verrier, Urbain Jean Joseph (1811–1877) French astronomer and director of the Paris Observatory, whose investigation of the irregularity in the motion of Uranus led to the discovery of Neptune in 1846 by German astronomer Johann Galle (1812–1910).

Lexell's Comet a comet discovered in 1770 by French astronomer Charles Messier (1730–1817) but named after Finnish-born mathematician Anders Johan Lexell (1740–1784), who calculated its orbit. Prior to 1767 the comet had a period of 11.4 years, but a close approach to Jupiter in 1770 changed this to 5.6 years, and the next close approach to Jupiter, in 1779, changed this period to a calculated 174 years. The 1779 approach perturbed the comet so that it has a perihelion distance of 5.4 AU and, because it has always been too far away from Earth, has not been seen since. The 1770 approach to Earth was the closest ever by a comet.

In 1781, Lexell calculated approximations of a circular orbit for Uranus that demonstrated that, unlike any known comet or planet of that time, Uranus—it seemed to be violating the law of gravity by its orbital path—was indeed in a planetary orbit. That orbit enabled astronomers to predict more accurately where Uranus would be found. See PERIHELION.

Libra (Lib) the Balance, a dim zodiacal constellation in the Southern Hemisphere between Virgo and Serpens. Alpha Librae, a green second-magnitude star, and the brightest star in Libra, is also called Zuben El Genubi or the Southern Claw. Beta Librae is the second brightest. It is also known as Zuben Eschamali or the Northern Claw.

librations the real or apparent oscillatory motions of the moon over a period of time that enable the observer to see more than half of the moon's surface.

life zone a region around a star within which a planet can have temperatures that would accommodate the presence of liquid water.

lift-off the action of a rocket vehicle as it separates from its launch pad in a vertical ascent.

light visible radiation considered in terms of its luminous efficiency.

light curve a graph that indicates the variations in light output of a variable star or an eclipsing binary system as the variations occur over a period of time. See VARIABLE STAR and ECLIPSING BINARY.

light energy see LUMINOUS ENERGY.

lighthouse theory the supposition that a neutron star, as it rotates, produces pulses of radiation by sweeping radio beams around the sky.

light microsecond the distance a light wave travels in free space, a perfect vacuum—where the light wave is not reflected or refracted—in one-millionth of a second.

light pollution a problem of modern times, the excess light in the sky, the reduced viewing of the stars by manmade light sources, such as street lights, which is difficult to overcome. Natural light sources include the moon, airglow, and other atmospheric effects. See AIRGLOW and ZODIACAL LIGHT.

light speed or **velocity of light** 300,000 kilometers per second, or 186,000 miles per second.

light time the elapsed time taken by electromagnetic radiation to travel from a celestial body to the observer at the time of observation. The *American Ephemeris and Nautical Almanac* uses a light time of 498.8 seconds for one astronomical unit (AU).

light-year a unit of stellar distance equal to the distance light travels through space in one mean solar year. One light-year equals 0.3066 parsec (PC) or 63,240 astronomical units (AU). See ASTRONOMICAL UNIT.

limb the edge of the apparent disk of a celestial body—the sun, a planet, or a moon.

limb darkening a condition sometimes observed on celestial objects in which the brightness of the object decreases as the edges, or limbs, of the object are approached. The sun and Jupiter exhibit limb darkening. See LIMB.

limb of the Earth the edge of Earth at the horizon. See LIMB.

Lindblad, Bertil (1895–1965) Swedish astronomer who served as director of the Stockholm Observatory and was known for his research in stellar and galactic dynamics, the study of the motion of material bodies under the influence of forces, including that of gravity.

line of apsides 1. the major axis of an ellipse;

2. a line connecting the two points of an orbit that are nearest and farthest from the center of attraction, as the perigee and apogee of the moon or the perihelion and aphelion of a planet;

3. the major axis of any elliptical orbit and extending indefinitely in both directions. See APSIDES, PERIHELION, APHELION.

liner *acronym for* *l*ow *i*onization *n*arrow *e*mission-line *r*egion, a galaxy in which gas is apparently heated by a very faint quasarlike nucleus, lacking the broad-line emission of Seyfert galaxies. See SEYFERT GALAXY.

line of nodes 1. a straight line connecting the two points of *intersection* of the orbit of a planet, planetoid, or comet and the *ecliptic*;

2. the line of intersection of the planes of the orbits of a satellite and its primary.

line of position in navigation, a line representing all possible locations of a craft at a given instant. In space this concept can be extended to sphere of position, plane of position, etc.

Linke scale or **blue-sky scale** a type of cyanometer, which is an instrument used to measure the blueness of the sky. Skyblueness study, or cyanometry, is a means of studying atmospheric turbidity. See TURBIDITY.

Linne a crater 1600 feet in depth located in the northern hemisphere on the near side of the moon at 28° N and 12° E. The crater appears to be a white patch 7 miles in diameter inside Mare Serenitatis (Sea of Serenity, a large but rather dark lava flow) near the Caucasus and Apennine mountains. Apollo 15 made its lunar landing near this site, and astronauts David R. Scott, James B. Irwin, and Alfred M. Worden used a Lunar Roving Vehicle to drive about, covering a total of 27.9 km in exploring the area.

German astronomers Johann Madler (1794–1874) and Wilhelm Beer (1797–1850), who produced the first really good map of the face of the moon in 1837–1838, described Linne in 1832 as a small, but deep and well-formed crater in Mare Serenitatis. Another German astronomer, Johann Schmidt (1825–1884), announced in 1866 that the crater had disappeared and had been replaced by a white patch. Madler wrote in 1868 that Linne looked just the same to him as it had in 1832.

Apollo photographs show that Linne is a now a small, deep crater of regular form, with a bright area around it, but it appears quite certain that there has been no general alteration in the the appearance of Linne.

Lion the common name for the Leo constellation. See LEO.

Lippershey, Hans (c.1570–c.1619) Dutch optician who applied for a patent on his telescope in 1608. He was one of several possible inventors of the telescope.

liquid oxygen or **lox** oxygen cooled below its boiling point, -183° Celsius. One of its major uses is as a rocket propellant.

liquid propellant a rocket propellant in liquid form, for example, the fuels alcohol, gasoline, aniline, liquid ammonia, and liquid hydrogen; or the oxidants liquid oxygen, hydrogen peroxide, or nitric acid. *Fuel* for a liquid-propellant rocket engine is ordinarily distinguished from *oxidizer*, which is a substance that supports the combustion of a fuel or propellant.

lithometeor a mass of dry, solid matter suspended in the atmosphere, as smoke, dust, dry haze, etc.

lithosphere 1. the solid part of Earth. See Fig. 46.
2. the crust of a planet.

Little Bear or **Lesser Bear** common names for Ursa Minor, the northernmost constellation. Ursa Minor contains the stars that make up the Little Dipper. See LITTLE DIPPER.

Little Dipper the northern constellation Ursa Minor, also called the Little Bear. It is a region of the north celestial pole, near Draco and Ursa

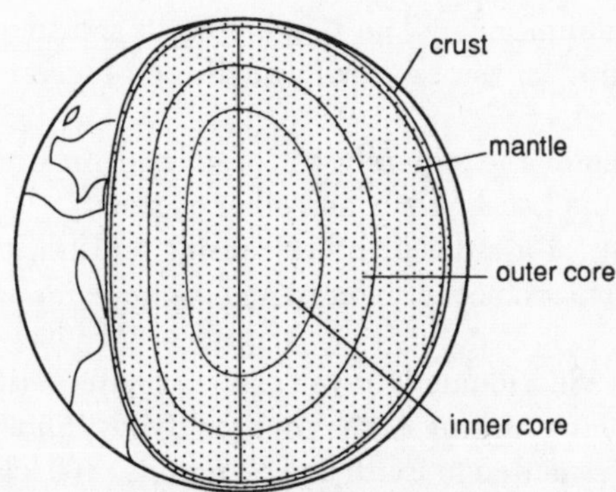

Fig. 46. **Lithosphere.** The layers of the lithosphere are identified here in a cutaway view of Earth.

Major. The Little Bear was said by the ancient Greeks to have been the first constellation named by the astronomer Thales of Miletus (c.625–545 BC). The earliest reference seems to have been made by the poet Callimachus of the 3rd century BC, who reported that Thales "measured out the little stars of the Wain by which the Phoenicians sail." Phoenicians navigated by reference to Ursa Minor rather than Ursa Major. The Little Bear is smaller and fainter than the Great Bear, but lies closer to the pole and so provides a better guide to true north. Aratus called Ursa Minor Cynosura, meaning dog's tail. See BIG DIPPER.

LM or **LEM** lunar module, also called lunar excursion module, used during the Apollo flights. See LUNAR EXCURSION MODULE.

LMC *abbreviation for* the Large Magellanic Cloud (galaxy). See LARGE MAGELLANIC CLOUD.

lobate scarp a curved or lobed cliff, for example, certain cliffs found on Mercury.

lobes the regions to the sides of the center of a radio source, from which high-energy particles are radiating.

local apparent noon the time at which the center of the sun is on the observer's meridian. See MERIDIAN.

Local Group a small group of galaxies, the one to which our Milky Way belongs. Andromeda Galaxy, Leo I, and the Large Magellanic Cloud are also members of the Local Group, which includes 25 or more galaxies. See LARGE MAGELLANIC CLOUD.

local mean time **1.** time defined by the distance that the sun travels at a constant rate along the ecliptic;

2. Greenwich mean time; local time at the Greenwich, England, meridian.

local meridian an imaginary line running north and south through the observer's zenith (in the sky) or through the observer's position (on Earth).

Local Supercluster the supercluster of galaxies in which reside the Virgo Cluster, the Local Group, and other clusters.

lock or **lock on** (of a radar or other sensing and tracking device) to acquire a particular object of interest and continue tracking it automatically.

Loki originally called Plume 2, a volcano on Jupiter's satellite Io. This volcano was active during both Voyager flybys. Photographs of its plume were transmitted to Earth and seen to rise 100 kilometers above Io's surface.

Lockyer, Joseph Norman (1836–1920) English astronomer who became famous for his studies of the spectrums of sunspots and solar prominences. He discovered the element helium on the sun before its discovery on Earth.

Lomonosov, Mikhail Vasilievich (1711–1765) Russian scientist and astronomer, who was the first to prove that Venus had an atmosphere. When Venus is approximately between Earth and the sun, sunlight backlights the upper atmosphere of Venus, revealing the hazy layer ringing the planet.

long-baseline system a trajectory-measuring or missile tracking system with receiving stations separated by distance in the order of magnitude of the distance to the target being tracked.

longitude 1. angular distance along a primary great circle from the adopted reference point, that is, the angle between a reference plane through the polar axis and a second plane through that axis;
2. of a planet in the solar system, the sum of two angles: the celestial longitude of the ascending node of the planetary orbit, and the angle measured eastward from the ascending node along the orbit to the position of the planet.

longitude, types of including the following: *terrestrial longitude*, the arc of a parallel, or the angle at the pole, between the prime meridian and the meridian of a point on Earth, measured eastward or westward from the prime meridian through 180° and labeled E or W to indicate the direction of measurement; *astronomical longitude*, the angle between the plane of the reference meridian and the plane of the celestial meridian; *geodetic longitude*, used for charts and sometimes called *geographic longitude*; and *celestial longitude*, the angular distance east of the vernal equinox, along the ecliptic.

longitudinal axis the fore-and-aft line through the center of gravity of a spacecraft.

Longomontanus a walled plain in the Clavius crater on the near side of the moon, in the south polar region, near the Tycho crater. Mare Humorum lies to the northeast.

long-period comet a comet, for example, Kohoutek and Ikeya-Seki, whose orbital period is longer than two centuries.

looming a mirage effect produced by above-normal refraction in the lower atmosphere, by which objects below the horizon appear to be raised above their true position. This is a common occurrence in the Far North.

Looped Nebula (NGC 2070) also known as 30 Doradus and Tarantula Nebula. The Looped Nebula is a very extensive luminous emission nebula in the Large Magellanic Cloud.

Lost City Meteorite a chondrite that fell near Lake Murray, in southern

Oklahoma, in 1970. The actual fall was photographed. See CHONDRITE.

Lowell, Percival (1855–1916) American astronomer known for his observations of Mars, which were intended to prove the existence of artificial canals on the planet; for his prediction of the existence of the planet Pluto; and for his work on the red shift of galaxies. His studies led to the discovery of Pluto in by American astronomer Clyde William Tombaugh (1906–). Tombaugh made his discovery in 1930, while working on the staff of the Lowell Observatory, Flagstaff, Arizona, which had been founded in 1894 by Percival Lowell as the Flagstaff Observatory. See RED SHIFT OF GALAXIES.

lower limb the half of the edge of the apparent disk of a celestial body having the least altitude; in contrast with the *upper limb*, which has the greatest altitude.

lower transit transit of the lower branch of the celestial meridian, also called *inferior tranit* and *lower culmination*. See CULMINATION.

lox 1. *(n.)* liquid oxygen, also called LOX and loxygen. See LIQUID OXYGEN.

2. *(v.)* load the fuel tanks of a rocket vehicle with liquid oxygen. The procedure is called *loxing*.

LRV *abbreviation for* LUNAR ROVING VEHICLE.

luminosity (L) the absolute brightness of a star in comparison with that of the sun, equal to the total energy radiated per second from the star. Thus, a star that has a luminosity of 24 has an intrinsic, or absolute, brightness that is 24 times the brightness of the sun.

luminosity class a classification of stars of any given spectral type according to their luminosity, as in the different regions of the H-R star diagram: supergiants (I), bright giants (II), giants (III), subgiants (IV), and dwarfs (V).

In the luminosity class of main sequence stars, luminosity decreases as temperature decreases. The luminosity of giant stars, however, increases with decreasing temperature. Further, the luminosity of supergiants drops and then rises with decreasing temperature. See HERTZSPRUNG-RUSSELL (H-R) DIAGRAM.

luminous cloud see NOCTILUCENT CLOUD.

luminous energy or **radiant energy** or **light energy** energy of visible radiation, weighted in accordance with the wavelength dependence of the response of the human eye. The energy emitted from a light source, for example, electronic radiation in the wavelength range for visible light has an average frequency of 10^{15} Hertz.

Luna the series of Soviet spacecraft with which the USSR—persisting despite a number of early failures—finally achieved the first soft-landing on the moon. Luna 9 was the spacecraft that achieved this feat, on February 3, 1966. The USSR had announced the successful launching of Luna 1, its first lunar probe on January 2, 1959, only a little more than a year after orbiting Sputnik 1. Luna 2 hit the moon nine months later, and Luna 3 took the first photographs of the dark side of the moon. After that came the attempts to make soft-landings. Luna 10, the first of the USSR's orbiting series, became the moon's first artificial satellite.

lunar 1. of or pertaining to the moon;
2. measured by the revolutions of the moon;
3. resembling the moon.

lunar albedo a measurement of the reflective power of the moon's surface, in terms of the ratio between the intensity of the sunlight reflected from a lunar surface and that striking the surface. The average albedo of Earth's moon is 0.07. See ALBEDO.

lunarbase a name often used for the material that makes up the moon's maria, or seas. It is dark volcanic rock, which is similar to the basalts found on Earth.

lunar basin see BASIN.

lunar crater a pit or depression, usually circular, on the surface of the moon. In most instances the crater is surrounded by a raised rim, called a ringwall. The largest craters are sometimes called walled plains. See WALLED PLAIN.

lunar cycle or **Metonic cycle** any cycle related to the moon, particularly the Callippic cycle or the Metonic cycle (a Saros eclipse cycle of about 18 years). A *Metonic cycle* is a period of 19 years after which the phases of the moon will occur on the same days of the year as they did 19 years before. The period contains 6932.6 days. Since it is almost equals 20 eclipse years (6932.4 days), it is possible for a series of four or five eclipses to occur on identical dates at intervals of 19 years. The cycle was discovered by the Greek astronomer Meton in the 5th century BC and was used in determining how intercalary months could be inserted into a lunar calendar so that the calendar year and tropical (seasonal) year were kept in step. A *Callipic cycle* equals four Metonic cycles, or 76 years. A *Saros cycle* is an eclipse cycle of about 18 years. At the end of each Saros, the sun, moon, and line of nodes return to approximately the same relative positions, and another series of eclipses begins. See CALLIPPUS, METONIC CYCLE, and SAROS.

lunar day or **tidal day** the duration of one rotation of Earth on its axis, with respect to the moon. The average length of a lunar day is about 24 hours 50 minutes of mean solar time. See SOLAR DAY.

lunar domes the rounded volcanic hills up to 20 kilometers in diameter that are found in the maria areas of the moon. See MARE.

lunar eclipse a phenomenon observed when the moon enters the shadow of Earth. A lunar eclipse is called *penumbral* when the moon enters only the penumbra of Earth, *partial* when the moon enters the umbra of Earth without being totally immersed, and *total* when the moon is entirely immersed in Earth's umbra. See Fig. 47.

lunar excursion module (LM or **LEM)** the spider-like two-section vehicle that carried two astronauts at a time from an orbiting command and service module (CSM) down to the surface of the moon. The LEM provided the astronauts with an operations base, life support systems, and the ability to take off again and rejoin the CSM in lunar obit before the subsequent return to Earth.

Apollo 9 was the first manned operation in space that would lead eventually to an actual landing of astronauts on the moon, in the LEM. Apollo 9 lifted off on March 3, 1969, and five days later crew members James McDivitt and Russell Schweikart took a test flight in the LEM and then returned to the mother ship.

Apollo 10—crew members: Thomas Stafford, John Young, and Eugene Cernan—took off on May 18, 1969; scouted a future Apollo landing site; and returned to Earth on May 26. The mother ship made 31 revolutions of the moon. Cernan and Stafford, with Young in orbit, flew the LEM to within 9 miles above Mare Serenitatis, the site chosen for the eventual landing. In initiating the return to Apollo, with Cernan at the LEM controls, the LEM began to gyrate, and Stafford took the controls. He damped the gyrations and piloted the LEM back into lunar orbit to dock with the mother ship. The successful return to Earth proceeded.

Apollo 11—crew members: Neil Armstrong, Edwin Aldrin, and Michael Collins—took off on July 16, 1969, and achieved a successful landing of men on the moon. This time, it was Collins who stayed behind on the mother ship and, after a successful touchdown of the

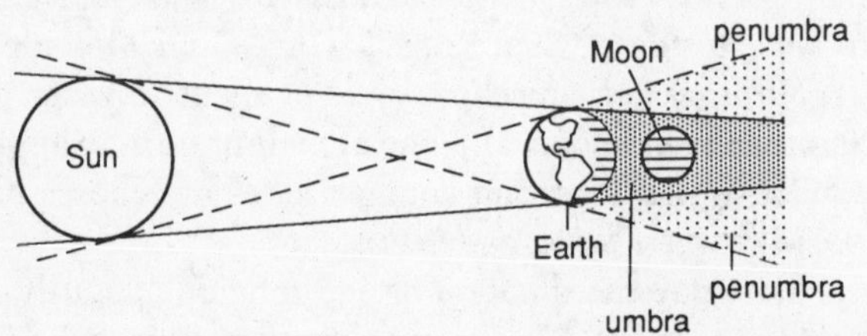

Fig. 47. **Lunar eclipse.** See entry.

Lem on the moon, Armstrong became the first man to walk on the moon's surface. On July 21, he and Aldrin fired up the LEM ascent engine, leaving behind near the landing site their boot marks, an American flag, and the landing legs that had supported their LEM. After docking with the mother ship, Apollo 11 began its successful return to Earth.

Apollo 12—crew members: Charles Conrad, Jr., Richard Gordon, Jr., and Alan Bean—made a successful round trip to the moon, taking off on November 14, 1970, and returning on November 17. They deployed six lunar experiments, including a seismometer and a small nuclear power station to operate them. They also collected 75 pounds of lunar rock samples.

Apollo 15—crew members: David Scott, Richard Irwin, and Alfred Worden—made a successful round trip to the moon, taking off on June 26, 1971, and returning on July 7. This was the first crew to use the Lunar Roving Vehicle (LRV), a battery-operated jeep-like vehicle. They logged more than 18 hours of LRV travel in the foothills of the Apennine Mountains and Hadley Rille. After the LEM returned to the mother ship, the successul return to Earth began. On the way home, Worden made a walk in deep space, more than 197,000 miles from Earth, to retrieve film from cameras aboard the LEM, since the LEM was normally discarded before the landing on Earth.

Apollo 17—crew members: Eugene Cernan, Ronald E. Evans, and Harrison H. Schmitt—was the last lunar landing and exploration of the moon in the Apollo program. The crew returned to Earth with 243 pounds of lunar rock samples. See also APOLLO.

lunar gravity the force imparted by the moon to a mass that is at rest relative to the moon. Lunar gravity is approximately one-sixth that of Earth. The explanation for this lies in the concept of mass, a property of matter that determines both the inertia of an object and the resultant gravity field that can be produced by the object. The moon is smaller than Earth, has a mass that is less than the mass of Earth, and thus has a weaker gravitational field. A practical example of the difference between lunar gravity and terrestrial gravity: a person who weighs 120 pounds on Earth would weigh one-sixth as much on the moon, that is, 20 pounds.

lunarite a substance of unknown composition (as yet unknown) that is believed to constitute the bright areas of the moon's surface.

lunar highlands see HIGHLANDS, LUNAR.

lunar limb the extreme edge of the moon's apparent disk. See LIMB.

lunar maria the ring plains of the moon. Expanses of iron-rich basaltic lavas of low albedo that were erupted onto the lunar surface. The maria are largely confined to the near side of the moon. See ALBEDO, MARE, and RING PLAINS.

lunar mascons the gravity anomalies on the moon that were discovered during early Apollo satellite tracking. Mascons are massive concentrations of high-density material beneath the surface of the moon.

lunar module see LUNAR EXCURSION MODULE.

lunar month 1. the period of revolution of the moon about Earth, also known as a *synodical month*;

2. a period of time (29.531 days) based on the cycle of phases of the moon, that is, full moon to full moon. See SIDEREAL MONTH.

lunar mountains raised regions on the moon, most of which consist of crustal blocks uplifted, that define multiple ring structures of impact basins.

lunar orbit the orbit of a spacecraft around the moon. A nominal altitude for a lunar orbit would be about 70 miles. Such an orbit can be established if provision is made for a reduction of velocity in the vicinity of the moon. At a predetermined distance from the moon, near the point of closest approach, the velocity of the vehicle must be reduced to a value that will allow the moon to capture the vehicle as a satellite. A representative value for this velocity change would be of the order of 4000 feet per second, about half the value required for a lunar landing.

Lunar Orbiter a series of five NASA spacecraft launched at 3-month intervals from August 1966 to August 1968. All the missions were intended to build toward landing a man on the moon by 1970. Following the successful Ranger flights, which yielded the world's first close-up television pictures of the moon's surface, five Lunar Orbiter vehicles were placed in lunar orbit in 1966 and 1967, some as close as 25 miles from the moon. The primary objective of the 860-pound spacecraft was to photograph the lunar equatorial regions to help select landing sites for the Apollo lunar modules. Other Lunar Orbiter objectives were to study variations in lunar gravity and to monitor radiation and meteoroids in the vicinity of the moon.

The spacecraft succeeded in photographing objects as small as 3 feet across and provided the first real atlas of the moon, including the so-called hidden side. The first four orbiters were deliberately crashed onto the surface of the moon when their work was completed, in order to prevent any possible radio-frequency interference with later missions. The fifth orbiter, launched on August 1, 1967, remained in lunar orbit as a tracking target for NASA's Manned Spaceflight Network while it still had sufficient fuel to power a controlled crash. The fifth orbiter finally impacted the moon on January 31, 1968.

The Lunar Orbiters measured 5-1/2 feet in height when folded for launch. With solar panels and antennas deployed, the panels and antennas provided a windmill shape 18-1/2 feet across the antenna booms, and 12 feet 2 inches across the solar panels.

lunar orbit insertion (LOI) the process of putting a spacecraft or other satellite into lunar orbit. For example, an Apollo spacecraft reaching the moon is placed in circular lunar orbit in two maneuvers. After passing behind the moon for the first time, the spacecraft is turned so that the main rocket engine faces forward. At a precisely calculated moment, the 20,500-pound service propulsion system is fired. In the case of Apollo 11, firing lasted 6 minutes, 2 seconds. This so-called retrograde burn reduced the forward speed by about 2000 mph and put the spacecraft into a lunar elliptical orbit of 69 miles at pericynthion (the point at which a spacecraft, having been been launched from Earth, and having been put into lunar orbit, is nearest to the moon) and 195 miles at apocythion (the point at which a spacecraft, having been launched from Earth, and having been put into lunar orbit, is farthest from the moon).

The Apollo 11 rocket firing mentioned, the first of two, consumed about 12 tons of fuel. The second firing, again behind the moon—always a shorter maneuver burn—lasted 17 seconds and further reduced speed by 107 mph. This put Apollo 11 into a not-quite-circular orbit of 63 by 75 miles. This was desirable because the Apollo 8 and Apollo 10 missions had shown that variations in the moon's gravitational pull would result in the orbit's becoming a circular 69 miles by the 30th revolution, when the lunar module would be docking with the command module.

lunar parallax the horizontal or geocentric parallax of the moon. See PARALLAX.

lunar parking orbit (LPO) a maneuver first used on Apollo 8, when the spacecraft was parked—left in lunar orbit—for ten revolutions. During landing missions, vehicles are usually parked for two revolutions both before and after separation and redocking of the lunar module. This is done to rest the astronauts and to give them time for system checks.

lunar rays the bright streaks that radiate from some of the moon's principal craters, among them Aristarchus, Tycho, Giordano Bruno, Kepler, Copernicus, and Clavius. The most pronounced system of rays extends outward from Tycho, in the southern lunar hemisphere.

lunar rock see MOONROCK.

lunar roving vehicle or **lunar rover** (LRV) a battery-driven car used by

United States astronauts on the moon. See LUNAR VEHICLES, LUNAR PROBES, and LUNOKHOD.

lunar satellite any man-made satellite that makes one or more revolutions about the moon.

lunar terminator the line on the surface of the moon that separates the dark and light hemispheres. Certain features, such as craters, can be seen best when they are on or near the lunar equator.

lunar tide a very slight bulging of the moon caused by the tidal force of Earth upon it.

lunar valley a canyon on Earth's moon resulting from a radial fracture associated with an impact basin or lunar crater. See IMPACT BASIN and LUNAR CRATER.

lunar vehicles (LRV) the self-propelled vehicles that carried astronauts to various areas of the lunar surface. The USSR version was unmanned. See LUNOKHOD and LUNAR PROBES.

lunation the interval between successive new (or full) moons, also called a *lunar month* or *synodical month*: 29 days, 12 hours, 44 minutes, and 2.9 seconds.

Lunik one of a series of lunar probes launched by the USSR to approach the vicinity of the moon or launched to actually impact the moon. See LUNOKHOD.

Lunokhod or **Lunik probes** **1.** a series of Soviet lunar probes that included the first craft to reach the vicinity of the moon (Lunik 1, January 2, 1959); the first to photograph the far side of the moon (Lunik 3, October 4, 1959); the first crash landing (Lunik 2, September 12, 1959); the first soft lander (Luna 9, January 31, 1966); the first orbiter (Luna 10, March 31, 1966); the first unmanned sample-return mission (Luna 16, September 12, 1970); and unmanned roving vehicle missions (Luna 17 and Luna 21, November 17, 1970, and January 8, 1973, respectively);

2. Lunokhod, an eight-wheel unmanned lunar roving vehicle, soft-landed by Luna 17 and 21. Lunokhod 1 was equipped with a laser reflector for lunar ranging experiments. It was active in Mare Imbrium for ten months, during which time it completed a 10-km traverse, performing photographic tasks, magnetic field measurements, and x-ray and cosmic-ray analyses. Lunokhod 2 traveled 17 km in four months in the vicinity of the Le Monnier crater on the border of Mare Serenitatis.

Lupus (Lup) the Wolf, a constellation in the Southern Hemisphere, near the Milky Way, containing no named or bright stars, and lying between Centaurus and Norma. It was known to the Greeks and Romans. Arab scientists observed this group of stars and called it by a name meaning leopard or panther. The ancient Greeks called Lupus by the name Therium, an unspecified wild animal, and the Romans called it Bestia, the Beast. It was visualized as impaled on a *thyrsus*, a long pole, which was held by Centaurus.

Lynx (Lyn) a constellation in the Northern Hemisphere between Ursa Major and Auriga. NGC 2419 is located in this constellation. Known as the Intergalactic Wanderer, NGC 2419 is the most distant of the Milky Way's globular star clusters and is tentatively classified by some authorities as an extragalactic object.

Lyot, Bernard F. (1897–1952) French astronomer and inventor of the coronagraph, which makes possible the study of the solar corona and prominences at times other than during a solar eclipse. By using the coronagraph with monochromatic filters, Lyot greatly expanded the knowledge of the sun's corona.

Lyra (Lyr) the Lyre, a compact but prominent northern constellation between Cygnus and Hercules. Its brightest stars include a blue star called Vega, sometimes known as Alpha Lyrae, Wega, the Falling Eagle, or the Harp Star. Vega is the fifth-brightest in the sky and is one of the three stars forming the Summer Triangle, consisting of Vega, Deneb, and Altair. Another of Lyra's brightest stars is Sheliak, also known as Beta Lyrae or the Tortoise. The famous Ring Nebula in Lyra is probably the best-known example of a PLANETARY NEBULA.

Lyrids or **April Lyrids** a minor meteor shower in the northern sky that maximizes on or about April 21. In the past it was much more active, the last great Lyrid shower occurring in 1803. The Chinese described a remarkable display in 15 BC. The associated meteor stream has the same orbit as Comet 1861 I and is associated with that comet.

Lysithea the smallest moon of Jupiter, approximately 15 kilometers in diameter. Along with three other faint moons, it was discovered in 1938 by American astronomer Seth Barnes Nicholson (1891–1963), who also made measurements of the temperatures of the planets and of the moon in eclipse. Lysithea orbits Jupiter at a mean distance of 11,710,000 kilometers. Its sidereal period is 259.2 days.

M

M see MESSIER CATALOG and MESSIER NUMBER.

M1 (NGC 1952) the Crab Nebula in Taurus considered to be the remains of a supernova. See CRAB NEBULA.

M8 (NGC 6523) the Lagoon Nebula in Sagittarius.

M13 (NGC 6205) the Great Globular Star Cluster in Hercules. M13 is the finest cluster of its type in the Northern Hemisphere and one of the most spectacular telescopic objects in the heavens. It was first mentioned by English astronomer Edmond Halley (1656–1742) in 1715, but was discovered in the previous year. French astronomer Charles Messier (1730–1817), coming across it in 1764, described it as a round "nebula containing no stars." The cluster is located in the Keystone of Hercules, about a third of the way along a line drawn from Eta to Zeta.

M17 the Swan, or Omega Nebula, in Sagittarius.

M20 (NGC 6514) the Trifid Nebula in Sagittarius.

M26 (NGC 6853) the Dumbbell Nebula, a planetary nebula in the constellation Vulpecula.

M31 (NGC 224) the Andromeda galaxy.

M43 (NGC 1976) the Orion Nebula.

M51 (NGC 5194) the Whirlpool spiral galaxy in Canes Venatici.

M57 (NGC 6720) the Ring Nebula, a planetary nebula in Lyra.

M97 (NGC 3587) the 11th-magnitude planetary Owl Nebula in Ursa Major, at 12,000 light-years from Earth.

Maasym the common name given to the orange star Lambda Herculis. Kaasym, the Wrist, is a giant K4 star of magnitude 4.48, at a distance of 233 light-years from Earth.

Mach 1. a number expressing the ratio of the speed of a body or of a point on a body with respect to the surrounding air or other fluid, or the speed of a flow with respect to the speed of sound in the medium;

2. the speed represented by this number. If the Mach number is less than 1, the flow is called *subsonic*, and local disturbances can propagate ahead of the flow. If the Mach number is greater than 1, the flow is called *supersonic*, and disturbances cannot propagate ahead of the flow. Supersonic flows result in the formation of shock waves.

Mach, Ernest (1838–1916) Austrian physicist and philosopher who pioneered studies of bodies in wind tunnels. His work in establishing the ratio of the speed of a body to the speed of sound in undisturbed air is important in the theory of flight.

Maculae the dark patches seen on Europa, which is a satellite of Jupiter.

Madler, Johann Heinrich (1794–1879) German astronomer who produced the first map of Mars and, in 1836, the first good map of the moon. He also studied double stars. See DOUBLE STAR.

Madler Continent see MADLER LAND.

Madler Land or **Madler Continent** the old name for Chryse, the Martian plain, diameter 100 km, located at latitude -11° and longitude 357°, on which Viking 1 landed in 1976. Madler Land was named after Johann Madler. See MADLER, JOHANN; VIKING PROBES; and CHRYSE PLANITIA.

Maffei galaxies two galaxies hidden behind the dust clouds of the Milky Way, in the constellation Cassiopeia. Discovered in 1968 by the Italian astronomer Paolo Maffei, who studied infrared photographs of the sky, the galaxies are infrared objects. Maffei 1, the brighter of the two, is a large elliptical galaxy, and Maffei 2 appears to be a spiral galaxy of medium size.

Magellan a NASA spacecraft launched on May 4, 1989, from the space shuttle as a high-resolution radar mapper. It reached Venus in August of 1990 and went into orbit. The primary mission of Magellan was conducted over a period of 243 Earth days and covered Venus in 1842 mapping swaths. The resolution of Magellan was so great that it was able to show details as small as 250 meters across and 30 meters high. It mapped up to 90% of the planet's surface, including a 4200-mile winding canyon, the longest in the solar system, and the large impact crater Golubkina, which is 34 km in diameter.

Magellanic clouds two small, irregular galactic clusters that are close neighbors (satellites) of our own Milky Way galaxy, being the nearest independent star systems to the Milky Way. Both clouds can be seen with the naked eye in the Southern Hemisphere. They are named after Ferdinand Magellan, the Portuguese explorer who first described them in 1519: Large Magellanic Cloud (LMC) and Small Magellanic Cloud (SMC). See LARGE MAGELLANIC CLOUD, SMALL MAGELLANIC CLOUD.

Magellanic streams the gas filaments connecting the Magellanic clouds to the Milky Way.

Maginus a walled plain 177 kilometers in diameter, located at -50° S and -5° W, near the Clavius area of the moon. See WALLED PLAIN.

magma underground molten material within Earth's crust, from which igneous rock is formed. See LAVA.

magma ocean the primordial layer of molten lava on the initial surface of the moon and planets.

magnetic braking the slowing of rotation of a star or planet caused by interaction of its magnetic field with surrounding ionized material.

magnetic crotchet a sudden change in Earth's magnetic field due to an increase in the conductivity of the lower ionosphere.

magnetic declination or **declination** (D) the angle between the geographical meridian and the magnetic meridian at any given location, that is, the angle between true north (the geographic north pole) and the magnetic north pole. See VARIATION and Fig. 48.

magnetic dip (i) the angle at any point between the horizontal and the direction of a line of force of Earth's magnetic field. The magnetic dip is also called *magnetic inclination*, *magnetic latitude*, *inclination*, and *dip*. See MAGNETIC FIELD.

magnetic disturbance daily variation the periodic variation of Earth's magnetic field that is in phase with electromagnetic radiation during increased solar activity. See MAGNETIC FIELD.

magnetic equator an imaginary line on the surface of Earth or other celestial body connecting all points at which the magnetic dip is zero. Also called the *aclinic line*. See MAGNETIC DIP.

magnetic field 1. the space surrounding a magnet;

2. a region of space in which any magnetic dipole will experience a magnetic force or torque. (A dipole is any object or system, such as a magnet, that is oppositely charged at two points or poles.) This magnetic field is often represented as the geometric array of the magnetic lines of force that exist in relation to magnetic poles. For a depiction of the magnetic field surrounding Earth, see Fig. 49.

magnetic flux density a measure of the strength of a magnetic field. In electromagnetism it is the integral over a specified surface of the com-

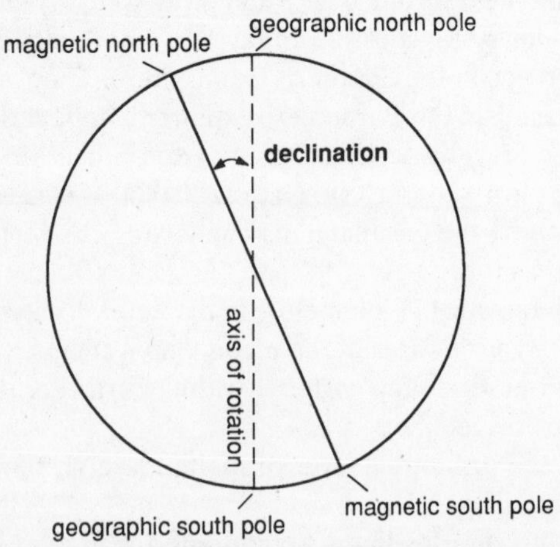

Fig. 48. **Magnetic declination.** See entry.

ponent of magnetic induction perpendicular to the surface. See MAGNETIC LINES OF FORCE.

magnetic inclination see MAGNETIC DIP.

magnetic lines of force imaginary lines so drawn in a region containing a magnetic field as to be everywhere tangent to the magnetic field intensity vector. These lines of force are merely convenient conventions for delineating the geometry of a magnetic field.

magnetic lunar daily variation (L) the periodic variation of Earth's magnetic field that is in phase with the transit of the moon. This phenomenon is essentially a tidal effect. The amplitude of the variation changes with the phase of the moon, the seasons, and the sunspot cycle.

magnetic north the direction north at any point as determined by Earth's magnetic lines of force. Magnetic north is the reference direction for measurement of magnetic directions.

magnetic pole either of the two places on the surface of Earth or other celestial body at which the magnetic dip is 90 degrees. See MAGNETIC DECLINATION.

magnetic star or **magnetic variable** a star that has a detectable and often very large magnetic field. This type of star was first observed in 1948. Magnetic stars, for example, Vega and Sirius, are usually of spectral type A—bluish-white or white and having a surface temperature of 7500 to 10,000 K—but they do not appear to be restricted to any particular spectral class or sector of the H-R diagram. Many show either periodic or irregular variations of magnetic field, and some show a

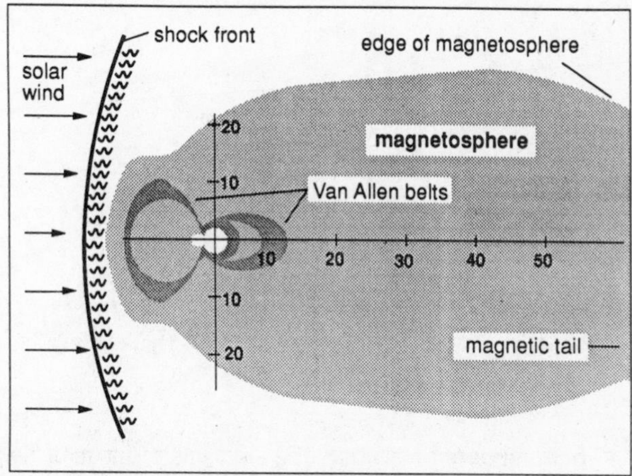

Fig. 49. **Magnetic field of Earth.** See entry.

reversal of polarity. Magnetic variability is usually accompanied by very small changes in brightness.

Magnetic stars are studied by measurements of the Zeeman effect. Periodic variations in magnetic field can result from the tilting of the magnetic axis of a star with respect to its rotational axis so that areas of different magnetic field strength are presented to the observer as the star rotates. See ZEEMAN EFFECT and HERTZSPRUNG-RUSSELL DIAGRAM.

magnetic storm or **geomagnetic storm** a worldwide disturbance of Earth's magnetic field. Such storms are frequently characterized by a sudden onset, in which the magnetic field undergoes marked changes in the course of an hour or less, followed by a very gradual return to normal. Magnetic storms are caused by solar disturbances and are more frequent during years of frequent sunspot activity. A magnetic storm sometimes can be linked to a particular solar disturbance. In these cases, the time between solar flare and onset of the storm is about one or two days, suggesting that the disturbance is carried to Earth by a cloud of particles thrown out by the sun. When these disturbances are observable only in the auroral zones, they may be termed *polar magnetic storms*. See AURORA and SUNSPOT.

magnetic variable see MAGNETIC STAR.

magnetopause the boundary between the magnetosphere of a planet, for example, Earth, and interplanetary space.

magnetosphere the volume of space around a planet in which the motion of charged particles is dominated by the planet's magnetic field rather than by the solar wind. The magnetosphere includes any radia-

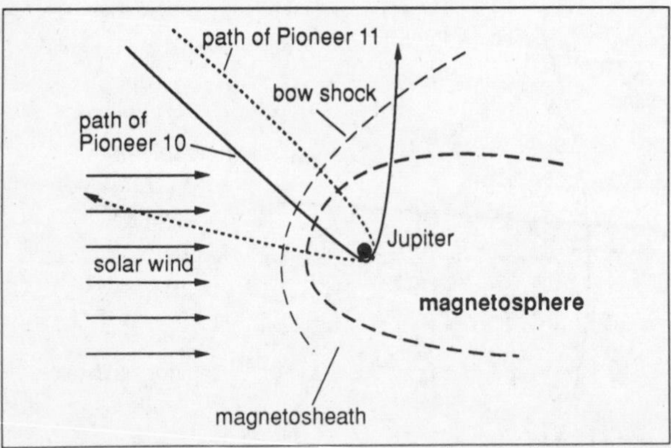

Fig. 50. **Magnetosphere of Jupiter.** The elements of Jupiter's magnetosphere are shown, along with the paths of the Pioneer 10 and 11 spacecraft, which flew by the planet on their journeys into even deeper space.

tion belts of the planet, such as the Van Allen belts of Earth. Earth's magnetosphere extends to 60,000 km on the sunward side of the planet but is drawn out by the solar wind to many times this distance on the side away from the sun. (See Fig. 49.) Above the magnetosphere is a *magnetopause* and then a layer of turbulent magnetic field, called the *magnetosheath*, which is enclosed by a shock wave where the smooth flow of solar-wind particles past the planet is first interrupted. Mercury and Jupiter also have magnetospheres. See Fig. 50.

magnitude or **stellar magnitude** or **apparent magnitude** a measure of the relative luminance (brightness) of stars and other celestial objects. The brighter the object, the lower its assigned magnitude. The brightest objects have negative magnitudes (sun: -26.8; full moon: -12.5; Venus at brightest: -4.3; Jupiter at opposition: -2.3; Sirius: -1.6; Vega: 0.2; Polaris: 2.1). The faintest stars visible to the naked eye on a clear dark night are of about magnitude 6.

Maia the common name for the blue-white star 20 Tau in the Tau constellation of the Northern Hemisphere. Maia is a member of the Pleiades, or Seven Sisters.

Maiden the common name for the equatorial constellation Virgo.

Main a crater 48 km in diameter that crosses into Challis, on the near side of the moon at 81° N and 9° E, in the north polar region near Mare Frigoris.

main sequence stars a sequence of stars on the color-magnitude diagram, containing the majority of stars, that runs diagonally from the upper left to the lower right. Main sequence stars make up over 90 percent of the stars in the sky. The hottest main-sequence stars shine with a blue or blue-white light and are located in the upper left corner of the H-R (Hertzsprung-Russell) diagram. Cool, dim main-sequence stars appear in the lower right corner of the diagram. See HERTZSPRUNG-RUSSELL DIAGRAM.

major axis **1.** the axis of an ellipse that passes through the two foci of the ellipse;

2. the longest line segment that can be drawn through an ellipse, intersecting both foci.

major planets the planets revolving about the sun: Mercury, Venus, Earth, Mars, Jupiter, Saturn, Uranus, Neptune, and Pluto, which have diameters significantly larger than the 1003 km diameter of Ceres, which is the largest minor planet (asteroid). Occasionally, the four largest planets—Jupiter, Saturn, Uranus, and Neptune—are referred to as major planets and as giant planets.

man-machine integration the matching of the characteristics and capabilities of man and machine in order to obtain optimum conditions and maximum efficiency of the combined system.

mantle **1.** the greatest part of Earth's interior, lying between the crust and the core;

2. a region of intermediate density surrounding the core of a planet.

March equinox see VERNAL EQUINOX.

Marduk also known as Plume 7, an active volcano on Jupiter's satellite Io. Marduk's plume rises 120 km above the surface of Io.

mare *plural* **maria** the name, originally Latin meaning *sea*, applied to **1.** the dark, relatively smooth features that cover about 17% of the moon. See Fig. 51.

2. a dark-colored region on a planet or satellite;

3. a region of basaltic lava flow. The term is also used in reference to Mars.

Mare Australe the Southern Sea, at -49° S and +78° E, a series of dark, flooded craters on the southeastern limb of the near side of the moon.

Mare Crisium a 500-km region of dark gray lava surrounded by mountains, at +18° N and +58° E, in the 1st quadrant of the eastern hemisphere of the moon. See Fig. 51.

Mare Fecunditatis the Sea of Fertility, one of the major lunar seas. It is a relatively craterless plain at -4° S and +51° E in the equatorial region on the west limb of the near side of the moon. Two large craters, Langrenus and Vendelinus, line its borders. See Fig. 51.

Mare Humboldtianum Humboldt's Sea, a minor lunar sea at +57° N and +80° E, in the 1st quadrant of the moon, on northeastern limb. See Fig. 51.

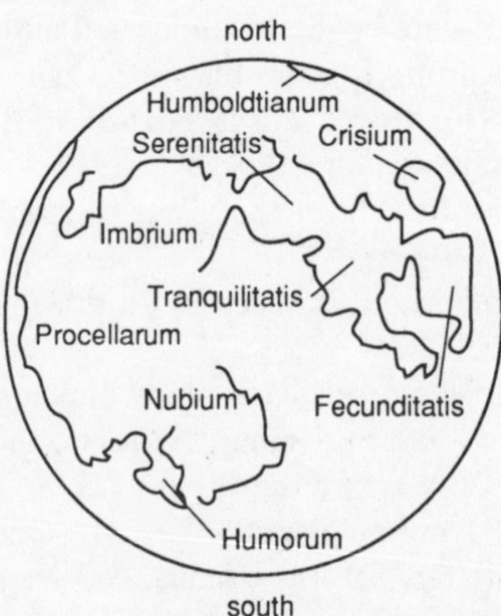

Fig. 51. **Maria.** The lunar seas.

Mare Humorum the Sea of Moisture, a lunar sea at -23° S and -38° W, west of Mare Nubium, in the 3rd quadrant of the moon, on the moon's southeastern limb. It has a comparatively smooth floor and no major craters. See Fig. 51.

Mare Imbrium the Sea of Showers, a dark plain 1300 km in diameter, at +36° N and -16° W, in the 2nd quadrant of the moon, north of the moon's equator. It is bordered on the east by the Jura Mountains, on the north by Plato Crater.

Mare Ingenii a lava-flooded lunar sea 330 km wide, at 34° S and 164° E on the far side of the moon. It contains several large craters.

Mare Marginis an irregular, lava-inundated area of the face of the moon, at 13° N and 87° E, north of Mare Smythii. See MARE SMYTHII.

Mare Moscoviense a 250-km wide lava-flooded lunar region, at 28° N and 148° E, in the 4th quadrant of the far side of the moon.

Mare Nectaris the Sea of Nectar, a multi-ring, lava-flooded structure south of the moon's equator, at -14° S and +34° E, in the moon's 4th quadrant. The mare is associated with a lunar mascon and with major lunar faults.

Mare Orientale the Eastern Sea, a lunar mare discovered by Patrick Moore and H.P. Wilkins in 1948. It is the moon's extreme western limb on the far side, at -20° S and -95° E. Its outer ring, the Cordillera Mountains, is over 965 km in diameter. Mare Orientale is probably the result of the impact of a small asteroid.

Mare Serenitatis the Sea of Serenity, one of the major lunar seas, in the 1st quadrant of the moon's near side, at +30° N and +17° E, adjoining Mare Tranquillitatis to the east. The largest crater is Bessel, which is the site of the controversial surface formation known as LINNE. See Fig. 51.

Mare Smythii or **Mare Smithii** a lava-inundated area at -1° S and +88° E in the equatorial region of the far side of the moon, near the lunar equator.

Mare Spumans the Foaming Sea, a small dark lunar area, at +1° N and +65° E on the near side of the moon's 1st quadrant, south of Mare Crisium and east of Mare Fecunditatis.

Mare Tranquillitatis the Sea of Tranquility, an area of dark lava floors at +9° N and +30° E, in the eastern hemisphere of the moon's 1st quadrant. It contains the fault Rupes Cauchy, and Hadley Rille, a relatively shallow, meandering valley. As far as the human race is concerned, this is probably the most historic site on the moon. It was here, specifically at 0° 67′ N and 23° 49′ E, that mankind first reached out and touched another world. On July 20, 1969, Neil Armstrong and Edwin Aldrin,

Jr., in the Apollo 11 mission, exiting from the Eagle lunar module, made the first human footprints on an unearthly landscape. Barring accident, the prints will last for eons. See LUNAR EXCURSION MODULE and Fig. 51.

Mare Undarum the Sea of Waves, a small, dark lava area at +6° N and +5° E, in the 1st quadrant of the moon, just south of the Mare Crisium.

Mare Vaporum the Sea of Vapors, a lava region at +14° N and +5° E, in the moon's 1st quadrant, near the center of the face of the moon and bordered on the north by the Apennine and Haemus mountains.

maria see LUNAR MARIA and MARE.

Mariner a series of United States spacecraft sent on a planetary fly-by to the planets Venus, Mercury, and Mars. On December 14, 1962, Mariner 2 passed within 22,000 miles of Venus. Mariner 9 (launched May 30, 1971) came within 900 miles of Mars. It was the first spacecraft to go into orbit around a planet other than Earth. It was also the first to photograph, measure, and collect other data about Mars while in orbit. The entire Martian surface was mapped, and close-up views were obtained of Mars' two small natural satellites, Deimos and Phobos. Mariner 10 (launched November 3, 1973) came within 3600 miles of Venus and 450 miles of Mercury, taking close-up views of both worlds. This was the first probe of Mercury. Mariner 11 and Mariner 12 were renamed Voyager 1 and Voyager 2. See Fig. 52.

Mariner missions and dates of launch

Mariner 2: August 1962, the first successful interplanetary probe, a flyby of Venus. Interpretation of its data led to accurate determination of the planet's mass and accurate assessment of the high temperatures of the planet.

Mariner 3: November 1964, Mars flyby. The space probe failed to achieve its intended trajectory to Mars, and all communication with the spacecraft was eventually lost.

Mariner 4: November 1964, Mars flyby. The spacecraft reached Mars on July 14, 1965. It photographed a heavily cratered, moonlike surface and found that the Martian atmosphere is thin, with less than 1% the pressure of Earth's atmosphere, and composed largely of carbon dioxide.

Mariner 5: June 1967, Venus flyby. It encountered a weak magnetic field and very dense atmosphere.

Mariners 6 and 7: February and March 1969, Mars flybys. Their findings were that nitrogen is virtually absent from the Martian atmosphere, solid carbon dioxide (dry ice) occurs in the clouds and near the polar caps, and the dust particles of its atmosphere probably consist of silicate materials derived from the planetary surface.

Mariner 8: May 1971, Mars orbiter mission. The launch vehicle failed.

Mariner 9: May 1971, the first Mars-orbiting spacecraft, November 1971. It transmitted 7400 pictures covering all of the Martian surface as well as the planet's small moons, Phobos and Deimos. The data show that Mars is a two-part world, with an anciently cratered surface in its southern hemisphere, and a geologically younger surface, with volcanoes, canyons, and dry river channels in its northern hemisphere—it has a huge canyon, some enormous volcanoes, and sinuous channels that appear to have been riverbeds. Landforms resembling lava flows occur in flat regions. Layered deposits in the polar regions suggest glacial periods in past times. Solar ultraviolet light is not absorbed by its atmosphere and reaches the planetary surface. Periodic global dust storms were observed. Phobos and Deimos are very dark and have irregular shapes and cratered surfaces.

Mariner 10: November 1973, Venus flyby February 5, 1974; Mercury flyby March 29, 1974. The spacecraft trajectory around the sun swung it back for a second encounter with Mercury in September 1974 and for a third encounter in March 1975. The data from Venus show no significant magnetic field; a notable disturbance in the solar wind is produced as it flows past Venus; Venus is closer to being a perfect sphere than is Earth; ultraviolet images of the atmosphere reveal streamline and circular patterns; the upper atmosphere rotates much more rapidly than Venus itself; and hydrogen and helium are present in the atmosphere. The data from Mercury show desolate landscapes, remarkably similar to our moon's, with huge craters and long, narrow valleys; long scarps or cliffs, features unique to Mercury; and a huge circular impact basin—Mare Caloris (Caloris Basin) about 13,000 km in diameter. The data also show that Mercury is closer to being a perfect sphere than Earth is; that it is not only the smallest planet, but the densest, with a

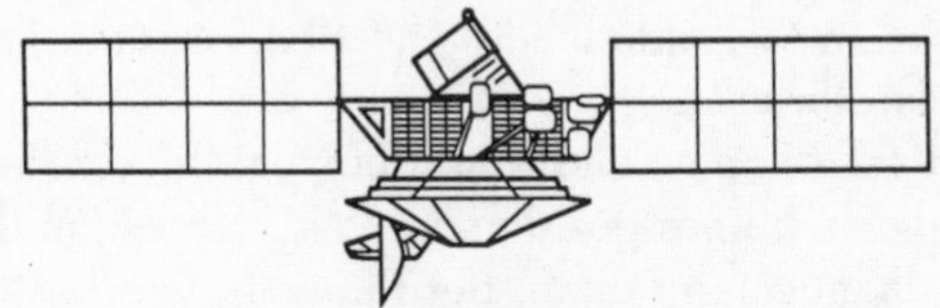

Mariner 10 probe 1973
Length: 6.7 m Weight: 500 kg
Propulsion: chemical

Fig. 52. **Mariner 10.** See entry for Mariner.

metal-rich core; its tenuous atmosphere includes such exotic gases as argon, neon, and helium; its magnetic field is about a tenth as strong as Earth's; and the temperatures are extreme, ranging from 425° to -183° Celsius.

Mariner Valley or **Valles Marineris** the largest canyon on Mars, at latitude 1° N to -18° S and longitude 24° to 113°, in the equatorial region of the southern hemisphere. It was photographed by Mariner 9. Mariner Valley is 3000 miles (5000 km) long. If it were on Earth, it would stretch from New York City to San Francisco. At some points the enormous canyon is 3 miles (5 km) deep and 150 miles (240 km) wide. Earth's Grand Canyon would be lost inside Valles Marineris.

Marius a lunar crater in Oceanus Procellarum, at 12° N and 51° W in the moon's equatorial region, close to the Kepler Crater.

Marius, Simon (1570–1624) German astronomer, one of the first to use an astronomical telescope. He observed sunspots in 1611 and the Andromeda constellation. He also claimed discovery of Jupiter's four largest satellites (1609) and gave them the names Io, Europa, Ganymede, and Callisto, but his contemporaries credited Galileo.

Markab a white giant that is the brightest star in the Great Square of the constellation Pegasus. The other three stars are Scheat, Algenib, and Alpha Andromedae (Alpheratz). Markab is 32 parsecs from Earth.

Markarian galaxies a number of very distant galaxies, associated with quasars and Seyfert galaxies, that were discovered by the Armenian astronomer B.E. Markarian in the 1970s and found to be strong ultraviolet sources showing a bright blue light.

Mars the Red Planet, the fourth planet from the sun and the nearest to Earth. Mars is the most earthlike of all the planets in our star system. It has an orange-brown surface with distinct darker markings and two white polar caps composed of water ice and carbon dioxide. The atmosphere is 95% carbon dioxide gas, making its air almost one hundred times thinner than the air on Earth. It has only one-thousandth as much water vapor as Earth's atmosphere. This small amount forms occasional Martian fog and clouds. The Red Planet is known for its planet-wide dust storms.

The Italian astronomer Giovanni Schiaparelli (1835–1910) first reported seeing dark lines on Mars in 1877. He called them *canali*, which means channels in Italian, but the word was mistranslated as canals. American astronomer Percival Lowell later came to believe incorrectly that intelligent Martians had built canals there. In actuality, the irregular patterns are dark surface rock that have been uncovered by dust storms.

However, there are channels and canyons on Mars, and they look as though they were carved by great rivers. These channels are deep and winding. The largest is called Valles Marineris (Mariner Valley). It is 3000 miles long and at some points is 3 miles deep and 150 miles wide. There are also gigantic volcanoes on Mars. The largest is Olympus Mons, whose top pierces the clouds at a height of 15 miles above the surface. Olympus Mons is more than twice as tall as Mauna Kea, the tallest volcano on Earth. The enormous Martian caldera (crater) is 50 miles wide. The entire state of Rhode Island could easily fit inside this huge Martian crater.

Mars has two small satellites (moons). They are small, cratered chunks of rock. Phobos, the inner moon, is about 21 kilometers in diameter. It zips around Mars every seven and a half hours. Phobos is covered with parallel grooves and with rows of small craters. Deimos, the outer moon, is slightly smaller than Phobos and orbits Mars every thirty hours. More unmanned spacecraft (Mariner and Viking series) have explored Mars than any of our other neighboring planets. See MARINER MISSIONS.

Mars-crossing asteroids loosely called the Amor Group, the asteroids Eros, Ivar, Beira, Atami, etc., whose orbits cross the orbit of Mars. Dozens of Mars-crossers are known.

Marsik (7 Herc) the common name for the yellow star Kappa Herculis, 28.2 parsecs from Earth and magnitude 5-6, in the northern constellation Hercules.

Mars probes the unmanned spacecraft sent to study Mars (Mariner series, Zond series, Mars series, and Viking series). Unfortunately, the USSR's Zond probes missed Mars and returned no data. See MARINER MISSIONS.

Marsquake seismic activity resembling that of an earthquake. Both Viking spacecraft, which made soft landings on Mars in 1976, carried seismographs. The instrument on Viking 1 failed, but that of Viking 2 gave readings, which may have been influenced by strong wind vibrations of the spacecraft. During its 5 months of operation, no large quakes were detected, though one possible event of Richter magnitude 3 was recorded. Martian winds provided a high seismic noise level during much of the 5-month interval.

Mars is considered to be less seismically active than Earth and perhaps close to our moon in level of activity, which is about 3000 quakes per year.

Mars' rotation period the Martian day, 24 hours and 37 minutes, only slightly longer than that of Earth.

Martian air pressure the pressure exerted by the very thin Martian air. On the surface of Mars, the air pressure is only about 0.7% of that at Earth's surface.

Martian air temperature night temperatures about -123°F, day temperatures colder than soil temperatures, which approach or exceed freezing except near the equator, where the temperatures may reach 80°F.

Martian atmosphere composed of carbon dioxide (95.3%), water vapor (0.03%), and oxygen (0.2%). The bulk of the rest is nitrogen and other inert gases such as argon. Several types of clouds have been observed. Of these, two are outstanding: cirruslike clouds (formed from crystals of ice and carbon dioxide) and dust clouds. The dust clouds more often than not are stationary for long periods of time. The dust clouds have been known, however, to move at high speeds. Dust storms have been estimated to sweep across Martian deserts at 200 mph. Mariner 9, which arrived on Mars in November of 1971, was enveloped for nearly 8 weeks in a severe dust storm—global dust storms reach altitudes of 48 km—soon after it reached its assigned orbit. A careful examination of the data collected suggests that dust storms occur often when Mars is in its perihelion position, that is, when it is closest to the sun. See MARINER MISSIONS.

Martian canals the nonexistent canals once believed to have been features of the Martian topography. As established by the Mariner spaceflights of the 1960s, they are nothing more significant than tricks of the eye. For the background of the Martian canal legend, see MARS.

Martian meteorites a handful of meteorites believed to have been blasted off Mars.

Martian polar caps the two variable white areas at the Martian poles, visible to observers on Earth. The north pole is capped by ice that is formed of frozen water. Ice on the south pole is mostly frozen water, with some frozen carbon dioxide (dry ice). See MARTIAN ATMOSPHERE.

mascon or **mass concentration** a positive gravitational anomaly associated with lunar maria. The anomaly is characterized as positive because gravity attraction is somewhat greater over such a region. The first evidence concerning the interior of our moon was obtained in 1960 by the five Lunar Orbiters. Careful tracking of the orbits of these satellites was used to study variations in the moon's gravity. Gravity anomalies, or areas in which lunar gravity is slightly stronger or weaker than average—Mare Orientale is an example—cause spacecraft to deviate from their ideal orbits. Deviations of the orbital paths of the Lunar Orbiters occurred over many maria, indicating that mass concentrations, or mascons, were present under the spacecraft. As an orbiter flew over a mare, the additional mass pulled it slightly closer to the moon. See LUNAR MASCONS.

maser *acronym for m*icrowave *a*mplification by *s*timulated *e*mission of *r*adiation, a device that generates microwave energy by exciting molecules and then utilizes the resulting emission as an energy source. Such a device, when used to generate emissions within the wave frequencies of light, is called a *laser*.

Maskelyne a lunar crater 24 km in diameter at +2° N and +30° E, in the 1st quadrant of the moon, in Mare Tranquillitatis and not far from the original landing site of Apollo 11, the first manned lunar landing mission. The crater was named for English astronomer Nevil Maskelyne (1732–1811), who began issuing the *Nautical Almanac* in 1766. He later issued a four-volume reference catalog of 90,000 observations of the solar system and 36 reference stars.

mass (m) the amount of matter (material) in an object. See MATTER.

mass concentration see MASCON.

mass-luminosity ratio the mass per unit of light or total radiation emitted from an object such as a galaxy.

mass-luminosity relation the relation between the mass of a main-sequence star and its total radiation rate; the more massive, the greater the luminosity.

mass wasting the downhill movements of sediments caused by gravity.

Matar a common name for the yellow giant star Eta Pegasi, type G8 II. Matar, the Fortunate Rain, is next to Scheat in the northern sky and 360 light-years from Earth.

material coordinates see LAGRANGIAN COORDINATES.

matter anything that has mass and takes up space.

Maunder butterfly diagram a graph showing the latitude of sunspots plotted against time. The diagram, first plotted by English researcher Edward Walter Maunder (1851–1928) in 1904, showed a distribution that resembled a butterfly. At the Royal Greenwich Observatory, during his study of long-term patterns in sunspot variations, he determined that practically no sunspots had been seen between 1645 and 1715. Weather records show that the climate of Europe was unusually cool during this period.

Maunder Crater an impact basin on Mars, diameter 84 km, latitude -50° and longitude 358°, in the Noachis Quadrangle. The crater is named after British astronomer Edward W. Maunder (1851–1928). Noachis is one of the 30 major regions of Mars.

Maunder minimum the interval from 1645 to 1715, when solar activity was very low. See MAUNDER BUTTERFLY DIAGRAM.

Maupertuis, Pierre Louis Moreau de (1698–1759) French astronomer who journeyed to Lapland, no mean feat in his day, to measure the size and shape of Earth. He published his results in his book *La Figure de la terre* (1738).

Maurolycus a walled plain in the fourth quadrant of the face of the moon. It is 105 km in diameter.

maxima the times when a variable star reaches its maximum brightness.

maxwell 1. (Mx) a cgs (centimeter-gram-second) electromagnetic unit of magnetic flux, equal to the magnetic flux that produces an electromotive force of 1 abvolt in a circuit of one turn linking the flux, as the flux is reduced to zero in 1 second at a uniform rate;

2. the unit of magnetic flux in the cgs system, now replaced by *weber*, the SI unit.

Maxwell, James Clerk (1831–1879) Scottish physicist and astronomer of many accomplishments. In addition to studying the stability of Saturn's rings, he demonstrated that electromagnetic action travels through space in transverse waves similar to those of light and having the same velocity.

Maxwell Montes a mountain range on Ishtar Terra, one of the regions of highest elevation in the northern hemisphere of Venus. Located at latitude 60° N and longitude 5°, on the eastern end of Ishtar Terra, the mountains rise 11 km above the mean surface level of the planet.

mean center of the moon the central point for a lunar coordinate system.

mean density the mass of an object divided by its volume. See MASS.

mean motion (n) of an object in orbit, a measure of angular velocity.

mean noon the instant when the mean sun is over the upper branch of the reference meridian: twelve o'clock mean solar time, also called civil time.

mean solar day 1. the duration of one rotation of the Earth on its axis with respect to the sun, giving 24-hour, 3-minute, 56.555-second days throughout the year;

2. the average length of an apparent solar day.

mean solar time the time shown by conventional clocks, determined by the sun's mean motion averaged over the year, also called mean time.

Mebsuta the common name for the supergiant yellow star Epsilon Gemini, in the northern constellation Gemini, which also contains such bright stars as Castor and Pollux. Mebsuta has a magnitude of 2.98 and lies at a distance of about 1100 light-years from Earth. It has a luminosity of 5700 times that of the sun. Mebsuta was occulted by Mars on April 7, 1976, an extremely rare occurrence. Mebsuta is also called Epsilon Geminorum.

Mechain, Pierre (1744–1805) French astronomer best known for his discovery of eight comets. The most famous of these is Encke's comet. Mechain's calculation of the elliptical orbit of Uranus in 1783 enabled astronomers to predict more accurately the future location of Uranus in the sky. See ENCKE'S COMET.

megaparsec (Mpc) one million parsecs. See PARSEC.

Megrez or **Delta Ursae Majoris** a dwarf white star of the main sequence, magnitude 3.30, lying 63 light-years from Earth and found in the northern constellation Ursa Major (the Big Dipper, Great Bear, the Wagon, the Plow). Megrez is the so-called root of the bear's tail.

Mekbuda also called Zeta Geminorum and Zeta Gemini, a pulsating giant yellow star of magnitude 3.00 in the northern sky and about 1500 light-years from Earth. Its luminosity is about 5700 times that of the sun.

Melpomene (Asteroid 18) a minor planet in our solar system, discovered in 1852 by English astronomer John Russell Hind (1823–1895). It is 150 km in diameter and has a rotation period of 11.6 hours.

Menelaus a brilliant crater in the Haemus Mountains, 16° N and 16° E on the near side of the moon, in the equatorial region near Mare Tranquillitatis. Menelaus is 32 km in diameter.

Menkalinan the common name for the white dwarf star Beta Aurigae, found in the northern constellation Auriga. Called the shoulder of the rein-holder (charioteer), this star has a magnitude of 1.90 and is 88 light-years from Earth.

Menkar the orange-red star Alpha Ceti, in the Whale's head of the southern constellation Cetus, the Sea Monster. Often called the nose of the whale, this 2.54 magnitude star is 130 light-years from Earth.

Menkhib or **Menkib** the common name for the blue-white star Zeta Persei in the northern constellation Perseus. Menkhib was formerly referred to as the shoulder of Perseus, the Hero, but is now called the ankle. An 07 star of magnitude 4.05, Menkhib is 2100 light-years from Earth.

Mensa (Men) the southern constellation originally named Mons Mensae (Latin for table mountain) by Lacaille, suggesting the Table Mountain above Cape Town, South Africa. He placed it near the south celestial pole. Later, the word *Mons* was dropped, so that sometimes this constellation is called merely the *Table*. It contains no bright stars, but at its border is the Large Magellanic Cloud (galaxy). Close by is the Tarantula Nebula. See NICOLAS LACAILLE.

mensae the designation for small plateaus or table lands on maps of Mars. Examples are Aedlis Meansae, Cydonia Mensae, and Protonilus Mensae.

Merak the white dwarf star Beta Ursae Majoris, the southern, and fainter, of the Pointers to the Pole Star in the northern constellation Ursa Major, often called the Bear and located between Draco and Leo. Merak is sometimes referred to as the loins of the bear. This 2.37-magnitude star is 78 light-years from Earth.

Mercury sometimes called the morning star, the innermost planet, and the first planet from the sun. Mercury, named for the Roman messenger of the gods, is the second smallest planet in our solar system. It orbits the sun in 88 days and has no natural satellites (moons). Only 36 million miles from the sun, Mercury is the fastest of all the planets. It travels at about 108,000 miles per hour around the sun—Earth has a mean orbital speed of 6700 mph. Dust covers Mercury's heavily cratered surface. Caloris Basin, the largest impact crater, measures 930 miles across, a distance greater than the width of Alaska. See MARINER 10.

Mercury in transit Mercury seen in the form of a black disk against the brilliant face of the sun. Since the orbit of Mercury is inclined to the ecliptic by 7°, at most inferior conjunctions Mercury passes either above or below the sun as seen from Earth. Occasionally, however, the three bodies move into a direct line. It is at such a time that Mercury is said to appear in transit. The only planets that can appear in transit are Mercury and Venus. This was realized by Kepler in 1627. Transits of Mercury have been predicted for November 5, 1993; May 7, 2003; and November 8, 2006.

Mercury Project a series of one-man spacecraft in which Americans first gained experience in space flight. See Fig. 53. The seven astronauts in the program were Scott Carpenter, Gordon Cooper, John Glenn, Virgil Grissom, Walter Schirra, Alan Shepherd, and Donald Slayton. Six of them made a Mercury flight.

Manned Flights of Project Mercury:

(1) Freedom 7, launched by Mercury-Redstone 3 on May 5, 1961, carrying Alan Shepherd. This suborbital flight, 15 minutes, 22 seconds in duration, put the first American in space.

(2) Liberty Bell 7, launched by Mercury-Redstone 4 on July 21, 1961, carrying Virgil Grisson. This suborbital flight, 15 minutes, 37 seconds in duration, was successful even though the spacecraft sank shortly after splashdown.

(3) Friendship 7, launched by Mercury-Atlas 6 on May 21, 1962, carrying John Glenn. This three-orbit flight, 4 hours, 55 minutes in duration, placed the first American into orbit.

(4) Aurora 7, launched by Mercury-Atlas 7 on May 24, 1962, carrying Scott Carpenter. This orbital flight, 4 hours, 56 minutes in dura-

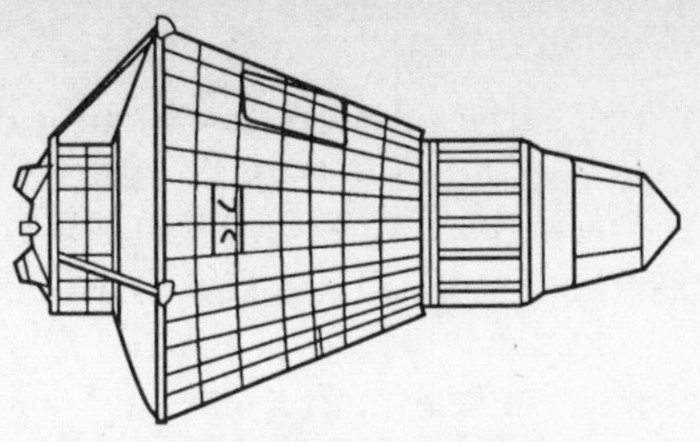

Mercury-Atlas 1961 – 1963
Length: 3.4 m Weight: 1.5 tons Ship's complement: 1
Propulsion: chemical

Fig. 53. **Mercury-Atlas.** See entry for Mercury Project.

tion, confirmed the success of Friendship 7.

(5) Sigma 7, launched by Mercury-Atlas 8 on October 3, 1962, carrying Walter Schirra. This six-orbit engineering test flight was 9 hours, 13 minutes in duration.

(6) Faith 7, launched by Mercury-Atlas 9 on May 15, 1963, carried Gordon Cooper. This final Mercury mission, 34 hours, 19 minutes in duration, completed 22 orbits to evaluate the effects of spending an entire day in space.

Mercury's rotation the rotation of Mercury relative to the stars, 58.6 days. This means that every part of the surface of Mercury is exposed to sunlight at some time or other. For many years it was thought that Mercury must have a captured, 88-day, rotation period, so that the same hemisphere was always illuminated by the sun, and the other hemisphere always turned toward the cold and darkness. In 1962, W.E. Howard and his colleagues at Michigan measured radar emission from Mercury and showed that the dark hemisphere was much warmer than could possibly have been the case if it were always turned away from the sun. Radar measurements then were made and established the real rotation period of Mercury relative to the stars. It is interesting to note that the average time between successive sunrises as seen from any point on Mercury—its solar day—is 176 Earth years, or 2 Mercury years.

Merez or **Nekkar** the common names for the yellow giant star Beta Bootis, magnitude 3.45. Merez is in the northern constellation Boötes, near Virgo and Canes Venatici. *Nekkar* is the Arabic name of the entire Boötes constellation.

Merga the common name for the yellow-white star 38 Boötes, seen in the northern sky constellation Boötes.

meridian 1. a north-south reference line;

2. a great circle through the geographical poles of Earth.

Meridiani Terra a dark surface feature 2045 km in diameter near the Martian equator, at longitude 17° to 341°, latitude 0° to -15°. When Mars is well placed, Meridiani Terra can easily be seen with the aid of a small telescope. The feature is also known as Terra Meridiani and Sinus Meridiani.

Meroe Patera a volcanic crater with irregular edges on Mars at 7° N and 291° W, in the large cratered plain called Syrtis Major Planitia.

Merope star 23 Tauri in the Pleiades, of the northern constellation Taurus, the Bull.

Mesarthim the common name for the white star Gamma Aurigae, apparent magnitude 4.8, found in the prominent northern constellation Auriga, near the star Capella.

mesosphere the layer of Earth's atmosphere that extends from the stratopause to an altitude of 80 kilometers.

mesosiderites stony-iron meteorites. See SIDERITES.

Messier, Charles (1730–1817) French astronomer noted for his deep-sky catalog of 100 brightest nebulas and star clusters. In Messier's catalog, celestial objects are designated by the letter M, as in M31 (Andromeda Galaxy).

Messier Catalog (M) also called *nebula catalog*, a listing of nonmoving, nonstellar, deep-sky objects such as nebulae, star clusters, and galaxies published by Charles Messier in 1787. See MESSIER NUMBER.

Messier number the catalog number of a nebula or star cluster (galaxy) in *Messier's Catalog.* Examples include M17, which is the Omega Nebula in Sagittarius; M1, which is the Crab Nebula; and M31, which is the Andromeda galaxy.

metagalaxy **1.** the total recognized assemblage of galaxies and intergalactic space;

2. the entire contents of the universe and the space it occupies.

Metallah or **Mothallah** or **Triangle** the common names for the yellow-white subgiant star Alpha Triangulum, in the northern sky near Aries and Andromeda. Metallah is a star of magnitude 3.42 and spectral type F6IV. It is one of three main stars that form the Triangle. It is 65 light-years from Earth.

metamorphic rock any rock produced by physical and chemical alteration of another rock that has been subjected to high temperature and pressure.

meteor a shooting star, the cometary debris (sand, rock fragments, frozen gases) that passes through Earth's atmosphere. It is seen by people as a streak of light that appears in the clear night sky when a small particle of interplanetary dust or meteoroid burns itself out in

Earth's upper atmosphere. The term *meteor* is generally used to designate any of the small chunks of iron and stone that inhabit the solar system, but is used more precisely to designate such material while it is entering Earth's atmosphere. Before it enters Earth's atmosphere, it is appropriately referred to as a *meteoroid*. If it survives its journey and lands on Earth, it is appropriately called a *meteorite*.

Meteor Crater an impact crater located between Flagstaff and Winslow, Arizona. It is some 1,200 meters in diameter and 183 meters deep. Also called the Crater Mound, the Winslow Crater, and the Arizona Meteorite Crater.

meteorite the interplanetary debris that strikes Earth's surface without being completely vaporized. Meteorites are classified as stony, chondrite, stony-iron, iron, and achondrite. Thus far, only about 2000 meteorites have been positively identified. The largest meteorites that have been found are one weighing 50 tons (in Grootfontein, South Africa) and another weighing 2300 pounds (Kansas). See also METEOR.

meteorite crater or **impact crater** **1.** a circular impact structure produced by meteorite bombardment;

2. a depression in planetary surfaces caused by explosions as meteorites crash into the surfaces at high speeds. These depressions are known as astroblemes if they occur in Earth's crust.

meteorite types see METEORITE.

meteoritics the study of meteorites and related phenomena.

meteoroid **1.** the term applied to meteoritic debris in the solar system;

2. a solid object moving in interplanetary space, considerably smaller than an asteroid and larger than an atom or molecule. It is estimated that 100,000 tons of meteoroids fall annually;

3. the natural objects in Earth-crossing orbits that are potential meteorites. See **ASTEROID.**

meteor path the projection of the trajectory of a meteor in the celestial sphere as seen by the observer on Earth.

meteor shower **1.** a number of meteors with approximately parallel trajectories;

2. the increase in observed rate of appearance of meteors when Earth crosses through a meteor stream. The effect is that of a brilliant display of fiery meteors. Meteor showers are associated with comets and are named for the constellation from which they appear to be bursting. See METEOR STREAM.

meteor storm or **meteor swarm** a meteor shower with an enormous rate of appearance that occurs when Earth intersects a new meteor stream close to the originating comet. The most famous meteor storm was the

Leonid storm of November 1833, with a rate that exceeded 10,000 visible meteors an hour. Individual observers often saw 20 per second. See LEONIDS.

meteor stream **1.** a collection of meteoroids around the orbit of a decaying comet;

2. a group of meteoric bodies with nearly identical orbits. See Fig. 54.

meteor swarm any large number of meteoroids moving in parallel paths. See Fig. 55 and METEOR STORM.

meteor train anything, such as light or ionization, that is left along the trajectory of a meteor after the head of the meteor has passed.

Meteosat either of two European Space Agency (ESA) geostationary satellite systems, launched in 1977 and June 1981, used for meteorological and climatological studies of Europe.

meter the basic unit of length in the metric system, equal to 39.37 inches.

methane a hydrocarbon gas that is present in many planetary and satellite atmospheres and, as an ice, in comets, satellites, and Pluto.

Metis (Asteroid 9) a minor planet discovered in 1848; its diameter is 150 km.

Metonic cycle a period of about 19 years, after which the various phases of the moon fall on approximately the same days of the year as in the previous cycle. Meton was an Athenian astronomer of the 5th century BC.

M giant a giant star of spectral class M, having a temperature in the 5000° F range, for example, the orange-red star Antares, in Scorpius.

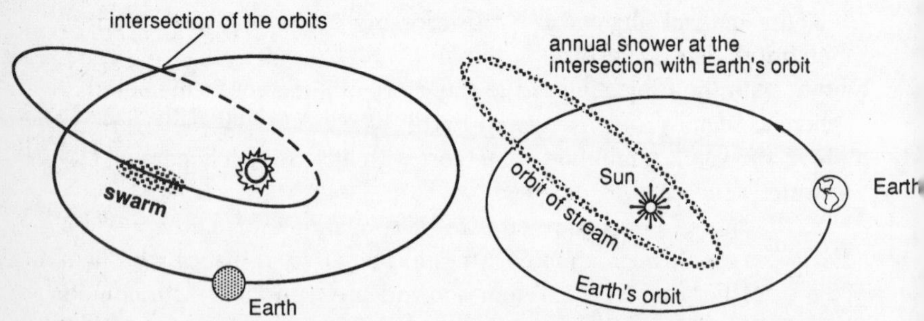

Fig. 54. **Meteor stream.** This drawing shows the orbit of the meteor stream that moves around the sun.

Fig. 55. **Meteor swarm.** Meteoroids moving in parallel paths, in this case around the sun. Their orbits intersect with Earth's orbit.

Miaplacidus the common name for the northern white giant star Beta Carinae. Miaplacidus is an A0111 star, magnitude 1.68, 85 light-years from Earth.

microlock a low-power, lightweight satellite telemetry system. Incoming satellite signals are relayed to the ground-based receiver through a phase-locked receiver that is the heart of the telemetering equipment, making possible correlation and detection of the signal.

micrometeorite a meteorite or meteoritic particle with a diameter less than about a millimeter. See METEORITE.

micrometer an instrument used to measure the perceived dimensions of remote celestial objects in order to estimate their true dimensions. Early micrometers used some means of projecting the background stars on a wire grid or similar device in the focal plane of a telescope so that it was viewed through the eyepiece together with the stars to be measured. Modern micrometers use more elaborate schemes to achieve the desired end.

Microscopium (Mic) a faint constellation south of Capricornus and east of Sagittarius. Composed of 5th-magnitude stars, it was intended to complement the new constellation Telescopium nearby. These constellations were originated by Lacaille to commemorate the exploration of the microcosm and the macrocosm, the smallest and the largest aspects of the universe. See LACAILLE.

microwaves a band of very high frequency radio waves just beyond the infrared band.

microwave turbulence the irregular and fluctuating gradients of microwave refractive index in the atmosphere. This index is the ratio of the velocity of a wave in a vacuum to the velocity of a wave in a specified medium, such as the atmosphere. It is measured at microwave frequencies.

Midas (Asteroid 1981) one of the Apollo asteroids discovered by the modern American astronomer Charles Kowal, working at the Palomar Observatory. He also discovered Leda, a moon of Jupiter; and Chiron, an asteroid that orbits between Saturn and Uranus.

midnight sun the sun visible at midnight in midsummer from locations in the arctic and antarctic regions.

Mie Crater a large Martian crater, 100 km in diameter, situated east of the robot Viking 2 spacecraft landing site at longitude 220°, latitude 48°.

Milky Way the galaxy to which the sun and its planets belong. As seen at night from Earth, the Milky Way is a faintly luminous belt of stars. The light is due to the fact that the vast majority of stars in our galaxy are located along this narrow band on the celestial sphere. The ancient Greeks named the faint band of light *galáxias kyklos*, the milky road. Today we can recognize the Milky Way as the glow of 200 billion stars whirling in a great wheel-like system.

millisecond pulsar a pulsar with a pulse period of only a few milliseconds. See PULSAR.

Mimas the innermost satellite, and one of the largest satellites of Saturn, orbiting at a distance of 186,000 km from the planet. Its orbital period is 22 hours.This icy moon is heavily cratered and has a diameter of 400 km. The dominant feature is a large impact crater, Herschel, six miles in depth. Mimas was discovered in 1789 by William Herschel.

minerals the chemical compounds, usually in the form of crystals, that constitute rocks.

minima the times of a variable star's minimum brightness.

Minkar the common name for the red-orange star Epsilon Corvi, apparent magnitude 3.2. It is located between Gienah and Alchiba in the southern constellation Corvus. Its distance from Earth is 140 light-years. The Ring-Tail Galaxy (NGC 4038) is also located in this constellation.

minor axis the shorter axis of an ellipse or ellipsoid that is perpendicular to the major axis at a point equidistant from the foci. See MAJOR AXIS.

minor-planet families see HIRAYAMA FAMILIES.

minor planets another name for *asteroids* or *planetoids*, the small solar system bodies of which 95% orbit the sun in a main belt (asteroid belt) between the orbits of Mars and Jupiter. They include members of the Amor, Apollo, and Trojan groups. Asteroids are irregular in shape, which causes them to vary in brightness as they rotate every few hours. Asteroids shine by reflected sunlight but only one, Vesta, located in the main asteroid belt, between Mars and Jupiter, is bright enough to be seen with the naked eye. More than 100,000 minor planets may be bright enough for photographic observation and discovery, but only a few more than 2100 have received official minor planet numbers to date. The largest minor planet is Ceres, in the main asteroid belt between Mars and Jupiter. See VESTA and CERES.

Mintaka Delta Orionis, the westernmost star of of the three forming the Belt of Orion. Mintaka is a bright blue giant eclipsing binary star very near the celestial equator. Mintaka, magnitude 2.2 and lying 1500 light-years from Earth, is 20,000 times as luminous as the sun.

minute of arc an angle equaling 1/60 of a degree.

Mir (commune) a long-duration space station launched by the USSR in 1986 as a step toward achieving permanent manned observations in space. Mir has six docking ports, at least four of which are building-block modules dedicated to specific scientific disciplines. Early in 1987 the USSR launched Kvant (quantum), a 20-ton astrophysics module, which was joined to the growing Mir. Kvant has a variety of telescopes, aimed primarily at investigation of x-ray and gamma-ray sources and used to study the 1987 supernova in the Large Magellanic Cloud.

Mira (the Wonderful) also **Mira Ceti** and **Omicron Ceti.** A red giant star in the equatorial constellation Cetus. Mira, 130 light-years from Earth, is the first known variable star. It changes in brightness from 2.0 to 10.1 magnitude and back again in a period of 332 days. Small wonder that Polish astronomer Johannes Hevelius (1611–1687) gave it the name Mira. See MIRA STARS.

Mira Ceti see MIRA.

Mirach a red giant star that is the second-brightest in the constellation Andromeda and is known as the girdle of Andromeda's gown. Mirach is 24 parsecs from Earth and has a magnitude of 2.06.

Miram the common name for the star Eta Persei, apparent brightness 3.9. Miram is part of the northern constellation Perseus, lying next to Andromeda and near Cepheus, Cassiopeia, and Auriga.

Miranda the innermost and fifth largest of the 15 moons of Uranus. It was discovered in 1948 by astronomer Gerard Kuiper, working at the Palomar Observatory. Miranda, with a diameter of 300 miles, orbits Uranus at a mean distance of 124,000 km and is noted for its puzzling fractured and grooved terrain. See KUIPER.

Mira stars or **Mira variables** a group of long-period variable stars, also called red variables. One example is the variable Omicron Ceti. See MIRA.

Mira variable see MIRA STARS.

Mirfak the common name for the yellow-white dwarf star Alpha Persei (a Per). Mirfak, the brightest star in the northern constellation Perseus, is 570 parsecs from Earth.

mirror altitude the altitude 1000 to 5000 km above Earth about the equator at which electrically charged radiation impinging upon Earth is reflected by the geomagnetic field.

Mirzam the bright blue-white giant star Beta Canis Majoris, a pulsating variable or Beta Cephei star, in the southern constellation Canis Major, the Great Dog, between Puppis and Leo. Sirius, Alpha Canis Majoris, is the brightest star of the constellation Canis Major. Mirzam, the second brightest, is referred to as the announcer of the rising of Sirius.

Misam the common name for the dim star Kappa Persei, just above

Algenib (Alpha Persei) in the northern constellation Perseus. Near Misam are M76, a planetary nebula of the 11th magnitude, and M34, a 6th-magnitude open star cluster.

missile, ballistic a missile designed to operate primarily in accordance with the laws of ballistics, covering the motion, behavior, and effects of projectiles, especially bullets and the like. A ballistic missile, also called a guided missile, is guided during a portion of its flight, usually the upward portion, and is not under thrust from its propelling system during the subsequent portion of its flight.

Mitchell, Maria (1818–1889) the first famous American woman astronomer, who made a special study of sunspots, nebulae, and satellites. She discovered a telescopic comet in 1847, an accomplishment for which she was awarded a gold medal by the king of Denmark. Mitchell was the first woman elected to membership in the American Academy of Arts and Sciences.

Mizar the star Zeta Ursae Majoris. This white star, one of the brighter stars of the Big Dipper, in the region of the north celestial pole, is 26 parsecs from Earth.

molecular cloud any interstellar cloud of gas and dust with greater than average density and dust content, and with a high concentration of molecules. The largest molecular cloud is Sagittarius B2, an immense—diameter 40 parsecs—dark molecular cloud of hydrogen gas and dust lying around the galactic center. Sagittarius B2 was discovered by means of radio astronomy.

momentum a measure of the state of motion of an object: the mass of the moving body multiplied by its velocity.

monitor to observe, listen in on, keep track of, or exercise surveillance over, as in *monitor radio signals* and *monitor the flight of a spacecraft*.

Monoceros the Unicorn, a southern constellation east of Orion. It fills a large area between Hydra and Orion, separating Orion's two dogs. Its brightest stars are only of 4th magnitude, but it lies in the Milky Way and contains the Rosette Nebula (NGC 2244), a wreath-shaped mass of glowing gas with embedded stars.

Mons and **Montes** (plural) **1.** designations used for a mountain and a mountain range on Mars, for example, Olympus Mons and Tharsis Montes;

2. designations used for surface features of Venus, for example, Maxwell Montes; and Mercury, for example, Montes Caloris.

Monster an infrequently used name for the constellation Hydra, which is more often called the Water Snake because it winds a quarter of the way around the equatorial region of the sky. Except for its size, there is nothing prominent about Hydra. Its only star of note is the 2nd-magnitude Alphard.

montes see MONS.

month the average period of revolution of the moon around Earth. A *sidereal month*, determined by using a fixed star as a reference point, is equal to 27 days, 7 hours, and 41 minutes. A *synodic* or *lunar month*, the average time between successive new, or full moons, is equal to 29 days, 12 hours, and 44 minutes.

moon 1. the only natural satellite of Earth and our nearest neighbor in space, lying 384,000 km away. Its surface gravity is only 1/6 that of Earth. The moon has a captive rotation, which means that it keeps the same side facing toward Earth as it revolves. The two main surface features are the marias (seas) and the highlands. See Fig. 56 and MARIA;
2. any satellite.

moon illusion the false impression that the full moon looks larger when low in the sky than when it is higher in the sky.

moonquake a localized seismic disturbance inside Earth's moon. This phenomenon was detected by the Apollo seismic network. Seismographs left on the moon by the Apollo 15 and 17 expeditions in 1971 and 1972 have revealedmuch about the lunar interior. Moonquakes occur less frequently and less energetically than earthquakes do—moonquakes average 1 to 2 on the Richter scale, earthquakes 5 to 8. As an aid in understanding the lunar interior, spent rocket stages and used lunar modules were sent crashing into the moon's surface to produce moonquakes of known intensity for study from Earth. Apollo scientific equipment that was left behind on the moon remained in operation for almost a decade and sent back much moonquake information.

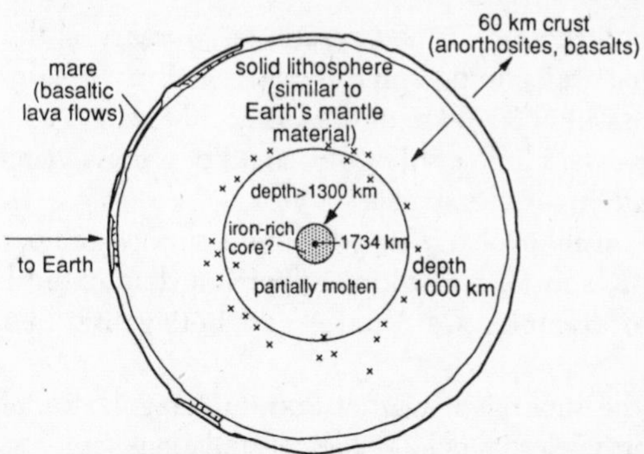

Fig. 56. **Moon.** A cross-sectional view of the moon, showing its internal composition.

moonrise the crossing of the visible horizon by the upper limb of the ascending moon. See MOONSET and LIMB.

moonrock a sample of lunar material. Moonrock was returned to Earth by Apollo and Luna spacecraft.

moonset the crossing of the visible horizon by the upper limb of the descending moon. See MOONSET and LIMB.

Moretus a high-walled crater, 105 km in diameter, at -70° S and -4° W, on the near side of the moon, in the south polar region.

morning star also called *Phosphorus*, not a star at all but any bright planet, especially Venus, that is visible in the sky just before sunrise. The term is normally applied to Venus when it shines brightly in the eastern sky before sunrise, but it sometimes refers to the morning visibility of Mercury.

Mothallah see METALLAH.

mountain a natural planetary landform that reaches high elevations above the usual land surface. See MONS.

Mount Huygens a high peak in the lunar Apennines at +20° N and -3° W, southeast of Mare Imbrium, in the northern hemisphere of the near side of the moon.

Mount Olympus also called *Olympus Mons*, the largest volcano on Mars—at the base its diameter is 600 km. It was photographed by the Viking 1 orbiter in 1976. The top of this gigantic volcano pierces the clouds at a height of 15 miles above the surface. Olympus Mons, at latitude 18° N and longitude 133°, is more than twice as tall as Mauna Kea in Hawaii, which is the tallest volcano on Earth. The volcano is crowned with an enormous caldera, or crater, 50 miles wide. All of Rhode Island could easily fit inside this huge Martian crater. See OLYMPUS MONS.

Mozart crater a 225-km diameter crater on Mercury, at the very edge of a region that was photographically surveyed in 1974 by Mariner 10, which came within 6000 km of the surface. Mozart is at 8° N and 191° W, on the western limb of Mercury, south of Caloris Planitia.

Mpc *abbreviation for* megaparsec.

M star a relatively cool red star, having a surface temperature of less than 3500 K and an absorption spectrum dominated by molecular bands. Two examples are Antares and Betelgeuse. See ABSORPTION SPECTRUM.

Mu Cephei the supergiant Garnet Star, an irregular variable star lying near the north celestial pole, in the constellation Cepheus.

Mufrid or **Muphrid** the common name for the yellow subgiant star Eta

Bootis, in the northern constellation Boötes and 32 light-years from Earth.

Muliphein the common name for the blue-white star Gamma Canis Majoris in the southern constellation Canis Major. Muliphein is 325 light-years from Earth.

multiple star 1. any system of three stars (trinaries) or more stars lying close together in the celestial sphere and usually united in a single gravitational field, therefore orbiting around one another. Examples of trinaries are Alpha, Beta, and YY Gemini—Castor (A), (B), and (C)—and Alpha, Beta, and Proxima Centauri—Centauri (A), (B), and (C); See VISUAL TRINARY;

2. a term sometimes or loosely applied to binary stars. An example is Zeta Ursa Majoris, comprising Mizar (A) and Mizar (B).

Mundrabilla meteorite a shower of large irons, or iron meteorites, that long ago blasted into pre-Cambrian quartzite at Wolf Creek, in Western Australia. Its remains were first recognized in 1948: Only tiny specks and thin veins of the metal are now visible on the cut surfaces of meteorites that fell untold hundreds of thousands of years ago as solid masses of nickel-iron.

Muphrid see MUFRID.

Murasaki crater a 125-km diameter crater at latitude -12° S and longitude 31°, in the southern hemisphere of Mercury, just south of the dark equatorial region Phaethontia, located on G.V. Schiaparelli's 1877 map of Mercury. (The term *Phaethontia* is not identified on more recent maps.) The wall of the crater is broken by the ray crater Kuiper. See KUIPER CRATER.

Murchison meteor a large carbonaceous meteorite that fell in Canada in 1969, at a time when many laboratories were preparing for analyses of the first Apollo lunar samples. This meteorite was widely studied as a dry run for work on the Apollo moon samples. Murchison is best known for the variety of organic, or carbon-bearing, chemicals it has yielded; the meteorite also contains 16 amino acids, 11 of which are rare on Earth.

Musca (the Fly) a small southern constellation lying to the south of Crux, the Southern Cross. The stars of Musca are unnamed, and its brightest star is of third magnitude.

Museida the common name for the star Pi Ursa Majoris, in the region of the north celestial pole, near Draco and Leo.

mutual recession the movement away from Earth of all distant galaxies. The farther away they are, the faster they recede.

N

nadir the point on the celestial sphere that is directly beneath the observer on Earth and diametrically (180°) opposite the zenith.

naked singularity a singularity that is not surrounded by an event horizon and therefore is kept from our view. See SINGULARITY.

Naos (Zeta Puppis) a blue-white supergiant star in the southern constellation Puppis, near Canis Major and Pyxis. Lying at 2300 light-years from Earth, Naos has an absolute magnitude of -7.1 and is one of the most intrinsically luminous stars—60,000 times that of our sun—at a distance of 2400 light-years from Earth. Naos is comparable to Rigel in energy output. If such a star were as near to Earth as is the star Vega, Naos would appear to us to be about 12 times brighter than Venus at its best.

NASA *acronym of* *N*ational *A*eronautics and *S*pace *A*dministration, formed in 1958, the agency responsible for civilian aeronautical and space activities of the United States. NASA achievements include the Apollo program, Mercury project, Gemini, Skylab, and the Space Shuttle orbiter.

Nash another name for the orange star Nushaba in Sagittarius. See NUSHABA.

Nashira the common name for the yellow-white star Gamma Capricorni, an F2 type star with an apparent magnitude of 3.8. This dwarf star lies 109 light-years from Earth.

Nath also called Beta Tauri, a blue-white star next to the bright orange star Aldebaran in the northern constellation Taurus. Nath has an apparent magnitude of 1.8 and lies 300 light-years from Earth.

natural motion the Aristotelian notion that objects move toward their natural places; that is, fire and air move upward, and earth and water move downward.

nautical mile the average length of an arc on Earth's surface that makes an angle of one minute (1/60 degree) at the center of Earth.

nautical twilight the period during which the upper limb of the sun is below the visible horizon, and the center of the sun is not more than 12 degrees below the celestial horizon. See LIMB.

navigation the practice or art of directing the movement of a spacecraft from one point to another. Navigation usually implies the presence of a human navigator aboard the craft.

navigational planets the four planets commonly used in celestial surface and air navigation: Venus, Mars, Jupiter, and Saturn.

navigational satellite a satellite designed specifically as a navigational aid for shipping and aircraft. The first navigational satellite, Transit B, launched in 1960, transmitted information about its orbit and position, and the signals were picked up ships at sea. A later series, Timation, produced even more accurate positions. A further series, Nav-Star, numbered 11 launches in all. Seasat, a satellite designed to monitor the oceans on a global scale, was terminated due to contractual, not scientific, problems.

navigational stars the 57 stars included in the main listing of the stars used in celestial navigation—ranging from Acamar to Vega. A navigator observing the positions of well-known heavenly bodies at a certain time, using a sextant and referring to tables, can determine the position of his or her craft. *The Nautical Almanac* is used for surface navigation by sailors of the United Kingdom and the United States.

navigational triangle a celestial triangle formed on the celestial sphere by the great circles connecting the elevated pole, the zenith of the assumed position of the observer, and a celestial body. Solving this triangle enables the navigator to compute altitude and azimuth.

neap tide 1. *neap:* the lowest or less extreme tides, which occur when the moon is near first- or third-quarter phase;

2. *spring*: the highest tides, which occur at full and new moon, when Earth is near perihelion and the moon is close to perigee.

near side the hemisphere of the moon that is permanently turned toward Earth. People on Earth always see the same side of the moon, because the moon rotates on its axis with the same period that it revolves around Earth. An astronaut standing on the near side of the moon finds Earth perpetually present in the sky, another demonstration of the fact that the near side of the moon is always visible from Earth.

nebula an interstellar region of dust or gas that can be seen in visible light as a luminous patch, a dark hole, or as a band against a brighter background. Widely known nebulae include the Crab, Lagoon, Crescent, Swan (Omega Nebula), Trifid, Dumbbell, Orion, Eskimo (or Clown-Face Nebula), North American (Pelican Nebula), Ring, Tarantula, Veil, and Owl.

The types of nebulae include (a) *diffuse*—a reflection nebula, which merely reflects starlight toward us without emitting any visible radiation of its own; (b) *planetary*—an emission nebula formed when a variable star sheds its outer layers, the radiation emitted being gas ionized by ultraviolet radiation from nearby stars; (c) *supernova remnant*—an emission nebula formed when a star rips itself apart as a supernova; (d) *bipolar* (or *biconical*)—formed from the light that has escaped to illuminate a reflection nebula; (e) *cometary*—a bipolar nebula in which one of the two lobes is hidden, normally by a dark nebula; (f) *cometary globule*—a dense blob of gas squeezed by a passing shock wave, as from a supernova, and usually having a long tail; (g) *Herbig-Haro object*—a tiny emission nebula with a distinctive spectrum; and (h) *zodiacal light*—the sun's own reflection nebula.

nebular variables also known as **T Tauri Stars**, very young stars that have begun to shine, but have not yet reached main sequence. See MAIN SEQUENCE STARS and VARIABLE STARS.

negative acceleration (of spacecraft, rockets, etc.) deceleration.

nekkar see MEREZ.

Neptune the 8th planet from our sun, discovered in 1864 by German astronomer Johann Gottfried Galle (1812–1910), and orbiting the sun every 165 years. Its atmosphere contains hydrogen, helium, and methane. It also contains a circulating region called the Great Dark Spot. The most distant giant planet from the sun, Neptune resembles Uranus in that it has a greenish disk. Neptune has a moon system similar to the moon systems of Jupiter and Saturn. Of its 8 moons, only Triton and Nereid are named. The other moons are listed by numbers: 1989N6, 1989N5, 1989N4, 1989N3, 1989N2, and 1989N1 (at 200-km in diameter, the largest of the smaller moons). Neptune also has a dark, narrow ring system, including several ring arcs, or partial rings. See VOYAGER and GREAT DARK SPOT.

Nereid the third largest moon—diameter 300 km—of Neptune, discovered in 1949 by American astronomer Gerard Peter Kuiper (1905–1973), born in Holland. Neptune's newly discovered moon (1981 N1) is the second largest Neptunian moon—diameter 420 km.

Nestor (Asteroid 659) a Trojan asteroid discovered in 1908. It is 102 km in diameter and lies 5.26 AU from the sun. See TROJAN GROUP.

neutrino a fundamental particle that has little or no mass and no charge, but does have spin and energy. Many astrophysically important processes release neutrinos, from fusion reactions in stars to supernova explosions.

neutron a stable elementary particle found in the nucleus of every atom except the ordinary hydrogen atom. It has no charge, and its mass is approximately equal to that of the proton.

neutron star a collapsed star consisting of immense numbers of densely packed neutrons, so that it will be of low luminosity but almost incredibly great density. Astronomers consider that a neutron star may possibly be the remains of a supernova. For example, the Crab Nebula is the remnant of a supernova that was seen to explode in 1054 AD by Chinese observers. It is now known that the remarkable radio sources known as pulsars are in fact neutron stars, and more than 400 have thus far been discovered. See PULSAR.

New General Catalog (NGC) a listing of nebulae, star clusters, and galaxies that has succeeded the catalog compiled by Charles Messier in 1787. See MESSIER CATALOG.

new moon 1. the moon at conjunction, when little or none of it is visible to an observer on Earth because the side illuminated by the sun is facing away from the observer. See Fig. 57;

2. the phase of the moon that occurs when the moon is between Earth and the sun. This new moon is also called the *change of the moon* and the *dark of the moon*.

New Quebec crater an impact (meteor) crater 3 km in diameter in the Canadian Shield, a vast region underlain by Precambrian rock of northern and central Canada. There is also an Old Quebec crater, which may be an old volcanic crater or an ancient impact crater whose meteoritic debris has been lost to erosion.

newton (n) a unit of force. One newton is the force needed to accelerate a mass of 1 kilogram by 1 meter per second in 1 second.

Newton, Isaac (1642–1727) an English mathematician, physicist, and astronomer. Newton formulated the law of gravitation and, in 1671,

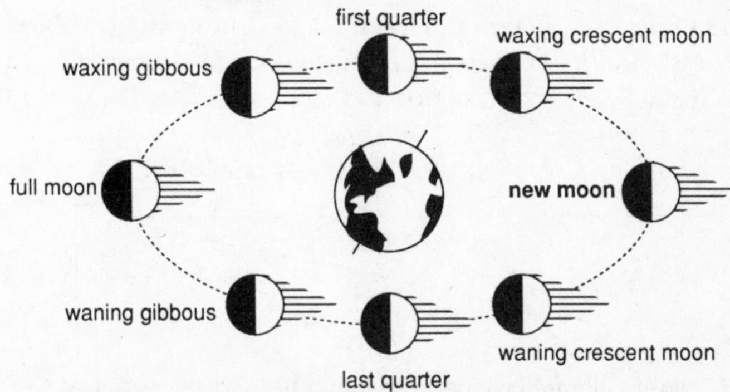

Fig. 57. **Moon phases.** Beginning at the new moon, farthest right in the drawing, one can see that little or none of the moon can be seen from Earth. Moving counterclockwise, one can see more and more of the moon until, at the extreme left, the moon is full, and the complete disk is visible. As the moon begins to wane, less and less is visible. The cycle soon ends, to begin again with another new moon.

built his first reflecting telescope. See NEWTON'S LAW OF GRAVITATION and NEWTON'S LAW OF MOTION.

Newtonian reflector a reflecting telescope that brings the rays of light from a distant object to a focal point near the side of the telescope tube. See Fig. 58.

Newton's Law of Gravitation the scientific law holding that every particle of matter in the universe attracts every other particle with a force acting along the line joining the two particles, proportional to the product of the masses of the particles and inversely proportional to the square of the distance between the particles.

Newton's Laws of Motion three principles that together constitute the basis of classical mechanics:

(1) Every body persists in its state of rest or of uniform motion in a straight line unless it is compelled to change that state by forces impressed upon it.

(2) The rate of change of momentum of a body is directly proportional to the force applied and takes place in the direction of that force.

(3) To every action there is always an opposed and equal action; the initial actions of two bodies upon each other are always equal and directed to contrary parts.

N galaxies galaxies that resemble quasars, whose light is dominated by a pointlike stellar nucleus. N galaxies are recognized as one of many groups of active galaxies between normal galaxies and quasars. See QUASAR.

NGC the prefix used before numbers assigned to nonstellar objects in the *New General Catalog*, published by Danish astronomer J.L.E. Dreyer in 1888. See NEW GENERAL CATALOG.

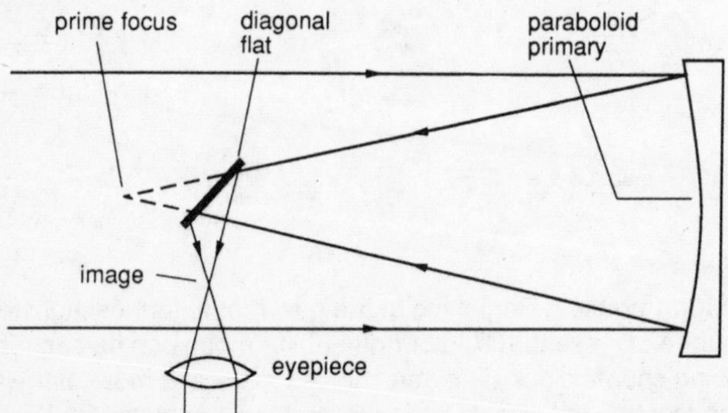

Fig. 58. **Newtonian reflector.** The user of this type of telescope views the image through the eyepiece at the side of the telescope.

Nicholson, Seth B. (1891–1963) American astronomer, working at the Mount Wilson Observatory, near Pasadena, California, who discovered four faint satellites (moons) of Jupiter and made thermocouple measurements of the temperatures of planets and the eclipsed moon.

Nihal or **Beta Leporis** a yellow giant star at the base of Lepus, a southern constellation just beneath Orion. Nihal, 113 light-years from Earth, is a double star, the primary being of magnitude 2.81. The companion star has a magnitude of 9.4.

Nimbus a weather satellite operating around the clock and designed to record temperature data on the ground and temperature and humidity data in the upper atmosphere. It photographs clouds in daytime by visible light and in nighttime by infrared light. It also detects ozone. Seven Nimbus satellites were placed in orbit by NASA between 1964 and 1978. See Fig. 59.

noctilucent cloud or **luminous cloud** a pearly white or blue cloud of unknown composition that occurs at great heights, 75–90 km above Earth. It resembles a thin cirrus, standing out against a dark night sky.

Noctis Labyrinthus a maze of Martian canyons (46,000 square miles in extent) located at latitude -4° to -14° S and longitude 95° to 110°, at the summit of the Tharsis Ridge.

node 1. a point of intersection of one orbit (say, the moon's) with the plane of another orbit (say, Earth's);

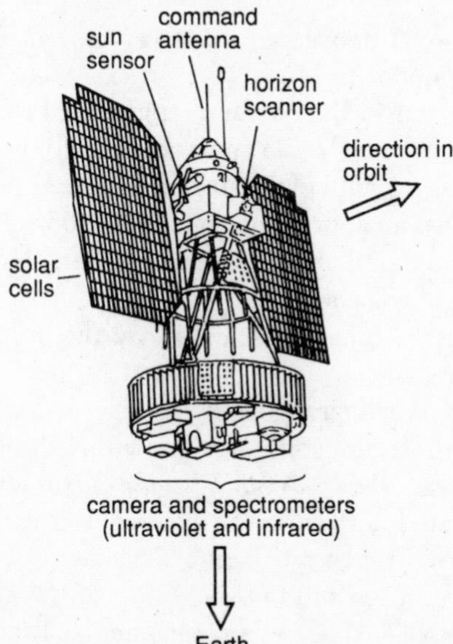

Fig. 59. **Nimbus.** The illustration shows NASA's Nimbus satellite in orbit and with its solar cells deployed.

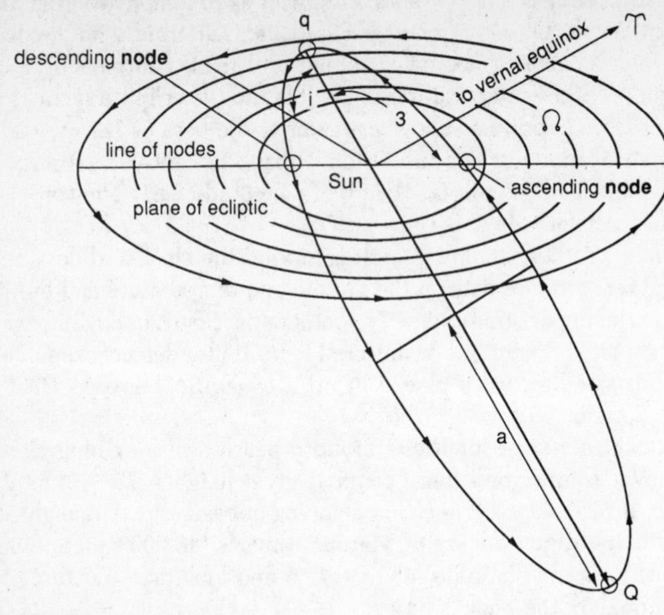

Fig. 60. **Nodes.** See entry.

2. one of two points where an orbit crosses a reference point. See Fig. 60.

nodical period the interval between successive passages of a satellite through the ascending node.

Nodus I a giant orange star in the northern constellation Draco. It lies 148 light-years from Earth and has an apparent magnitude of 3.2.

Nodus II Zeta Draconis, a giant yellow star of Draco. It lies 124 light-years from Earth and has an apprent magnitude of 3.06.

nontronite a clay mineral found in the fine dust of Mars. Nontronite is a product of weathering of volcanic lavas.

noon the instant at which a time reference is over the upper branch of the reference meridian.

norite the crustal rock in the lunar highlands.

Norma (Nor) the southern constellation known as the Carpenter's Square. Originally, it was called *Norma et Regula*, Latin for carpenter's square and level. Located north of and adjoining Triangulum, Norma was formed in 1752 by French astronomer Nicolas de Lacaille, who took some stars away from Ara and Lupus.

North America Nebula (NGC 7000) an emission nebula lying in the constellation Cygnus; famous for a luminous supergiant star called *Deneb*. See DENEB.

north celestial pole the point on the celestial sphere that is determined by the extension of Earth's axis in a northerly direction. See CELESTIAL SPHERE.

north circumpolar constellation one of the constellations, for example, Cepheus and Draco, that are near the north celestial pole. As seen from moderate northern latitudes, such constellations never set. See CIRCUMPOLAR STARS.

Northern Cross the Cygnus constellation. See CYGNUS.

northern lights or **aurora borealis** a display of diffuse changing colored light seen high in Earth's atmosphere in the north polar region. They are caused by charged particles from the solar wind or from flares that become trapped by Earth's magnetic field and interact with gases in the upper atmosphere. See AURORA.

north point a point on the observer's celestial horizon directly under the north celestial pole.

north polar sequence a list of stars near the north celestial pole arranged in order of photographic magnitude. These stars are used as reference stars in stellar photometry.

north pole the end of the axis of rotation of a celestial body (planet, moon, star) at which, when viewed from above, the body appears to rotate in a clockwise direction. Also known as the *celestial pole*, *ecliptic pole*, and *geographical pole*.

North Star or **Stella Polaris** any bright star that happens to be within a few degrees of the north celestial pole during a given era. At present, Polaris (Alpha Ursa Minor) is the north star or pole star. In Egyptian times, the star Thuban (Alpha Draconis) was the north star. See POLARIS.

nova (plural, *novae*) **1.** a newly visible star, or one that suddenly increases dramatically in brightness then gradually fades, and so is seen as a *new star*;

2. a highly evolved star in which there is a sudden and unpredictable increase in brightness by 10 magnitudes or more. A nova may result when gas is dumped from one member of a binary star pair onto the other. The tremendous outflow is pulled by the gravity of the companion star.

Nova Cygni the 1975 nova in Cygnus. This, the best-observed nova in history, provided the constellation Cygnus (the Swan) with a prominent extra star for a few days in that year. Most novae go unseen during the first hours of their explosion, but during the Cygnus event, many amateur astronomers in California were photographing the sky. One of them, Ben Mayer, of Los Angeles, was photographing the Cygnus area of the sky at the crucial time. He was searching fruitlessly for meteors, but when he heard about the nova, he retrieved his meteorless film from the trash and found that he had actually recorded Nova Cygni while it brightened. See NOVA and CYGNUS.

novae a plural form of *nova*. See NOVA.

Nova Herculis a nova that appeared in 1934, one of the brightest novae observed in the 20th century. It appeared near the Hercules-Lyra border. Nova Herculis was first seen by the British amateur astronomer J.P. Prentice, on the night of December 13, 1934.

Nova Mon see X-RAY TRANSIENT.

Nova Serpentis (1970 Serpens) a bright nova discovered by the Japanese astronomer M. Honda on February 13, 1970. It reached its maximum visual brightness on February 18 and after a few days duly appeared to begin its slow decline. Three months later the nova became, as viewed through infrared detectors, one of the most brilliant stars in the sky, magnitude -4.6.

N stars the N spectral class of very red stars. It is probable that all N stars are variable stars. See VARIABLE STAR.

Nubecular Major and **Nubecular Minor** alternative names for the Large and Small Magellanic Clouds.

nuclear bulge 1. the spherical cloud of stars that lies at the center of spiral galaxies;

2. any great barrier of stars. See GALAXY.

nucleosynthesis the production of elements heavier than helium by the fusion of atomic nuclei in stars and during supernovae explosions. See SUPERNOVA.

nucleus or **atomic nucleus** the central, positively charged, dense portion of an atom.

nucleus, cometary the solid chunk of ice and dust in the head of a comet, typically a few kilometers in diameter.

nucleus, galactic the central concentration of matter at the center of a galaxy, typically less than one light-year in diameter, and possibly containing a supermassive black hole. See BLACK HOLE.

Nushaba also known as *Nash* or *Gamma Sagittarii* an orange star with an apparent magnitude of 3.1 in the southern constellation Sagittarius, between Scorpius and Capricornus.

nutation a relatively small nodding motion of Earth's axis of rotation with a period of 19 years. This motion is superimposed on precession. See PRECESSION.

Nysa (Asteroid 44) a minor planet in the main asteroid belt, with the highest albedo (0.377) of any known asteroid. Its diameter is 82 kilometers. Nysa was discovered in 1857 by German astronomer Hermann Goldschmidt.

Nyx Olympica an early name for Olympus Mons. Italian astronomer Giovanni Virginio Schiaparelli (1835–1910) was the first to see, through a telescope, this giant volcano on the Tharsis Ridge of Mars. Its summit is about 4,000 meters high. The peak, about 70 km wide, contains a complex system of calderas, which at one time must have been the outlets for lava flows. Characterized by a flattened profile, Nyx Olympica belongs to the type known as *shield volcanoes*, which are formed by successive eruptions of low-viscosity lava. See CALDERA and OLYMPUS MONS.

O

OAO *abbreviation of* Orbiting Astronomical Observatories, specially equipped unmanned NASA spacecraft that made ultraviolet observations of stars and interstellar matter from Earth orbit during the early 1970s.

Oberon the outermost satellite of Uranus. This 1,600-km diameter moon has an icy, cratered surface and orbits Uranus at a mean distance of 586,000 km. English astronomer William Herschel (1738–1822) discovered Oberon and Titania, another moon of Uranus, in 1787. Two years later, he discovered two moons of Saturn—Enceladus and Mimas.

oblate a nonspherical shape formed by rotating an ellipse around its shorter axis. The equatorial diameter of an oblate body, such as Jupiter, is greater than its polar diameter.

oblateness the ellipticity or degree of flattening of a planet at its poles because of rotation. Saturn is the most oblate of the planets.

oblate spheroid a shape like that of Earth, which is flattened at the North and South Poles. See OBLATENESS.

obliquity the angle by which a planet's rotation axis is tipped relative to its orbit. There is wide variation in obliquity—Mercury, 0°; Jupiter, 3.12°; Earth, 23.45°; Uranus, 82.14°.

observatory, astronomical a structure built for astronomical study and equipped with telescopes. Skylab is an orbiting observatory. Examples of surface observatories are Mt. Palomar, Wilson, and Arecibo. See SKYLAB.

observed altitude see TRUE ALTITUDE.

Occam's razor the maxim that the simplest hypothesis with the fewest assumptions is most likely to be the correct one. Named after William of Ockham (c.1285–c.1349) an English philosopher. Occam's razor can be thought of as useful for cutting away false hypotheses.

occultation 1. the complete or partial obscuration of an astronomical object by the moon or a planet, for example, a solar eclipse;

2. the passage of an object of large angular size in front of a smaller object, for example, the moon in front of a distant star, or the rings of Saturn in front of the Voyager spacecraft. See Fig. 61.

ocean tide the moon's tidal stretching of the Earth, as observed on the ocean surface (as opposed to *body tide*). See TIDES.

Oceanus Procellarum the Ocean of Storms, a large mare on the near side of the moon, at 10° N and 47° W. It was the landing site of Apollo

12 in 1969. The lower portion of Procellarum lies across the lunar equator, running northward to Aristarchus. The region contains such ray-craters as Aristarchus, south of Oceanus Procellarum, and Kepler, west of Oceanus Procellarum. See MARIA.

octahedrite or **anatase** **1.** an iron meteorite—less than 4% of all meteorites found to date contain this mineral composition, titanium dioxide; **2.** a naturally occurring crystalline form of titanium dioxide.

Octans (Oct) the Octant, a constellation of the Southern Hemisphere, containing the south celestial pole. This star group was originally called *Octans Hadleianus* (Latin for Hadley's Octant) to commemorate the invention of the octant, a navigational instrument invented in 1730 by English mathematician John Hadley (1682–1744). An octant resembles a sextant, but its measuring arc is one-eighth of a circle. The octant can measure an angle (usually the altitude of a star above the horizon) up to 90°.

oculogyral illusion an apparent movement of an image in space, seen when the semicircular canals of the viewer's ears are stimulated. The viewer feels that he or she is also moving, and in the same direction as the image in space.

Odysseus a 400-km diameter crater on Saturn's satellite Tethys.

Oesel crater or **Kaalijarv** a group of six meteor craters in Estonia, identified by the presence of iron meteorites at the sites.

OGO *abbreviation of* Orbiting Geophysical Observatory.

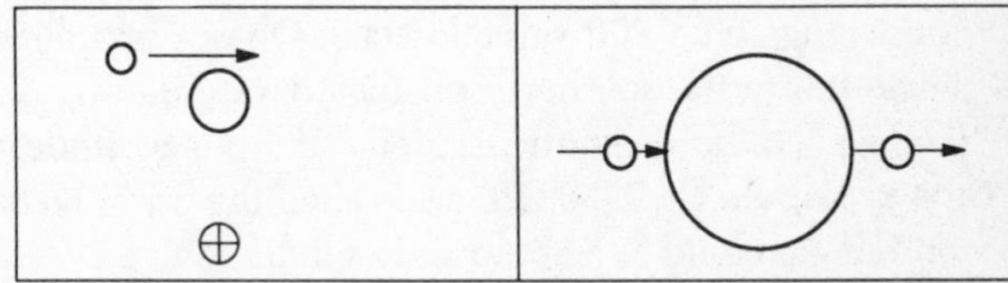

Fig. 61. **Occultation.** The term applies generally to any large astronomical body passing between a smaller body and the observer, shown on the left. It also applies to the passage of an object of large angular size in front of a smaller object, shown on the right.

Ogygis Rupes a mountain ridge 185 km in diameter on the planet Mars, at latitude -32° to -35° and longitude 53° to 55°, along the edge of the Argyre Quadrangle, a large impact basin.

Olbers, Heinrich (1758–1840) a German astronomer who searched for the missing planet between the orbits of Mars and Jupiter. He later discovered two of the first four asteroids, Pallas and Vesta. Olbers also discovered several comets, invented a method of calculating their orbits, and originated the so-called OLBERS' PARADOX.

Olbers' Comet a bright comet with a period of 69.47 years, thus far seen three times, in 1815, 1887, and 1956. Its path was first calculated by German astronomer Friedrich Bessel (1784–1846), who was the first to make a successful stellar parallax measurement of 61 Cygni, a star near the head of the Swan in Cygnus.

Olbers' Paradox the paradox stemming from the conflict between observation and theory as to why the night sky should be dark, or should not be dark, if the universe is filled with stars.

Oljto the common name for Asteroid 2201, an Apollo asteroid that may be the burned-out remains of a cometary nucleus. It was photographed first in 1947 and again in 1979. See APOLLO GROUP.

Olympus Mons the largest volcano on Mars and thought to be the largest in the solar system. Olympus Mons is in the Tharsis Quadrangle region, at latitude 18° and longitude 133°. Its base diameter is 550 km, its height is 25 km above the surface plain, and its caldera diameter is 80 km. See CALDERA, MOUNT OLYMPUS, and NYX OLYMPICA.

Omega Centauri a globular star cluster 17,000 light-years from Earth, containing some 200 variable stars. Omega was once thought to be a single star in the southern constellation Centaurus. To the unaided eye it appears to be a slightly fuzzy star of 4th magnitude.

Omega Nebula (NGC 6618) also called the Swan Nebula and M17, this ionized gas cloud in Sagittarius is a radio source.

Omicron Ceti see MIRA.

Omicron 2 also known as 40 Eridani. At a distance of only 16 light-years from Earth, this is the 8th nearest of the stars that can be seen with the naked eye. It is a remarkable triple star system that contains a classic example of a white dwarf star. Discovered in 1783 by English astronomer William Herschel (1738–1822), the companion stars are (a) a white dwarf and (b) a red dwarf forming a binary pair in retrograde motion around (c) a faint red dwarf.

Oort cloud a region of the solar system far beyond the planet Pluto in which move a cloud of comets—billions of them—in nearly circular orbits around the sun. This swarm of icy bodies is believed to lie in a spherical shell 50,000 astronomical units from the sun.

opacity the resistance of a gas, such as an atmosphere, to the passage of radiation.

open cluster see OPEN STAR CLUSTER.

open orbit or **escape orbit** an orbit that does not return to its starting point.

open space any celestial space that is uncurved or is curved in such a way as to have infinite volume and no boundaries.

open star cluster sometimes called **galactic cluster** a cluster of 10 to 10,000 stars with an open, transparent appearance. Clusters are located in the spiral arms or disk of a galaxy. In an open star cluster, the stars are not tightly grouped. The Pleiades is a well-known open star cluster. The Jewel Box, an open star cluster in Crux, contains only a few hundred stars in a region about 8 parsecs in diameter. (By way of comparison, the object known as *47 Tukanae* is a large globular cluster containing over 1,000,000 stars in a region about 50 parsecs in diameter.) See GLOBULAR STAR CLUSTER.

open system an airborne or spaceborne system that provides for the maintenance of human body's metabolism by providing for removal of respiratory products and waste from the cabin, combined with use of stored food and oxygen.

Ophelia (1986 U8) a 50-km diameter satellite of Uranus discovered by Voyager 2 in 1986. Because its orbit lies within the outer Epsilon Ring, Ophelia is called a shepherd satellite. Its orbital period is 0.377 days, and its mean distance from Uranus is 33,400 miles.

Ophir Chasma a prominent Martian canyon located at latitude 64° to 75° and longitude -3° to -9°, in the central part of Valles Marineris, in the Coprates Quadrangle, an equatorial region of Mars. The canyon, 660 km in diameter, is noteworthy for its erosional debris and mesas.

Ophiuchid meteors a minor meteor stream seen in the month of June close to the star Xi Ophiuchi, in the southern constellation Ophiuchus.

Ophiuchus (Oph) the Serpent Bearer, a constellation on the celestial equator between Libra and Aquila. In Greek legend the Serpent Bearer is the god Aesculapius, founder of medicine, ship's doctor for the Argonauts. He was so skillful that he brought a dead man back to life. This power so worried Pluto, god of the underworld, that he persuaded Jupiter to place Aesculapius among the stars, out of the way. The bright stars of Ophiucus include (Alpha) Ras Alhague, head of the serpent charmer; (Beta) Cebalrai, the heart of the shepherd; (Eta) Sabik, the preceding one; 70 Oph, which is the 46th-nearest star to Earth; and (Lambda) Marfik, the elbow.

A good example of a supernova is found in Ophiuchus. Nova 1604 was a brilliant new star first observed on October 9, 1604, when it reached a brightness exceeding that of any other star in the sky. It is interesting to note that the two planets Jupiter and Mars were in conjunction on the same night, attracting the attention of astronomers. For this reason, the nova was detected immediately. German astronomer Johann Kepler (1571–1630) made a special study of the phenomenon—which closely resembled Tycho's famous nova of 1572 in Cassiopeia—and the nova is often called Kepler's Star in his honor.

Ophiuchus Nebula a dark nebula located in the constellation Ophiuchus. The nebula is 250 parsecs from Earth. See OPHIUCHUS.

Oppolzer, Theodor E. (1841–1886) Austrian mathematician and astromomer who calculated the time and track of every lunar and solar eclipse from 1207 BC to 2163 AD. His work was published in the *Canon of Eclipses* in 1887.

opposition the situation of two celestial bodies having either celestial longitudes or sidereal hour angles differing by 180°. The term is usually used in relation to the position of a planet or the moon relative to the sun. See Fig. 62 and CONJUNCTION.

optical binary see OPTICAL DOUBLE STAR.

optical double star any two stars in nearly the same line of sight but differing greatly in distance from the observer on Earth—and thus not actually co-orbiting—as distinguished from a PHYSICAL DOUBLE STAR.

optically effective atmosphere that portion of the atmosphere lying below the altitude from which scattered light at twilight still reaches the observer with sufficient intensity to be discerned. Also called effective atmosphere.

optical maser see LASER.

optical path a line of sight, the path followed by a ray of light through an optical system.

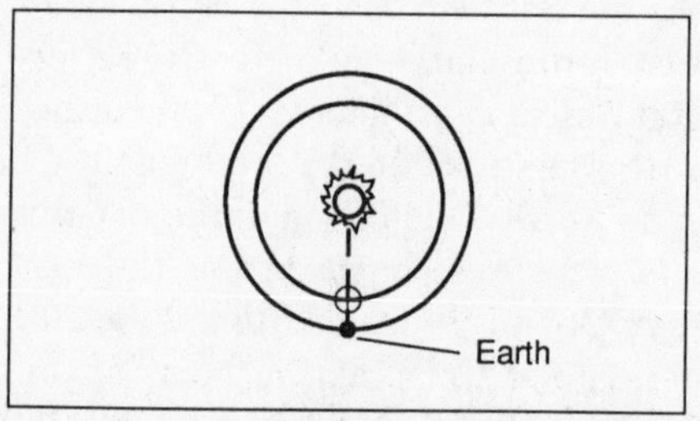

Fig. 62. **Opposition.** See entry.

optical pulsar a pulsar that flashes at visible wavelengths. Two examples are the Crab Nebula and the Vela Pulsar.

optical window the part of the electromagnetic spectrum at visible and near-infrared wavelengths that is transmitted by Earth's atmosphere.

orbit the path followed by an object in space that is influenced by a gravitational field. Two types of orbits are the *circular orbit* and the *elliptical orbit*. A circular orbit is one in which a satellite, usually a spacecraft, remains at all times at the same distance from the center of gravity of the influencing body. An elliptical orbit, also called an ellipse, is one in which the path is longer than it is wide, and the center of gravitational attraction is not always at the same distance from the body in orbit. Most planetary orbits are of this type.

It is worth noting that the term *orbit* is commonly used to designate a closed path, and *trajectory* a path that is not closed. Thus, we speak of the trajectory of a rocket and the orbit of a satellite.

orbital 1. taking place in orbit, as in *orbital refueling* and *orbital launch*; **2.** pertaining to an orbit, as in *orbital plane*.

orbital elements see ELEMENTS OF AN ORBIT.

orbital period or **period** the interval between successive passages of a satellite through the same point in its orbit.

orbital precession a slow, cyclical change in the orientation of the plane of an orbit.

orbital velocity the average velocity of a satellite or other orbiting body at any point in its orbit. The orbital velocity must be maintained to keep a planet or spacecraft in orbit. Earth's orbital velocity is 17,700 mph.

orbit decay the gradual slowing of a spacecraft in near-Earth orbit, that is, within 300 miles of the planet. Spacecraft in near-Earth orbits—unless they maintain an orbital velocity of 17,700 mph—gradually slow down until they reenter Earth's atmosphere.

Orbiter the Space Shuttle.

Orbiting Astronomical Observatory see OAO.

Orbiting Geophysical Observatory (OGO) a series of United States geophysical satellites, first launched in September of 1864 and moving mainly in highly elliptical orbits, that are used for studying Earth's atmosphere, ionosphere, magnetic field, radiation belts, and the influence of the solar wind on these phenomena.

Orbiting Solar Observatory (OSO) a series of eight United States observational satellites designed for making continuous observations of the sun and its atmosphere. OSO-1 was launched in 1962, and OSO-8 was launched in 1975. The OSO produced the first x-ray of a solar flare, discovered coronal holes, and mapped the solar disk.

order of magnitude a factor of 10. Two quantities of the same kind that differ by less than a factor of 10 are said to be of the same order of magnitude. The phrase *order of magnitude* is used loosely by many writers to indicate a pronounced difference in quantity, but the difference they have in mind is not made clear: it may be much less or much more than a factor of 10.

organic describing compounds that contain carbon in their molecular structure.

Orientale Basin a lunar basin, filled partially by mare lava. Orientale is situated on the western limb of the far side of the moon, at longitude -90° and latitude 20°, and is visible from Earth only at times of favorable libration. Its concentric ring structure of mountains and its ejecta blanket, the so-called Hevelius formation, are preserved. See LIBRATION.

Orion (Ori) the Hunter, a conspicuous constellation straddling the celestial equator, between Canis Major and Taurus. Its brightest stars include (Alpha) Betelgeuse, armpit of the central one; (Beta) Rigel, the brightest star in Orion; (Gamma) Bellatrix, the left shoulder of the constellation, named for an Amazon; and (Kappa) Saiph, the sword, Orion's belt. The constellation also contains the Horsehead Nebula.

Orionids a meteor shower of the Northern Hemisphere, sometimes associated with Halley's Comet. The average hourly rate of the mid-October shower is 15. Meteor showers appear to emanate from a radiant and are named after the constellation that contains the radiant; thus, Orionids takes it name from Orion. See RADIANT.

Orion Nebula (NGC 1976 & M42) the Great Nebula in Orion, the nearest to Earth—distance, 500 parsecs—and one of the brightest emission nebulae in the sky. Orion Nebula, one of the most prominent nebulae in our sky, forms what is perceived as the central star in Orion's sword.

oscillating universe theory or **big bang theory** the theory that the universe begins with a big bang, expands, is slowed by its own gravity, and then falls back to eventually create another big bang.

osculating orbit the elliptical orbit that a satellite or spacecraft would follow if all other outward forces were to cease, therefore leaving the orbiting body under control of the parent body's gravity alone.

OSO *abbreviation for* Orbiting Solar Observatory.

Oterma's Comet a comet that until recently had a period of 7.88 years. Its close approach to Jupiter in 1963 changed the comet's perihelion distance from the sun as well as the comet's period, which is now 19 years.

outer atmosphere 1. generally, the atmosphere at a great distance from Earth's surface;

2. a loose synonym for EXOSPHERE.

outer planets the planets with orbits larger than that of Mars. Also called the *distant planets*: Jupiter, Saturn, Uranus, Neptune, and Pluto.

outgassing 1. the release of gases from the interior of a planet;

2. the creation of a planetary atmosphere from the interior of a planet.

ovoid any of many egg-shaped features found on Miranda, a satellite of Uranus.

Owl Nebula (NGC 3587 & M97) a large planetary nebula of apparent magnitude 12 and a diameter of 1.5 light-years in the constellation Ursa Major, about 600 parsecs from Earth. The nebula lies 1.5° S and 2° E, following Merak, or Beta Ursae Majoris, in the Great Bear, or Ursa Major constellation. In the same area is a spiral galaxy, NGC 3556, which has a magnitude of 10.7 and thus is brighter than the Owl.

The Owl was discovered in 1781 by French astronomer Pierre-François-André Méchain (1744–1804). Its mass is 15% that of the sun. English astronomer William Herschel (1738–1822) described M97 as "a globular body of equal light throughout" and thought it might lie outside the Milky Way. In 1848, English astronomer William Parsons, Earl of Rosse (1800–1867), drew it with his 72-inch reflector telescope and described "two stars considerably apart in the central region: dark penumbra around each spiral arrangement." In 1853, he concluded that the nebula did not have a spiral form. His drawing, which looks rather like a man in the moon with a halo and extremely large eyes, shows M97 in a recognizable form, indicating why it was called the Owl.

oxidizer the propellant in a rocket that provides the oxygen needed to burn the fuel. Common oxidizers are liquid oxygen and nitrogen tetroxide.

Ozma Project or **Project Little Green Men** an attempt—thus far unsuccessful—to pick up intelligent messages from beyond the solar system.

ozone (O_3) an allotropic form of oxygen, whose molecules contain three atoms rather than two. It is used as an oxidizer in liquid propellant rocket engines. Formed when an electric spark passes through air or dry oxygen, ozone is an effective bleaching agent and powerful germicide. Its industrial uses include bleaching wood pulp, textile fibers, oils, and waxes; purifying water; and deodorizing rooms. It is a major factor in the atmosphere, contributing to the so-called greenhouse effect and to the reduction of lethal radiation. See GREENHOUSE EFFECT.

ozone layer see OZONOSPHERE.

ozonosphere or **ozone layer** the general stratum of the upper atmosphere in which there is an appreciable ozone concentration and in which ozone plays an important part in the radiation balance of the atmosphere. If the ozone layer is destroyed by overuse of freons (dichlorodifluoromethane, used as a refrigerant), it will not effectively filter out rays (ultraviolet radiation) from the sun, but will allow these rays to penetrate Earth's atmosphere to a degree capable of causing an increase in health hazards. See GREENHOUSE EFFECT and Fig. 63.

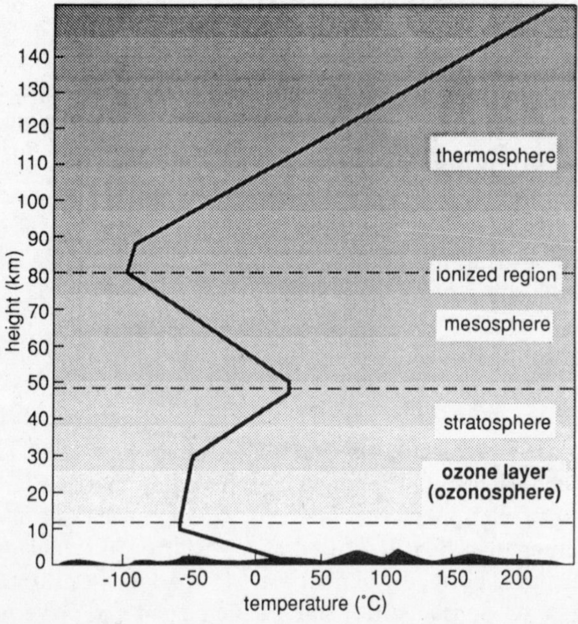

Fig. 63. **Ozonosphere.** It is this stratum of the upper atmosphere that has been attracting so much attention in recent years as reports keep coming in about the greenhouse effect and the loss of protection against harmful rays of the sun.

P

paddle-wheel satellite an artificial satellite, for example, Explorer VI, that has solar vanes or similarly shaped objects attached to convert solar radiation to a form of energy useful for the satellite.

Pallas (Asteroid 2) the second minor planet to be discovered. Observed first, in March of 1802, by German astronomer Heinrich Olbers (1758–1840), it is brighter than any other asteroid apart from Ceres and Vesta (which Olbers also discovered, in 1807). Pallas has a diameter of 608 km, making it the second largest asteroid. Pallas is found in the main asteroid belt, between Mars and Jupiter. Composed of silicate, it has a rotation period of 7.9 hours, a perihelion distance of 0.47 AU, and an aphelion distance of 1.20 AU.

pallasites the most common type of stony-iron meteorites, composed approximately equally of olivine (magnesium iron silicate) grains and metal.

Palomar Observatory an astronomical observatory on Mount Palomar, northeast of San Diego, California. The observatory houses one of the largest optical telescopes in the world, the Hale Telescope, as well as one of the largest Schmidt cameras in the world. The Palomar Observatory has contributed much to astronomical knowledge. For example, it has been used by the National Geographic Society Sky Survey to map the entire sky visible from Palomar.

palus a Latin word for swamp. The term has been applied to lunar areas that early observers considered swampy in appearance. Examples: Palus Somnii, Palus Putredinis, and Palus Nebularum.

Palus Epidemarium also called Epidemareum, a dark triangular plain area connecting Mare Humorum and Mare Nubium, in the south polar region of the near side of the moon, at latitude -32° S and longitude -29° W. It contains the Ramsden Crater, which has a distinctive system of rills and many small craters. See RILL.

Palus Nebularum also known as Nebularum Palus and as the Marsh of Clouds, a part of Mare Imbrium, in the northern hemisphere of the near side of the moon, at latitude +38° N and longitude +1° E. The craters Aristillus and Cassini border Palus Nebularum.

Palus Putredinis also called Putredinis Palus and the Marsh of Decay, an irregular plain that is part of the lunar Mare Imbrium, near Archimedes. Some of the outer walls of the plain reach heights of 12,000 feet. Putredinis forms the north border of the Apennine Mountains on the near side of the moon, at latitude +38° N and longitude -1° W. The Marsh of Decay was the site of the Apollo 15 base, in 1971. It was there that astronauts David Scott and James Irwin logged more than 18 hours of travel from the lunar module Falcon.

Pandora (XVII) the small (110 km × 86 × 66 km) moon of Saturn's F ring, discovered in 1980 by American astronomers S. Collins and D. Carlsen from Voyager 1 photographs. Its orbital period is 0.629 days.

parabola an open curve, all points of which are equidistant from a fixed point, called the *focus*, and a straight line.

parabolic orbit an orbit in the general shape of a parabola, considered to present the least eccentricity, equal to 1, possible for escape from an attracting body.

Paragould meteorite the third largest meteorite ever observed to fall and then be recovered. The largest was the 1947 Siberian fall, and the second largest was the 1948 Furnas County, Nebraska, fall. The Paragould meteorite weighs about 800 pounds and is on view in the Field Museum, in Chicago.

The meteorite fell at 4 AM on February 17, 1930, near Paragould, Arkansas. Most of the local people were awakened by its detonations. As far away as St. Louis, Missouri, people awake at the time mistook the meteor for an aircraft going down in flames. Not surprisingly, everyone who saw the fall—even the Missourians—believed that it had occurred less than a mile away. The Paragould meteorite made a hole eight feet deep and scattered clods of clay for more than 50 yards around.

parallactic inequality a secondary effect in the solar perturbations in the moon's longitude due to Earth's elliptical orbit.

parallactic motion the apparent motion of stars due to the orbital motion of Earth.

parallax the difference in the apparent direction or position of an object (such as a star) when viewed from different points. Parallax is expressed as an angle. For bodies of the solar system, parallax is measured from the surface of Earth and its center and is called *geocentric parallax*, varying with the body's altitude and distance from Earth. For stars, parallax is measured from the Earth and the sun, and is called *annual*, *heliocentric*, or *stellar parallax*. See Fig. 64.

parallel 1. an imaginary circle on the surface of Earth, parallel with the plane of the equator and connecting all points of equal latitude;

2. a circle parallel with the primary great circle of a sphere.

parallel of altitude an imaginary circle of the celestial sphere parallel with the horizon and connecting all points of equal altitude. Also called *altitude circle* or *almucantar*.

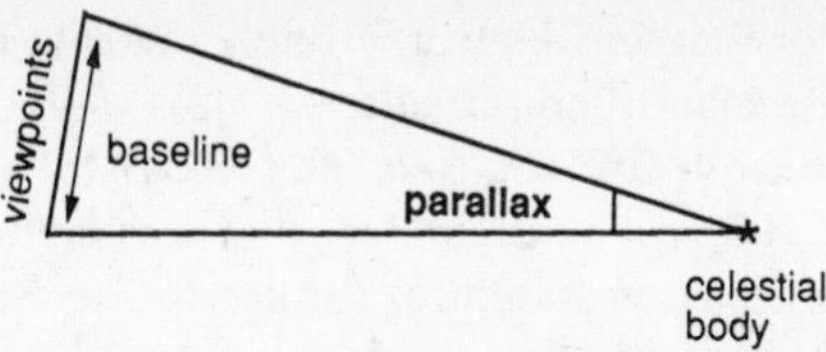

Fig. 64. **Parallax.** The diagram makes clear the difference in apparent direction of a celestial object when the viewer on Earth changes position.

parallel of declination an imaginary circle of the celestial equator. Also called *circle of equal declination*.

parallel of latitude 1. an imaginary circle on the surface of Earth, parallel with the equator and connecting points of equal latitude;

2. an imaginary circle of the celestial sphere, parallel with the ecliptic and connecting points of equal celestial latitude. Also called *parallel* and *circle of longitude*.

parcel see FLUID PARCEL.

Paris Observatory the oldest celestial observatory in the world still functioning. It was commissioned by King Louis XIV in 1667.

parking orbit 1. the orbit in which a spacecraft can be placed (usually less than two complete revolutions) at 117 miles altitude before being put into a final orbit or desired trajectory;

2. the orbit of a spacecraft around a celestial body, used for assembly of components, or to wait for conditions favorable for departure from the orbit.

parsec (pc) *from par*allax *sec*ond, a unit of distance. Parsec is usually used for distances beyond our own solar system. One parsec is equal to 3.2616 light-years. See LIGHT-YEAR.

Parthenope (Asteroid 11) discovered in 1850 by Italian astronomer De Gasparis, who also discovered Asteroid 10, Hygeia. Parthenope, which is located at the inner edge of the main asteroid belt between Mars and Jupiter, has a diameter of 150 km, a magnitude of 9.9, and a rotation period of 10.7 days.

Pasiphae (Jupiter VIII) a small satellite (moon) of Jupiter discovered in 1908 by English astronomer J.P. Melotte while he was working at the Greenwich Observatory. Pasiphae, which orbits Jupiter with a retrograde motion, is 70 km in diameter and has a period of 735 days and a magnitude of 17.0. See RETROGRADE MOTION.

pass 1. a single circuit of Earth by an artificial satellite. A pass begins when the satellite crosses the equator from the Southern Hemisphere into the Northern Hemisphere (*ascending node*), and ends when the satellite passes out of telemetry range;

2. the period of time in which an artificial satellite is within telemetry range of a data acquisition station.

Passive Geodetic Earth Orbiting Satellite (PAGEOS) a large metallized balloon, almost 100 feet in diameter, that was launched in June of 1966. Acting as a passive satellite, similar to the Echo satellites, it reflected sunlight and was photographed by ground stations around the world, thus establishing a worldwide triangulation network to map Earth's surface.

passive homing describing a spacecraft having the capability to direct itself toward the target by means of energy waves transmitted or radiated by the target.

path 1. the projection of the orbital plane of an artificial satellite on Earth's surface. Since Earth is turning under the satellite, the path of a single orbital pass will not be a closed curve. *Path* and *track* are used interchangeably;

2. the projection of the trajectory of a meteor on the celestial sphere, as seen by the observer. Also called *flight path*.

Patientia (Asteroid 451) with an estimated diameter of 276 km, this asteroid, found in the main asteroid belt is among the dozen largest known asteroids. Discovered in 1899, Patientia has an aphelion distance of 3.30 AU and a perihelion distance of 2.82.

Patroclus (Asteroid 617) the second Trojan asteroid to be discovered. It was first observed by Kopff in 1906. Patroclus has a diameter of 147 km and is located in the Lagrangian points of Jupiter's orbit, 60° ahead of and behind the planet. Its perihelion is 4.5 AU, and its aphelion is 5.9 AU. See LAGRANGIAN POINTS and TROJAN GROUP.

Pavo (Pav) the Peacock, a constellation in the Southern Hemisphere between Triangulum Australe and Indus. (Alpha Pavonis is also known as the Peacock.) Pavo is one of the twelve southern constellations introduced at the end of the 16th century by Dutch navigators and constellation mappers. Pavo was first depicted in 1598.

Pavonis Mons a 19-km high volcano at latitude 1° N and longitude 113° W, on the Tharsis Ridge of Mars. The volcano has a base diameter of 400 km, and the diameter of the large summit caldera is 45 km. Pavonis Mons is surrounded by radiating volcanic flows.

payload the section of a spacecraft or rocket that is provided in addition to what is necessary for flight operation of the vehicle.

pc symbol for PARSEC.

P Cygni also called **34 Cygni**, an important supergiant variable star located at 2° northwest of the center star of the Northern Cross. P Cygni is highly luminous and has an apparent visual magnitude of 5. It is 724,000 times more luminous than our sun, so P Cygni might be thought of as a permanent nova. It was first seen in 1600, by Dutch astronomer Willem Blaeuw (1571–1638), author of *Novus Atlas*. Over the years, the magnitude of P. Cygni varied between 3 and 3.5—it even vanished from sight at times—and finally reached 5 in 1715, where it has remained ever since. Modern studies suggest that P Cygni is one of the high-luminosity ejection variables, as typified by Eta Carinae. See CYGNUS.

Pegasus (Peg) the Winged Horse or the Flying Horse, a conspicuous constellation in the Northern Hemisphere, near Cygnus. This star group was seen as a winged horse, so its stars are named appropriately: Markab, Alpha Pegasi, is the saddle, 109 light-years from Earth; Scheat, Beta Pegasi, is the shoulder of the horse; and Algenib, Gamma Pegasi, is the wing or side of the horse. Together with Alpha Andromedae, these three stars form the distinctive Great Square of Pegasus, a landmark of the night sky. Other famous stars of Pegasus include Enif, the nose; Matar, fortunate rain; and Homan, lucky star.

Pegasus satellites a series of three NASA satellites, launched during 1965 and intended to determine the rate of meteoroid penetrations of the huge winglike panels of Pegasus, 30 meters tip to tip. The experiment established that interplanetary dust particles are about 10,000 times less abundant than indicated in earlier space experiments. Data collection from the satellites terminated in 1968.

Penelope a large crater on Saturn's satellite Tethys.

penumbra 1. at an eclipse, the part of Earth or moon's shadow from which part of the solar disk is visible. See Fig. 65.

2. the outer, less dark portion of a sunspot.

periapsis the point in an orbit that is nearest the center of gravitational attraction. The velocity of an orbiting body is maximal at periapsis, minimal at apoapsis. See LINE OF APSIDES.

periastron the point in the orbit of one member of a binary star system at which the stars are nearest to each other. The *apastron* is the point at which they are farthest apart.

pericythian the point in the trajectory of a space vehicle that is closest to the moon.

perigee the orbital point nearest Earth for the moon or a spacecraft, at which the velocity of the moon or spacecraft is at its maximum. The orbital point farthest from Earth is called the *apogee*. *Perigee* and *apogee* are used by some writers in referring to orbits of satellites,

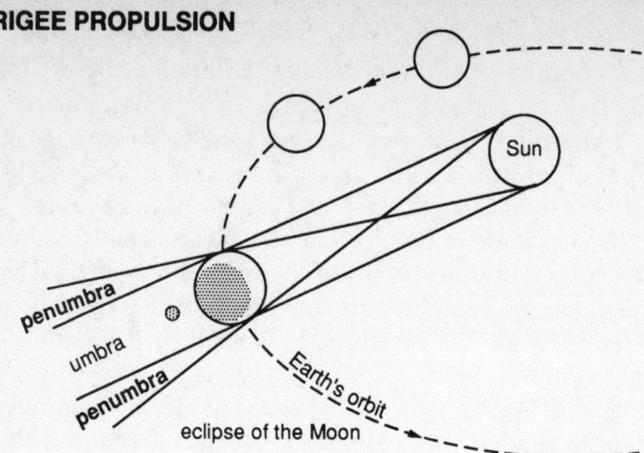

Fig. 65. **Penumbra.** In this representation of a lunar eclipse, it appears that the penumbra is in two parts. This is because the scene is shown in cross section. In fact, the penumbra is a cone of semidarkness, enveloping much of the Earth. Notice the moon, much smaller than Earth and shown here as entirely in the umbra.

especially artificial satellites, around any planet or satellite, thus avoiding coinage of new terms for each planet and moon. See Fig. 66.

perigee propulsion a technique for enabling a space vehicle to escape from the gravity pull of a planet, using programmed intermittent applications of thrust at perigee (when vehicle velocity is at its highest) combined with coasting periods.

perigee speed the speed of an orbiting body when at perigee.

perihelion the point in the orbit of a planet, comet, or satellite that is nearest the sun. The orbital point farthest from the sun is called the *aphelion*. See Fig. 67.

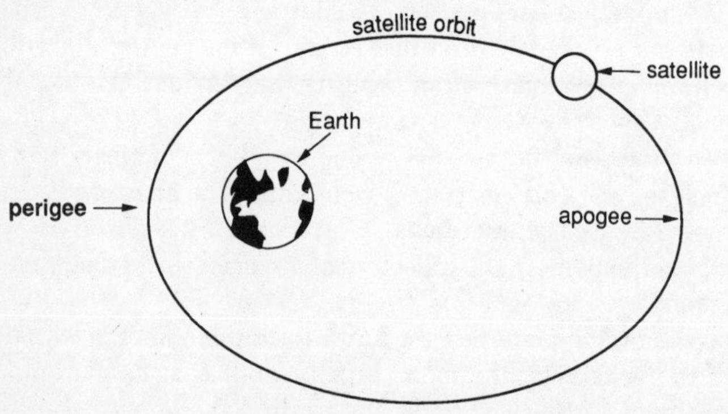

Fig. 66. **Perigee.** See entry.

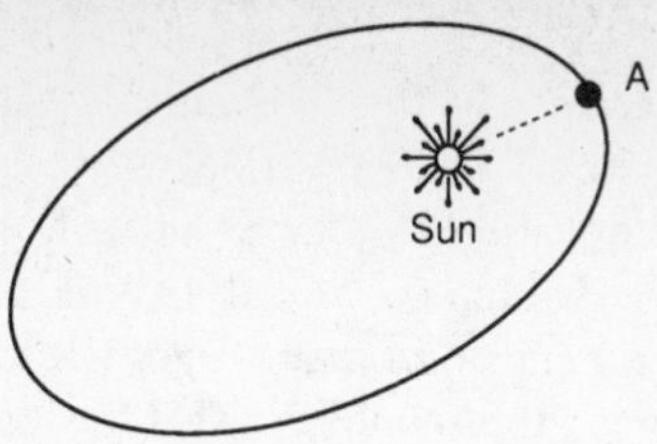

Fig. 67. **Perihelion.** See entry.

period the amount of time needed to complete a cycle, for example, an orbital period.

period-luminosity relation the relationship between the pulsation periods of Cepheid variable stars and their median luminosities or absolute magnitudes. The brighter the Cepheid, the longer its period. This relationship was established in 1912 by American astronomer Henrietta Leavitt (1868–1921) while working at Harvard College Observatory, in Cambridge, Massachusetts, where she was head of the Department of Photographic Photometry. The period-luminosity relation proved invaluable as the basis for a method of measuring the distance of stars. See CEPHEID VARIABLES.

Perrine, Charles Dillon (1867–1951) American astronomer on the staff of Lick Observatory, near San Jose, California. He became widely known for his discovery, observation, and calculations of the orbits of comets and for his determination of solar parallax from observations of the asteroid Eros. In 1901 he discovered light variations about the nova in Perseus. In 1904 and 1905 he discovered the sixth and seventh moons of Jupiter.

Perseids a major meteor shower in August, maximizing on or about August 12 with a zenithal hourly rate (ZHR) of about 70. Perseid meteors, seen throughout the two weeks each side of maximum, are bright and flaring, with fine trains. Italian astronomer Giovanni Schiaparelli (1835–1910) observed that the meteor stream is closely associated with comet 1862 III (Swift-Tuttle Comet). This was the first time that mathematical proof had been found linking meteor showers with periodic comets. Although the meteor display is regarded as being constant in hourly rate, there are exceptions. A ZHR of 250 was observed in 1921, and a ZHR of less than 10 in 1911 and 1912. The shower has been regularly observed for over 100 years. See ZENITHAL HOURLY RATE and SCHIAPARELLI.

Perseus (Per) a constellation of the Northern Hemisphere near Cassiopeia. The constellation takes its name from the youth of ancient Greek legend who slew the Gorgon Medusa and then saved

Andromeda from Cetus. In the Perseus constellation the youth still holds the Gorgon's head. Her eye, Algol, the Demon Star, still winks. (Some see this constellation as a large letter K or a fleur-de-lis.) The bright stars of Perseus include Mirfak (Alpha Persei or Algenib, the side); the prototype eclipsing binary Algol (Beta Persei, the demon); and Menkib (Xi Persei, the shoulder). This star group contains the California Nebula and the galaxy NGC 1275.

Perseus arm the spiral arm of our galaxy.

Perseus cluster (NGC 1275) a rich cluster of about 500 galaxies grouped around a Seyfert galaxy and lying about 70 megaparsecs away from Earth in the direction of the constellation Perseus. See SEYFERT GALAXY.

perturbation 1. any departure introduced into an assumed steady state of a system;

2. a small departure from a nominal path such as a desired trajectory. Specifically, a disturbance in the regular motion of a celestial body.

Petavius a crater 170 km in diameter, in the eastern limb of the near side of the moon, at -26° S and +60° E, in the south polar region. It has a complex central mountain group, characterized by multiple mountain peaks. The tallest is 8200 feet.

Petrarch a prominent crater south of Kuiper Crater on Mercury, at latitude -30° S and longitude +27° E. Its diameter is 160 km. See KUIPER CRATER.

Phad see PHECDA.

Phaethon (Asteroid 3200, originally known as 1983TB) the Apollo asteroid discovered by astronomers Simon Green and John Davies in 1983, during the IRAS mission, an international project involving the United States, The Netherlands, and the United Kingdom. Phaethon is only a few miles in diameter and has the smallest perihelion distance of any known asteroid, 0.14 AU.

About 30 small asteroids are now known to have orbits that cross Earth's orbit. These are called Earth-crossing asteroids or Apollo asteroids, named after the 1-km diameter minor planet Apollo. Apollo was discovered when it approached within 0.07 AU of Earth in 1932, but was lost to observers because of uncertainties over its orbit, and was rediscovered in 1973. Apollo orbits within the solar system, among the first four planets from the sun. It has never been part of the main asteroid belt.

Phakt the common name for the star Alpha Columbae, 140 light-years from Earth. It has a magnitude of 2.64 and is a spectral type B8V.

Phakt, from an Arabic word meaning ring dove, is the brightest star of the southern constellation Columba, the Dove, near Caelum and Puppis. Phakt lies in the top right corner of Columba.

phase front see WAVE FRONT.

phases of the moon 1. changes in the appearance of the moon's apparent shape during different times of the month, caused by variation in solar illumination resulting from changing positions (see Fig. 68);

2. changes in the apparent shape of a satellite or planet caused by variation in solar illumination resulting from changing positions.

Phecda or **Phekda** or **Phad** the common name for Gamma Ursa Majoris, located just to the left of the star Merak (Beta Majoris). Phecda is the thigh of the Great Bear—the contellation Ursa Major is in the region of the north celestial pole, near Draco and Leo. Phecda, one of the seven bright stars of the Big Dipper, which is part of the Great Bear, is an A0 star of magnitude 2.44 at 90 light-years from Earth.

Pherkad the common name for Gamma Ursa Minoris, which is the lower right star of the Little Dipper, in the north celestial pole constellation Ursa Minor, the Little Bear. Ursa Minor has the shape of a ladle, with Polaris at the tip of its handle. Pherkad is of magnitude 3.04 and lies 270 light-years from Earth.

Pherkard the common name for Delta Ursa Minoris, which is in the upper handle of the Little Dipper—Ursa Minor is a north celestial pole constellation—next to Polaris. Pherkard, apparent magnitude 4.4 and

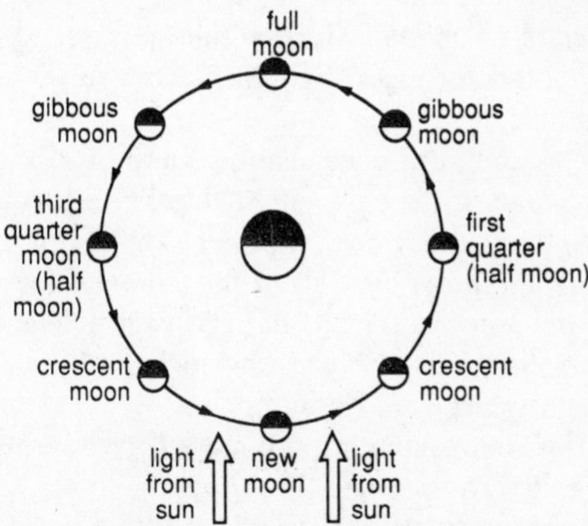

Fig. 68. **Phases of the Moon .** This second drawing of the lunar phases represents Earth (at center) in day and in night. To see the appearance of the moon in its phases, picture yourself observing the moon from the rising to the setting of the moon over a lunar month.

233 light-years from Earth, is also known as Yildun, meaning the surpassing star.

Phillips a crater west of W. Humboldt Crater in the southern hemisphere of the 4th quadrant, on the eastern limb of the near side of the moon, at -26° S and +77° E. Phillips has a central ridge and a diameter of 120 km.

Phobos the innermost and largest moon of Mars. This potato-shaped moon was discovered and named in 1877 by American astronomer Asaph Hall (1829–1907), who also discovered and named Deimos, the other moon of Mars. See MARS.

Phocylides a crater 97 km in diameter in the moon's south polar region, at -54° S and -57° W. It is a member of the Schickard group, the small craters of the moon's western limb, the largest bearing the name Schickard.

Phoebe (IX) the outermost satellite (moon) of Saturn, discovered in 1898. Phoebe, with an orbital of -550.48 days, is the only satellite to follow a retrograde orbit around a planet. Its mean distance from Saturn is 12,960,000 km. Phoebe was discovered in 1898 by American astronomer William Pickering (1858–1938).

Phoebe Regio a region on Venus close to the volcanic Beta Regio area. It has been the landing site for several unmanned USSR Venera probes. See VENERA PROBES.

Phoenicid meteors the minor meteor showers seen each year in the Southern Hemisphere, near the constellation Phoenix, and peaking about December 4 or 5.

Phoenicus Lacus a region of Mars on the southern edge of the Tharsis Ridge. It is noted for extensive lava flows and large fractures. See THARSIS RIDGE.

Phoenix (Phe) a southern constellation south of Fornax and between Hydrus and Sculptor. Phoenix, the mythical bird that in ancient Egypt was sacred to the god Ra, was supposed to live for 500 or 600 years in the Arabian wilderness, burn itself on a funeral pyre, and then rise afresh from the ashes to start its life cycle again. The brightest star of the constellation is Ankaa (Alpha Phoenicis), a K0 giant star at a distance of 93 light-years from Earth.

Phosphorus the Greek name for the morning star, especially Venus. In English it is called *Phosphor*.

photocell or **photoelectric cell** a light-sensitive device that produces electricity in an amount proportional to the amount of light striking it. Photocells are used in light meters, solar cells, TV cameras, etc.

photographic magnitude a stellar magnitude measured from a photographic plate exposed without filters.

photographic meteor a meteor of brightness sufficient to be detected by photography.

photology the study of light.

photometer an instrument used for measuring the intensity of light and radiation.

photosphere 1. the intensely bright, visible surface of the sun, which is a shallow layer of strongly ionized gases;

2. the boundary between the interior and the exterior of a star.

photovoltaic cell a transducer—a device capable of being actuated by energy from one or more transmission systems or of supplying related energy to one or more satellite systems—that converts electromagnetic radiation into electric current. The solar cells used on satellites and space probes are photovoltaic cells employing a semiconductor, such as silicon, which releases electrons when bombarded by photons from solar radiation.

phugoid oscillation in a flight path, a long-period longitudinal oscillation consisting of shallow climbing and diving motions about a median flight path and involving little or no change in angle of the path.

physical constant 1. an abstract number or physically dimensional quantity having a fixed or approximately fixed value;

2. a universal and permanent value, for example, the constant of gravitation.

physical double star any two stars in nearly the same line of sight and at approximately the same distance from the observer, as distinguished from an *optical double star*, two stars in nearly the same line of sight but differing greatly in distance from the observer. If the stars revolve about their common center of mass, they are called a *binary star*.

Piazzi, Giuseppe (1746–1826) Italian astronomer who discovered Ceres, the first asteroid, in 1801. He also established an observatory at Palermo, Italy, and began the compilation of a new star catalog of 6748 stars. It was published in 1803. See P CYGNI.

Picard, Jean (1620–1682) French astronomer who was the first to apply the telescope systematically in conjunction with graduated circles for the precise measurement of angles. He also provided the first accurate measurement of a degree of a meridian.

Pickering, William Henry (1858–1938) American astronomer whose research included studies of the surface features of Mars and observations of solar eclipses. In 1905, he received the Lalande Prize of the French Academy for his 1898 discovery of Phoebe, the 9th satellite of Saturn.

Pico a mountain in Mare Imbrium, at +46° N and -8° W, in the 2nd quadrant of the moon. See MARE IMBRIUM.

Pictor (Pic) the Painter's Easel, originally called Equuleus Pictoris, a faint southern constellation found by French astronomer Nicolas Lacaille (1713–1762) south of Columba and north of the Large Magellanic Cloud. The easiest way of locating it is to look west of Canopus. RR Pictoris, the bright nova of 1925, flared up here.

pilot's preference kit the small cloth bag carried by astronauts in space. It is intended to hold authorized personal possessions the astronaut wants to take along on a space flight. Most astronauts use the bag to carry family photographs, tape-recorded music, and the like. The need for the preference kit arose when astronauts in early flights smuggled aboard unauthorized articles, such as steak sandwiches.

Pioneer probes a series of United States unmanned intersolar system probes launched from 1958 to 1986. The first of the series was launched toward the moon, and the last (1986) is still sending back data from Venus. The Pioneer probes represented several successes: first United States probe to go anywhere near the moon; first to make a direct comet investigation; set a longevity record for solar orbit; first to obtain close-range data from Jupiter; first to probe Saturn, Uranus, and Neptune; and first to obtain detailed radar maps of virtually the entire surface of Venus. See Figs. 69, 70, and 71.The first eight Pioneers were designed as lunar probes. Because of launch vehicle failure, the program met with little success, and only Pioneer 4 reached the moon, in March 1959. Pioneer 1 discovered the radial extent of the radiation belts, Pioneer 2 returned data about the atmosphere, and Pioneer 3 discovered the second radiation belt.

Pioneer 10 (Pioneer Jupiter), launched March 3, 1972. On July 15, 1972, Pioneer 10 became the first spacecraft to enter the asteroid belt. Since this belt is too thick to fly over without prohibitively expensive launch vehicles, all missions to the outer planets must fly through it. Pioneer 10 made its Jupiter encounter on December 3, 1973. On June 13, 1983, it became the first spacecraft to leave the solar system. Its basic mission was the first flyby of Jupiter, but it also made the first flight beyond Mars and the first crossing of the asteroid belt. It provided the first close-up pictures of Jupiter's Great Red Spot and atmosphere, and it made the first crossings of the orbits of Uranus, Pluto, and Neptune.

Significant discoveries and achievements of Jupiter 10 include the following: (1) The heliosphere—sun's atmosphere—was found to extend much farther than previously thought and appears to breathe in and out once in every 11-year cycle. (2) It established that Jupiter is a liquid planet. (3) It provided the first model of Jupiter's huge magnetosphere. (4) It provided the first accurate measurements of the mass and density of Jupiter's planet-size moons. (5) It provided proof of the origin of zodiacal light.

Pioneer 11 (Pioneer Saturn), launched April 6, 1973. It made its Jupiter encounter on December 2, 1974. When it passed within 42,760 km of Jupiter's cloud tops, it relayed to Earth the only existing photographs of Jupiter's polar regions. After the Jupiter encounter, Pioneer 11 was renamed Pioneer Saturn. A total of 565 new discoveries resulted from the spacecraft's flight through the ring plane of Saturn and within the upper cloud tops of the planet itself.

As a result of this flight, it is now known that Saturn has a magnetic field, magnetosphere, and radiation belts. Its core is about twice the size of Earth. Its magnetic field is 1000 times stronger than that of Earth. It appears to have more and narrower belts and zones than Jupiter. Two new rings have been identified, and an 11th moon has been found. Measurements have been made of Titan, Saturn's largest moon. Additional evidence was found to discourage the idea that there is any possibility of life on the planet.

Pioneer Venus 1 launched May 20, 1978, reached Venus in December of 1978. It observed Venus for one complete rotation of the planet on its axis, globally surveyed its atmosphere and environment, studied its topography, and calculated its shape and density. The flight yielded

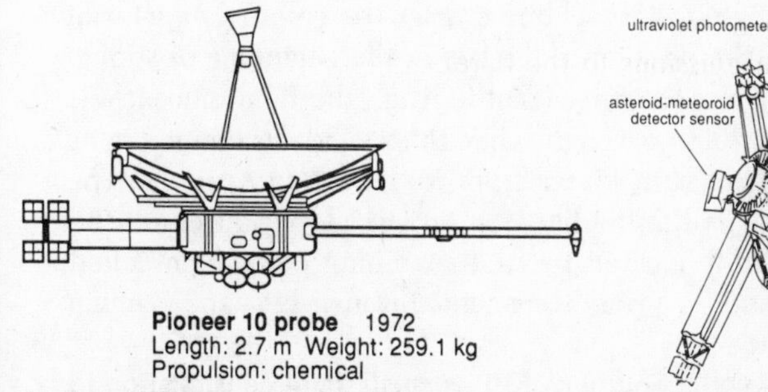

Fig. 69. **Pioneer 10.** See entry for Pioneer probes.

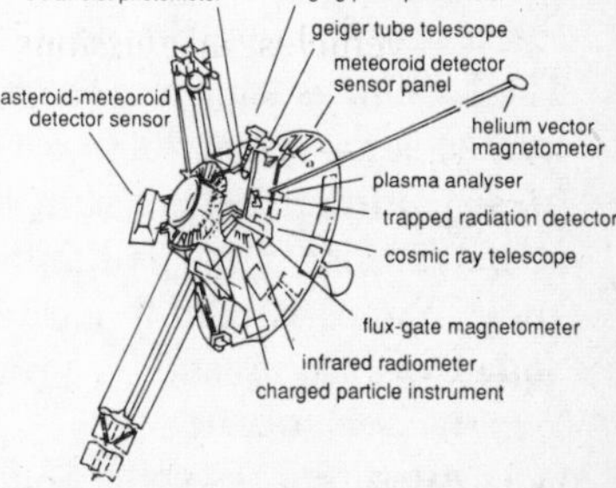

Fig. 70. **Pioneer 11.** See entry for Pioneer probes.

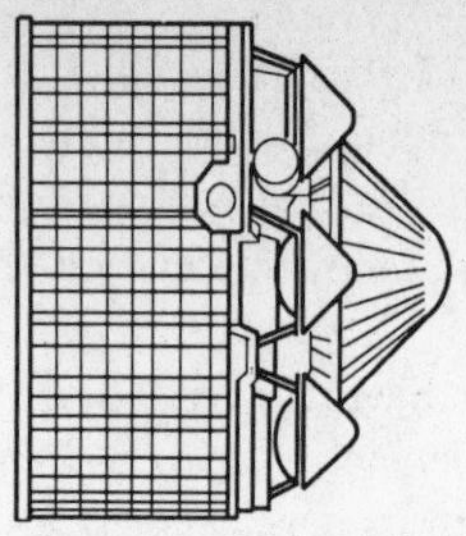

Pioneer Venus Probe 1978
Length: 132 cm Weight: 314 kg
Propulsion: chemical

Fig. 71. **Pioneer Venus.** See entry for Pioneer probes.

the following: (1) Venus has a turbulent, cloudy atmosphere, with bright cloud areas wrapped about both its polar regions and a Y feature covering most of the central part of its disk. (2) A thick, pale yellow opaque atmosphere obscures the surface of Venus, but radar scanning revealed flat, rolling plains, a mountain as high as Mount Everest, great rift valleys, continent-size highland areas, and two large volcanoes. (3) Measurements showed high-speed winds, changing global patterns of clouds and cloud-level winds, a high-altitude haze of sulfuric acid, and a surface temperature of 482° C.

Pioneer Venus 2 launched August 8, 1978, reached Venus December 9, 1978. The spacecraft measured the atmosphere from top to bottom. Smaller probes descended to the surface. They were not designed to survive impact, but one probe returned data for approximately 62 minutes. The data showed the presence of large amounts of rare gases in the atmosphere.

Pisces (Psc) the Fish, a zodiacal constellation in the Northern Hemisphere. In this star group the ecliptic crosses the celestial equator at the vernal equinox, the position of the sun at the beginning of spring. The location is known as the First Point in Aries, the Ram, since it was located at that point 2000 years ago, when the zodiac was defined in its present form. The sun is in Pisces from March 13 to April 19. The brightest Pisces star is the double star Alrisha (Alpha Piscium, the knot). Pisces is readily located by first searching out the so-called Square of Pegasus and then projecting a line through Beta and Gamma Pegasus. See ZODIAC.

Piscis Austrinus (PsA) the Southern Fish, a small, faint constellation in the Southern Hemisphere. Situated just below Aquarius, it is inconspicuous except for its brightest star, Fomalhaut (the fish's mouth), which skims the southern horizon when observed from Earth's mid-northern latitudes.

pitchover 1. a programmed turn from the vertical that a rocket or spacecraft takes as it describes an arc and points in a direction other than vertical;

2. a point in space where pitchover occurs.

PKLS2000-330 a very distant quasar. See QUASAR.

plage 1. a luminous area—clouds of calcium or hydrogen vapor—in the chromosphere of the sun that appears near a sunspot;

2. the bright flocculi on the sun. See FLOCCULI and FILAMENT.

Planck, Max Karl Ernst Ludwig (1858–1947) German theoretical physicist who made the assumption that radiant energy came in discrete packages—quanta—and in 1900 formulated the quantum theory, which revolutionized physics. His work successfully accounted for and predicted certain phenomena inexplicable in the Newtonian theory. Planck won the Nobel Prize for Physics in 1918.

Planck's constant (h) the constant of proportionality between the frequency of an electromagnetic wave and the energy of an equivalent photon, given by E = hv = hc/lambda. If v is taken as the frequency of the radiation, the energy of a quantum is hv, where h (known as Planck's constant) is a number that was first determined by fitting the theoretically derived distribution formula with the experimental data that Max Planck observed. The value of the constant is approximately 6.61×10^{-17} erg seconds. See PLANCK.

Planck's law a formula that describes the energy associated with each wavelength (color) in the spectrum as proportional to the frequency of the radiation. It shows that photons of blue light are more energetic than photons of red light. Max Planck was the first to observe that energy transfers in *quanta*, increments of energy proportional to the frequency of the corresponding radiation. See PLANCK'S CONSTANT and QUANTUM THEORY.

Planck time the timescale (10^{-43} seconds) within which the known laws of physics break down. See PLANCK.

planet a celestial body revolving around the sun or a star in a nearly circular orbit. The larger planets are called *principal planets* to distinguish them from asteroids, planetoids, or minor planets, which are comparatively very small. The larger planets are accompanied by satellites, such as the moon. The word *planet* is of Greek origin, meaning wanderer, appropriate because the planets appear to move relative to the stars. See Fig. 72 and INFERIOR PLANET, SUPERIOR PLANET, INNER PLANET, OUTER PLANET, and DISTANT PLANET.

planetarium 1. a building designed for studying the night sky by means of a model or representation of the solar system;

2. an optical device for projecting celestial images and effects above the viewers' heads onto a domed screen representing the night sky;

3. a room or building for housing such a projector.

planetary aberration a displacement of the apparent position of a planet in the celestial sphere due to the relative movements of observer and planet.

symbol	planet
☿	Mercury
♀	Venus
⊕	Earth
♂	Mars
♃	Jupiter
♄	Saturn
♅	Uranus
♆	Neptune
♇	Pluto

Fig. 72. **Planet symbols.**

planetary alignment a lineup of the two outer planets, Jupiter and Neptune, which occurs every 178 years. The most recent planetary alignment, called the Jupitar Effect, occurred in 1981–1982.

planetary boundary layer the layer of the atmosphere from a planet's surface to the geostrophic wind level including, therefore, the surface boundary layer and the Ekman layer. Above this layer lies the free atmosphere, also called the *friction layer* or the *atmospheric boundary layer*. See EKMAN LAYER, EKMAN SPIRAL, and GEOSTROPHIC WIND LEVEL.

planetary circulation or **general circulation** a system of large-scale disturbances in a planet's troposphere when viewed on a hemispheric or worldwide scale.

planetary configuration the apparent positions of the planets relative to one another and to other bodies of the solar system, as seen from Earth.

planetary nebula a shell of gas ejected by a dying star that contains about as much mass as the sun. About 1000 planetary nebulae have been catalogued. The term was first coined by William Herschel in 1785. Noteworthy nebulae include the Butterfly Nebula in Scorpius, the Dumbbell Planetary Nebula in Vulpecula, the Owl Planetary Nebula in Ursa Major, and the Ring Planetary Nebula (M 57) in Lyra. See WILLIAM HERSCHEL.

planetary precession the apparent slow movement of a planet's celestial poles. In the case of Earth, it is caused by the pull of the moon and the sun exerted on Earth's equatorial bulge. Earth behaves rather in the manner of a child's top that is running down and beginning to topple, but the movement is very gradual. The pole describes a circle on the celestial sphere, centered on the pole of the ecliptic, which is 47° in diameter and takes 25,800 years to complete. Because of precession, the celestial equator also moves, and this in turn affects the position of the vernal equinox, which shifts eastward along the ecliptic by 50 seconds of arc each year. See PRECESSION.

planetary probe any unmanned spacecraft on an exploratory mission to the planets and their moons. Examples are Mariner, Pioneer, Viking, and Voyager.

planetary satellites the satellites of the planets of a star system, for example, the solar system.

planetary system a group of planets and other bodies that orbit a star (sun).

planetary volcanism see VOLCANISM.

planetesimals the bodies ranging in size from dust particles to hundreds of kilometers across that are believed to have combined under the force of gravity to form the planets of the solar system. The Planetesimal Theory of American geologist Thomas Chrowder Chamberlin (1843–1928) suggested that a passing star caused the sun to eject filaments of material. The filaments condensed into the planetesimals from which the planets formed.

planetographic referring to positions on a planet measured in latitude from the planet's equator and in longitude from a reference meridian.

planetoid a minor planet or an asteroid. See these terms.

planetology the study of the planets of the solar system.

planet X **1.** the unofficial designation for American astronomer Percival Lowell's hypothetical planet orbiting the sun beyond the orbit of Neptune. (See Fig. 73.) Pluto was discovered beyond Neptune's orbit by another American astronomer, Clyde Tombaugh, in 1930;

2. the term used to designate a yet-undiscovered planet beyond Pluto.

Plaskett's Star or **Plaskett's Twins** (HD47129) a giant binary system, usually regarded as the most massive pair of stars yet identified in our

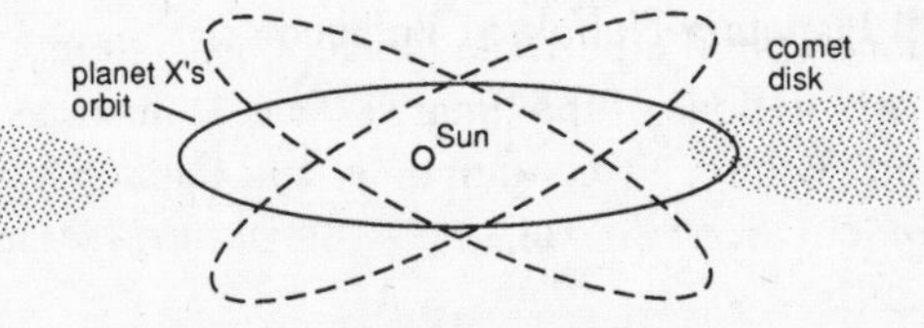

Fig. 73. **Planet X.** See entry.

galaxy. Located southeast of 13 Monocerotis, the supergiant—an exceptionally massive O-type—was first investigated, in 1922, by Canadian astronomer John Stanley Plaskett (1865–1941), an authority on the motion of faint stars, the rotation of the Milky Way, and the matter in interstellar space. Plaskett determined that this spectroscopic binary has a period of 14 days and estimated that each component has a mass of 55 solar masses. While the distance from Earth of Plaskett's Star is not well determined, it is assumed to be at 2700 light-years from Earth.

plasma the envelope, or sheath, of ionized gas particles that surrounds a spacecraft as it reenters Earth's atmosphere. The resulting heat of reentry results in a temporary blackout of radio and radar reception and transmission. See PLASMA SHEATH.

plasma cloud a mass of ionized gas flowing out of the sun.

plasma sheath a boundary layer of charged particles between a plasma and its surrounding walls, electrodes, or other plasmas. The plasma sheath affects transmission, reception, and diffraction of radio waves, so it must be taken into account in designing equipment for spacecraft.

Plato a walled plain, 97 km in diameter, on the edge of Mare Imbrium, at +52° N and -10° W, in the 2nd quadrant of the moon's near side. Its very dark, smooth floor makes it easy to identify when it is in sunlight.

Pleiades or **Seven Sisters** a young open star cluster, with a diameter of about 30 light-years and lying about 541 light-years from Earth in the constellation Taurus. The Pleiades cluster contains about 3000 stars. The Seven Sisters—only six are easily visible to the naked eye—are the bright stars Alcyone, Maia, Atlas, Electra, Merope, Taygete, and Pleione. Since early legends associated the Pleiades with the number seven, the supposition is that the seventh star has become fainter.

Pleione the common name for the variable star 28 Tau. See PLEIADES.

Plinius a prominent crater at +16° N and +24° E, in the 1st quadrant of the moon's near side, between Mare Serenitatis and Mare Tranquillitatis. It has a diameter of 48 kilometers.

Plow also spelled **Plough**, the constellation Ursa Major, which is called the Big Dipper in the United States. *Plow* is a nickname for the seven main stars of Ursa Major (Alkaid, Mizar, Alioth, Megrez, Phad, Merak, and Dubhe).

PLSS (pronounced pliss) a *p*ortable *l*ife-*s*upport *s*ystem, part of the suit used during explorations of the lunar surface. It includes oxygen, water circulation and cooling, air conditioning, and telemetry and communications equipment. See PORTABLE LIFE SUPPORT SYSTEM and EMU.

Plume 2 see LOKI.

Plume 3 see PROMETHEUS.

Plume 7 see MARDUK.

Pluto the 9th and smallest planet. This distant planet was discovered by American astronomer Clyde Tombaugh (1906–). Pluto orbits the sun in 248 years. The planet is so far away—40 AU—and so small as seen from Earth that observers cannot see any details of its surface. Discovery of Pluto was a result of a long search for an additional planet by American astronomer Percival Lowell (1855–1916) that, together with Neptune, was causing perturbations in the orbit of Uranus. The planet's existence was mathematically calculated by Lowell. Finally, in 1930, Clyde Tombaugh found Pluto after a year of diligent study of photographic plates at the Lowell Observatory (now named Flagstaff Observatory), in Flagstaff, Arizona. Pluto's symbol is an interlocked P and L, representing the planet as well as the initials of Percival Lowell.

Pluto's atmosphere— The planet is not massive enough to retain much of an atmosphere, but a tenuous atmosphere of methane has been detected from spectral observations by the IRAS satellite. There is a dark equatorial band, and Pluto has bright polar caps of methane ice that vary over the Pluto year. See IRAS.

Pluto's moon— Charon was discovered by James W. Christy in 1978. While he was studying new photographic plates of Pluto, he noticed that some of the photographs seemed to show a bump on the side of Pluto's image. The bump turned out to be the moon Charon, which orbits the planet in 6 days, 9 hours, and 17 minutes. See CHRISTY, JAMES W.

Pluto's orbit— Pluto's most notable characteristic is the eccentricity of its orbit, which brings it as close as 2.7 billion miles from the sun at perihelion, and takes it as far as 4.6 billion miles from the sun at aphelion. Pluto reached perihelion most recently in 1989. Its 249-year orbit is so eccentric that part of it lies inside the orbit of Neptune. It is now in that part of its orbit and will remain there until 1999. In a sense, therefore, Pluto is temporarily the 8th planet.

Pluto's size— The equatorial diameter of the planet is 2345 km (1457 miles). Its moon, Charon, is half the size of Pluto and is separated from the planet by only about 8 Pluto diameters, compared with the 30 Earth diameters that separate Earth and the moon. Thus, Pluto and Charon are almost a double-planet system.

Pogson ratio an arbitrary number assigned to the differences in magnitude between constant stars, enabling development of a precise magnitude scale for stars. It was developed by English astronomer Norman Pogson, who also discovered R Cygni in 1852.

Pointers the two outer stars in the Big Dipper that lie on a line that may be thought of as pointing to Polaris, since the line passes near Polaris and can be used in finding Polaris. See POLARIS.

polar distance or **codeclination** the angular distance along a great circle from a celestial pole.

Polaris or **North Star** or **pole star** a pulsating variable star, topaz yellow in color, located at the tip of the Little Bear's tail in the Little Dipper, Alpha Ursae Minoris. See Fig. 74.

polar orbit a satellite orbit that passes over or near the north and south poles of a planet. See ORBIT TYPES.

polar tufts the small spikes visible in the solar corona near the sun's poles, formed by gas following the sun's magnetic field.

polar wandering the gradual shift in location of Earth's magnetic poles as a result of secular variation in terrestrial magnetism.

pole either of the two points on a sphere (planet, moon) that are 90° either side of the equator.

pole star Polaris, the star closest to true north. See POLARIS.

Pollux the common name for Beta Gemini, an orange giant star of the Gemini constellation. Pollux, the brightest star in the constellation, is the nearest giant star to Earth.

Pons, Jean-Louis (1761–1831) French astronomer, at various times director of the Lucca Observatory and the Florence Observatory in Italy, and one of the most successful comet hunters of all time. Between 1803 and 1827 he discovered 37 comets.

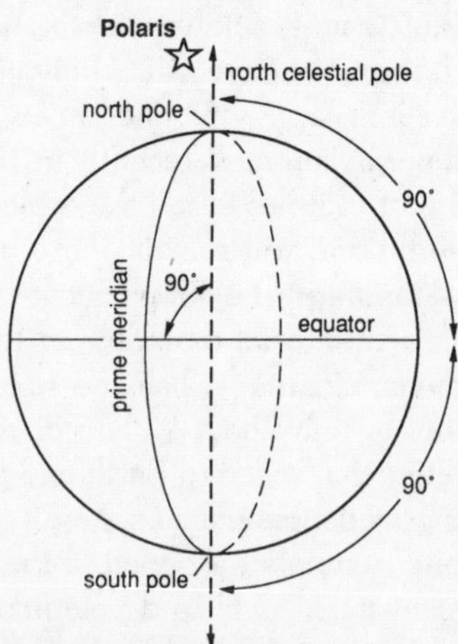

Fig. 74. **Polaris.** This is the star we all can find in the sky—if we live in the Northern Hemisphere.

Pons-Brooks Comet a comet discovered in 1812 by Jean-Louis Pons and rediscovered, in 1833, by W.R. Brooks. Its period is 70.9 years, and it was most recently seen in 1954.

Pons-Winnecke Comet a faint comet discovered in 1819 by Jean-Louis Pons and rediscovered, in 1858, by German astronomer Friedrich Winnecke (1835–1897). Its period is 6.4 years, and its most recently observed passage was in 1976.

Pontlyfni meteorite a stony meteorite, weighing 794 grams, that fell in Beddgelert, Wales, in 1931, and ripped through a hotel roof.

population I a region of stars rich in atoms heavier than helium. They are nearly always relatively young stars that are found in the disk of a galaxy.

population II a region of stars poor in atoms heavier than helium. They are nearly always relatively old stars found in the galactic halo—a spherical star cloud around the main part of a galaxy—or in globular clusters or the nuclear bulge. See NUCLEAR BULGE.

port 1. a place of access to a system at which energy may be supplied or withdrawn or at which system variables may be observed or measured. A designated pair of terminals is an example of a port;

2. an opening, for example, in a solid rocket.

portable life support system (PLSS) a backpack weighing 68 pounds and contoured to fit an astronaut comfortably, enabling the astronaut to operate independently in space or on the moon's surface for up to 4 hours at a time. In addition to an oxygen supply, circulating water for cooling the spacesuit, telecommunications equipment, and a power supply, it provides an emergency 30-minute supply of oxygen in two bottles in a separate pack mounted on top of the backpack and weighing an additional 40 pounds.

Posidonius a walled plain in the northern hemisphere of the 1st quadrant of the near side of the moon, on the eastern edge of Mare Serenitatis, at +32° N and +30° E. Its north wall contains multiple peaks reaching up 3000 feet.

posigrade rocket an auxiliary rocket that fires in the direction in which the spacecraft is pointed. Posigrade rockets are used to separate the sections of a multistage rocket.

position 1. the location of an object in space or on a sphere;

2. a crew member's station aboard a spacecraft.

Pourquoi Pas Rupes a major mountain ridge in the southern hemisphere of Mercury, at latitude -58° S and longitude 156° W, photographed by Mariner in 1974–1975. Its name, *Why Not Rock?* in English, makes one realize that whimsy is not alien to astronomers. For additional proof of this insight, see SUALOCIN and ROTANEV.

Poynting-Robertson effect the gradual decrease in orbital velocity of a small particle, such as a micrometeorite in orbit about the sun, due to its interaction with solar radiation, that is, the absorption and reemission of radiant energy by the particle.

Praesepe the Beehive, a large open cluster in the center of the northern constellation Cancer that contains over 100 stars. Also known as Messier 44 (M 44), Praesepe is 515 light-years from Earth and visible to the naked eye as a small, faint, fuzzy patch.

precession 1. the slow drifting of the orientation of Earth's axis over a period of 26,000 years (see Fig. 75);

2. a slow periodic change in the direction of the axis of rotation of a spinning body, for example, a gyroscope. The horizontal component of precession is called *drift*, and the vertical component is called *topple*. See PLANETARY PRECESSION.

precession of the equinoxes the conical motion of Earth's axis about the normal to the plane of the ecliptic, caused by the attractive force of the sun, moon, and other planets on the equatorial protuberance of Earth. The effect of the sun and moon, called *lunisolar precession*, is to produce a westward motion of the equinoxes along the ecliptic. The effect of other planets, called *planetary precession*, tends to produce a much smaller motion eastward along the ecliptic.

preset guidance a type of guidance system in which devices in the spacecraft are adjusted before launching to control the path of the craft during its journey.

Priamus (Asteroid 884) a Trojan asteroid discovered in 1917 by German astronomer Max Wolf. Priamus moves in virtually the same orbit as

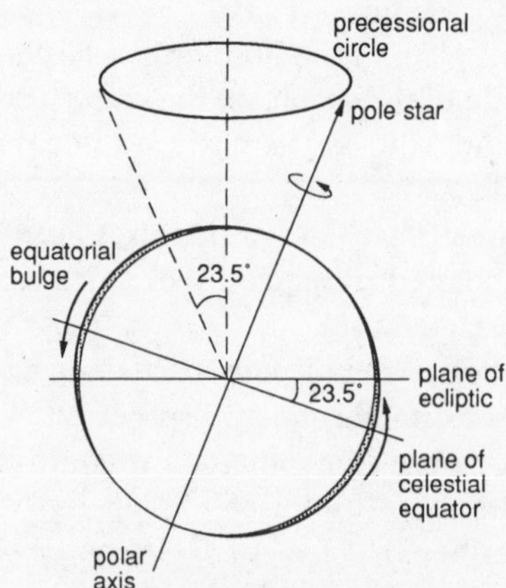

Fig. 75. **Precession.** See entry.

Jupiter, but is about 60° from Jupiter, so there is no fear of collision. See TROJAN GROUP.

Pribram fireball a fireball associated with the meteorite fall at Pribram, Czechoslovakia, on April 7, 1959.

primary body or **primary** a celestial body or central force field about which a satellite or other body orbits, or from which it is escaping, or toward which it is falling. The primary body of the moon is Earth; the primary body of Earth is the sun.

primary circulation the prevailing fundamental atmospheric circulation on a planetary scale that must exist in response to (a) radiation differences with latitude, (b) the rotation of the planet, and (c) the distribution of its land and oceans.

primary cosmic rays the high-energy particles originating outside Earth's atmosphere.

primary minimum in the light curve of an eclipsing binary, the deeper eclipse.

prime meridian longitude 0°, used as the origin for measurement of longitude. The meridian of Greenwich, England, is almost universally used for this purpose.

principal planets the larger bodies revolving about the sun in nearly circular orbits. The known principal planets are Mercury, Venus, Earth, Mars, Jupiter, Saturn, Uranus, Neptune, and Pluto.

probe an unmanned vehicle sent out from Earth for the purpose of obtaining information about space. Spacecraft that enter into orbit around the sun are called *deep-space probes*. Spacecraft designed to pass near or land on another celestial body are often designated as probes. For example, Surveyor, Lunar Orbiter, and Lunik are *lunar probes*; Mariner and the Venus probes are *planetary probes*; Pioneer and Voyager are *flybys*; and Viking 1 and 2 are *landers*.

Procellarum, Oceanus the largest of the great lunar plains (mare), which covers a major portion of the moon's western nearside, the Gargantuan Basin region. It is bordered on the east by the Kepler Crater, on the west by the Reiner Crater. Procellarum, often called the Ocean of Storms, was the landing site for Lunar 9 and Lunar 13, Surveyor 1 and Surveyor 3, and Apollo 12. It is located at latitude +10 N and longitude -47 W. See OCEANUS PROCELLARUM.

Proclus crater a brilliant crater just west of Mare Crisium, at +16° N and +46° E, in the moon's 1st quadrant. See MARE CRISIUM.

Procyon the common name for Alpha Canis Minoris, a conspicuous yellow-white star that is the brightest star in the Canis Minor constellation. Alpha Canis Minoris, sometimes called Elgomaisa, is a visual binary whose companion star is a white dwarf. The distance of Alpha Canis Minoris from Earth is 3.5 parsecs.

Prognoz a series of eight unmanned observatories launched by the USSR to monitor solar activity and the interaction of the solar wind with Earth.

prograde see RETROGRADE ROTATION.

Project Little Green Men see OZMA PROJECT.

prolate spheroid a celestial sphere stretched along its polar axis so its polar diameter is greater than its equatorial diameter.

Prometheus (1980 S26) a small inner shepherd satellite of Saturn's F ring, discovered in 1980 by American astronomers S. Collins and D. Carlson. Prometheus has a diameter of 100 km and a revolution period of 0.613 days.

Prometheus or **Plume 3** an active volcano on Jupiter's satellite Io. It was in eruption during the Voyager 1 and 2 passes.

prominences **1.** the clouds of gas in the sun's chromosphere;

2. the bright projections beyond the limb.

Prominences can be observed visually whenever the sun's disk is masked, as during an eclipse. They exhibit a great diversity of structure and are classified according to their behavior. *Quiescent prominences* are long-lived and are among the most stable of all solar features. Typically, they are hundreds of thousands of kilometers long, tens of thousands of kilometers high, and thousands of kilometers thick. They attain their greatest frequency a few years after the minimum of a sunspot cycle. *Active prominences* are relatively short-lived and may alter their structure appreciably in a matter of minutes. There are many characteristic types, for example, surges and sprays, in which chromospheric material is ejected into the inner corona; and loop prominences and coronal rain, in which the reverse occurs. Loop prominences are impulsive events that often accompany flares, while coronal rain represents the return of flare-ejected material.

Protonilus Mensa a mensa—a small plateau, or tableland—south of the Cassini Crater on Mars, at latitude 38° to 49° N and longitude 303° to 325° W.

Proton satellites a series of USSR satellites launched to monitor cosmic and gamma rays and to assist in development of the Salyut space station. See SALYUT.

proton storm a flux of protons sent into space by a solar flare.

protoplanet **1.** a planet in the making;

2. any one of the sun's planets as it emerged or existed in the formative period of the solar system.

protostar a collapsing cloud of gas and dust destined to become a star.

Ptolemaic system a model elaborated by Ptolemy and modified later by others that attempted to explain the observed motions of the sun, moon, and planets by proposing that Earth was the fixed center of the universe and all the other celestial bodies moved about it. See PTOLEMY and Fig. 76.

Ptolemy or **Claudius Ptolemaeus** (c. 90–168) a Hellenistic astronomer, mathematician, and geographer who lived in Alexandria. His conception of how the heavenly bodies relate to one another dominated scientific thinking until the 16th century. See PTOLEMAIC SYSTEM.

pulsar any one of several hundred rapidly rotating neutron stars that emit sharp pulses of radiation, especially radio waves, with a high degree of regularity. The pulse period ranges from about 0.0001 to 4 seconds. The first pulsar was discovered in 1967 by British astronomer Jocelyn Bell. Over 450 pulsars are now known, as a result of the use of radio telescopes. See CRAB PULSAR, CRAB NEBULA, VELA PULSAR, and NEUTRON STAR.

pulsating variable or **pulsating star** a variable star that periodically brightens and fades as its outer layers go through a cycle of expansion and contraction. The Cepheids are pulsating variables.

Puppis (Pup) a southern constellation that forms the stern of the ancient constellation Argo, the Ship. Below Puppis is Carina, the Keel; to the east is Vela, the Sail; and just beside Puppis on the deck is Pyxis, the Ship's Compass. To find Puppis, the observer first will locate Canopus and then look northward for a group of 2nd and 3rd magnitude stars. Two notable Puppis stars are Naos and Asmidiske. See ARGO.

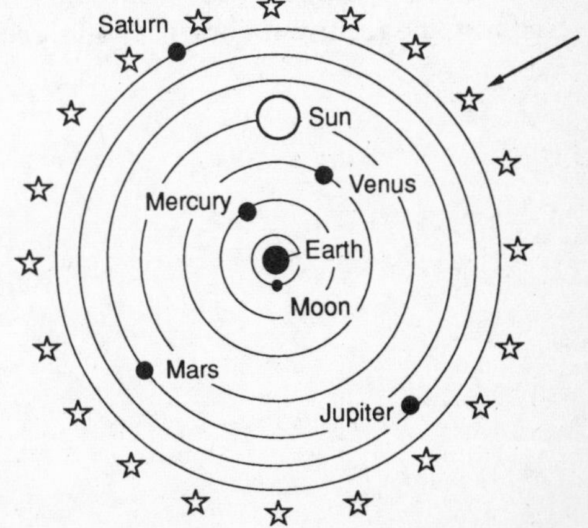

Fig. 76. **Ptolemaic system.** According to this early conception of the heavens, Earth was the center of the universe, and the sun and all the planets moved around Earth in circular orbits.

Purbach a walled plain about 120 km in diameter in the third quadrant of the face of the moon, at latitude -26° S and longitude -2° W, in the southern hemisphere, east of Mare Nubium. It forms a trio of craters with Regiomontanus and Walter.

Purbach, Georg von (1423–1461) Austrian mathematician and astronomer who contributed much to the advancement of astronomy. He calculated new tables of the planets, measured the obliquity of the ecliptic, and constructed a globe showing the motion of the stars from the time of Ptolemy to the year 1450. See PTOLEMY.

pyranometer or **solarimeter** an actinometer used to measure the combined intensity of incoming direct solar radiation and diffuse sky radiation. See ACTINOMETER.

Pythagoras (582–507 BC) Greek mathematician and philosopher whose name is known to schoolchildren for his theorem on right-angled triangles. Astronomers know him for his teaching that Earth is a sphere. He may observed the apparent sinking of ships as they sailed toward the horizon and may also have noticed that during a lunar eclipse, as the moon passed into Earth's shadow, the curvature of the edge of that shadow suggested the curvature of Earth. Pythagoras also taught that the planets orbit in circles.

Pythagoras crater a high-walled crater 113 km in diameter in the 2nd quadrant of the moon, at +64° N and -66° W, northwest of Sinus Roris, the Bay of Dew.

Pyxix (Pyx) the Ship Compass, a small southern constellation near Antlia and Puppis, identified by French astronomer Louis de Lacaille (1713–1762) in 1751 and 1752. Lacaille is known as the father of southern hemisphere astronomy. Pyxis contains no bright stars—its brightest ones being of only fourth magnitude—but it does show one object of interest, the recurrent nova T. Pyxidis, seen most recently in 1966.

Q

QSO *abbreviation for* *q*uasi-*s*tellar *o*bject. See QUASAR.

quadrant 1. the fourth part of the circumference of a circle;

2. a quarter section of a circle, for example, the face of a heavenly body, especially that of the moon seen from Earth. The moon face is thought of as divided by two perpendicular lines into four quadrants, numbered counterclockwise, beginning with the quadrant at the upper right;

3. an ancient astronomical instrument for measuring altitudes of the heavenly bodies.

Quadrantids a major meteor shower that maximizes on or about January 31. Its apparent origin (radiant) is in the constellation Boötes. The zenithal hourly rate (ZHR) at maximum is about 110 and is constant from year to year. The shower is named after the obsolete constellation Quadrans Murali, which is found in early 19th-century star atlases. See ZENITHAL HOURLY RATE.

quadrature 1. the position of a planet or moon in the solar system when its elongation is 90° from the sun, usually specified as east or west in accordance with the direction of the body from the sun, for example, when the angle sun-earth-planet is a right angle;

2. the position of the moon when it is at a right angle to the sun as seen from Earth. The moon is at quadrature when it is in its first and last quarters;

3. the situation of two periodic quantities differing by a quarter of a circle.

quake the violent shaking of the crust of a planet or moon, usually called *earthquake* because of our human frame of reference. When rocks rupture, shock waves travel from the site of the rupture and shake the ground far from the epicenter, the point on the surface immediately above the site of the rupture. Quake shock waves are called *seismic waves* and are detected by *seismometers*.

quanta see QUANTUM.

quantum a quantity or amount of uniform, discrete bundles of energy. A quantum of energy emitted as light is called a photon. See PHOTON and QUANTUM THEORY.

quantum leap or **quantum jump** a sudden alteration in the energy level of an atom or molecule together with the emission or absorption of radiant energy.

quantum mechanics a mathematical theory in physics that deals with atomic structure and begins with the assumption that energy is not infinitely divisible. See QUANTUM THEORY.

quantum theory a theory developed by German theoretical physicist Max Planck (1858–1947) stating that energy is not emitted from radiating bodies in a continuous stream, but only in discrete units or bundles. He named these uniform bundles *quanta* (singular, *quantum*). A quantum of energy emitted as light is called a *photon*. The particle-like and wave-like properties are related by Planck's constant. See PLANCK and PLANCK'S CONSTANT.

quarter moon the moon at half phase, when we see one-quarter of the entire surface. See Figs. 58 and 69.

quasar (QSO) any one of a thousand known compact extragalactic objects, each of which looks to us on Earth to be no more than a point of light in space but emits more energy than a hundred supergiant galaxies. They are starlike in appearance and characteristically have spectra with massive red shifts. Quasars, which are thought to be the most distant objects from Earth and the most luminous objects in the universe, were discovered in 1963 by American astronomer Maarten Schmidt (1929–), born in Holland. Schmidt found that the number of quasars increases with distance from Earth, an observation that gives credence to the so-called big bang theory of the origin of the universe.

The term *quasar* was formed from *qua*si-*s*tell*ar*, and early papers on the subject sometimes refer to *quasi-stellar galaxies* (QSG). About 1% of quasars are also radio sources and are referred to as *quasi-stellar radio sources* (QSS).

quasi-periodic object any of certain x-ray sources that appear to flicker rapidly for short intervals.

quasi-stellar galaxy (QSG) see QUASAR.

quasi-stellar object (QSO) see QUASAR.

quasi-stellar radio source (QSS) see QUASAR.

Queen the common name for the constellation Cassiopeia. Cassiopeia was the vain and boastful wife of Cepheus, king of Ethiopia, who lies next to her in the northern sky. The Queen sits on her throne circling the celestial pole. The constellation has a distinctive W shape, made up of its five brightest stars. See CASSIOPEIA.

Quetzalcoatl (Asteroid 1915) an Amor (Mars-crossing) asteroid with a librating orbit. It makes a close approach to Mars infrequently, about once in a million years. See LIBRATION and AMOR GROUP OF ASTEROIDS.

quiescent prominence a particularly long-lived solar feature and the most stable of all solar features. Quiescent prominences may persist for several months before breaking up. They typically measure a few hundred thousand kilometers in length and attain their greatest frequency a few years after the lowest point in a sunspot cycle. By way of contrast, *active prominences* are relatively short-lived and may alter their structure appreciably in minutes. There are many characteristic types of active prominences, for example, surges, sprays, coronal rain, and flares. See PROMINENCE.

quiet sun the sun at a time of minimal solar activity in the sunspot cycle, a period that occurs every 11 years. During such periods there is relative absence of unusual radio waves or thermal radiation such as that associated with sun spots. See SUNSPOT CYCLE.

R

R.A. see RIGHT ASCENSION.

radar *acronym for radio detecting and ranging*, an electronic system for determining by means of reflected signals (radio echoes) the distance, altitude, and direction of motion of objects in the path of a radio beam.

radar astronomy the study of astronomical bodies within the solar system by means of radiation originating on Earth but reflected from the body under observation. The uses of radar astronomy include mapping of planetary bodies, such as Venus and Mercury, and precise measurement of periods of rotation of these bodies. See RADIO ASTRONOMY.

radar range 1. the distance from a radar to a target as measured by the radar;

2. the maximum distance at which a given radar is effective in detecting targets.

radar reflector a device capable of, or intended for, reflecting radar signals.

radar scan or **scan** a continuous searching motion of a radar beam in any of various path configurations.

radial spokes the radian markings in Saturn's rings that appear to be fine dust suspended above the ring plane by electromagnetic forces.

radial velocity the movement toward or away from a celestial body, measured by the Doppler effect in its spectrum. If the spectral lines are red-shifted, the object is receding. If the shift is to the blue, the object is approaching. Conventionally, radial velocity is said to be positive with a receding body, negative with an approaching body. Among the 50 stars nearest to Earth, about half the radial velocities measured are more than 20 kilometers per second toward or away from Earth.

radiancy see RADIANT FLUX DENSITY.

radiant or **radiant point of meteors** the point on the celestial sphere from which a meteor shower appears to radiate. Meteor showers are usually named after the constellation that contains the radiant. For example, the August meteor shower has its radiant in Perseus, so the meteors are known as the Perseids. The meteors in a shower are really moving in parallel paths through the atmosphere, and the radiant effect is due to the perspective of the viewer.

radiant emittance see RADIANT FLUX DENSITY.

radiant energy any form of energy traveling in waves through space or through some medium, especially electromagnetic radiation, as heat, light, x-rays, gamma rays, infrared radiation, and ultraviolet rays. See LUMINOUS ENERGY.

radiant flux the time rate of flow of radiant energy.

radiant flux density the radiant flux per unit of area. When applied to a source of radiation, radiant flux density is called *radiancy* or *radiant emittance* (W). When applied to a receiver, it is called *irradiancy* or *irradiance* (H).

radiant point of meteors see RADIANT.

radiation 1. the process of emission and transmission of energy rays over a continuous range of wavelengths from an object through space or through some medium. The sun and all other stars give out various forms of electromagnetic radiation—visible and invisible—such as light, heat, infrared, ultraviolet, x-ray, and radio waves;

2. the electromagnetic energy transmitted by waves through space or some medium, usually referred to as *electromagnetic radiation*, but also as *radiant energy*;

3. a stream of particles, such as electrons, neutrons, protons or high-energy photons, alpha particles, or a mixture of these.

radiation belts or **zone** a region of charged particles surrounding a planet and lying above the planetary atmosphere. Mercury, Earth, Jupiter, Saturn, Uranus, and Neptune all possess radiation belts. For Earth's radiation belt, see VAN ALLEN RADIATION BELT.

radio astronomy 1. the study of space employing a radio telescope;

2. the study of celestial objects through observation of radiofrequency waves emitted or reflected by these objects;

3. astronomical studies carried out in the long wavelength region of the electromagnetic spectrum. The main instruments used are known as radio telescopes. They are of many types, ranging from so-called dishes, such as the 250-foot paraboloid at Jodrell Bank, in England, to long lines of antennas.

In 1931, Karl Jansky, an American radio engineer, was investigating the causes of static, when he found that his specially designed aerial was picking up long wavelength radiation from the Milky Way. This was the start of the new science of radio astronomy.

radio command a radio signal programmed to evoke a response from a spacecraft or artificial satellite—a change in direction, the initiation of a procedure, etc.

radio galaxy a galaxy that is a strong source of radio signals. Cygnus A, Centaurus A, and NGC 5128 are examples of radio galaxies. Radio galaxy M87, one of the brighter members of the Virgo cluster, is a giant elliptical galaxy.

radio guidance system a guidance system that uses radio signals to direct a spacecraft in flight.

radio hole a strong fading of the radio signal at some position in space. The effect is caused by abnormal refraction of radio waves.

radio interferometer 1. any of various types of instrumentation used in discovery and measurement of radio sources in the atmosphere by observing interference patterns of electromagnetic radiation at radio wavelengths;

2. a system using two or more radio telescopes whose signals are combined to achieve the resolving power of a telescope larger than either of the individual units. The farther apart the radio telescopes are placed—that is, the longer the baseline—the greater the accuracy in attempting to pinpoint the direction of a radio source. Since it is feasible to erect radio telescopes miles apart from one another, such telescopes simulate a telescope much bigger than any single type that can actually be built and erected on Earth. See VLA and VLB.

radio meteor a meteor that has been detected by the reflection of a radio signal from the meteor trail, which is of relatively high ion density.

radio source any celestial object, such as a pulsar or supernova, that emits radio waves. Within our solar system, Jupiter and the sun both emit powerful radio bursts. Extragalactic radio sources include spiral galaxies, radio galaxies, and quasars. See Fig. 77.

radio sun the sun mapped at radio frequencies.

radio telescope a system consisting of a receiver and a parabolic or dipole antenna designed for receiving, amplifying, and measuring the intensity of radio waves originating outside Earth's atmosphere. A radio telescope does not produce a visual picture of the celestial object under study. Instead, it collects radio waves from the heavens, which are the basic tool of radio astronomy. Most radio telescopes are of the dish type. They have a parabolic metal bowl that collects radio waves and focuses them on an antenna. The world's largest radio telescope is the 305-meter fixed position dish at Arecibo, in Puerto Rico. The largest steerable dish, 100 meters across, is at Effelsberg, near Bonn, Germany. See VLA and VLB.

radio waves from Jupiter the radio transmissions that result from electrical discharges along the Jovian field lines when the moon Io crosses them. The first detection of radio emissions from Jupiter was made in 1955 by radio astronomers Bernard Burke and Kenneth Franklin, who discovered that Jupiter was an intense source of radio emission. The bursts they observed, some as powerful as 10 million kilowatts,

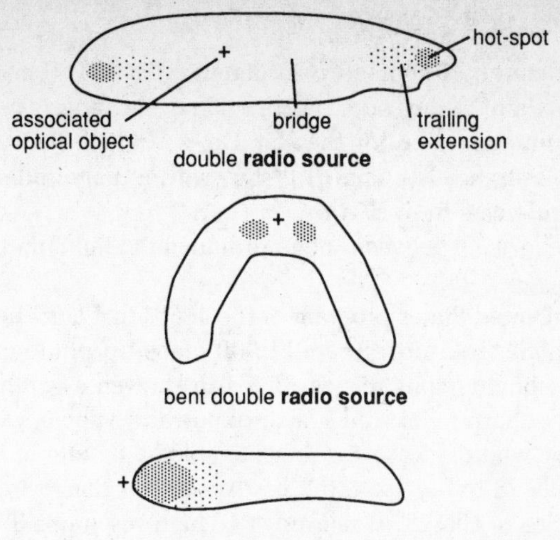

Fig. 77. **Radio sources.** Three types of radio sources are represented here: double radio source, bent double radio source, and radio-trail source.

occurred in rapid succession and lasted as long as two hours.

Astronomers have also discovered a continuous, unchanging emission at long rado wavelengths. It has been determined, and confirmed by Voyager 1 and Voyager 2, that this continuous emission from Jupiter comes from a gigantic radiation belt extending to a distance several times larger than the planet's radius.

radio window the range of wavelengths at which Earth's atmosphere is transparent to radio waves, ranging between .25 cm and 30 m in length.

radius vector 1. a straight line connecting a fixed reference point or center with a second point, which may be moving;

2. a straight line connecting the center of a celestial body with the center of a body that revolves around it, as in the radius vector of the moon.

Ram on old star maps the northern constellation Aries, not at all prominent. For modern astronomers the Ram assumes more prominence, since it is known that in ancient times, approximately 130 BC, Aries contained the cardinal point known as the vernal equinox. This is the point at which the sun crosses the celestial equator from north to south. Because of precession—the slow wobble of Earth's axis—the vernal equinox has moved some 30° and currently lies in the neighboring constellation Pisces. Despite this, the vernal equinox is still sometimes called the first point of Aries.

Ramsden a crater 24 kilometers in diameter, at -33° S and -32° W, in the 3rd quadrant in the south polar region of the moon's near side.

Rana the common name for the star Delta Eridani, between the stars Zibel and Zaurak. Rana is a dK0 star, with a magnitude of 3.72 and lying 29 light-years from Earth.

range the difference between the maximum and minimum of a given set of numbers.

Ranger the United States program of the 1960s that launched a series of probes which took more than 17,000 close-up photographs of the moon. The photographs relayed to Earth showed a gently rolling terrain with no sharp relief, and a layer of powdery rubble, with rocks and craters everywhere, measuring down to at least 1 meter in diameter.

Ranger 7 July 28 to 31, 1964, the first successful Ranger mission, landing at the Sea of Clouds. It relayed 4316 high-resolution TV pictures of the lunar surface, even showing objects less than 3 feet in diameter.

Ranger 8 February 17 to 20, 1965, landing at the Sea of Tranquillity and relaying 7137 photographs.

Ranger 9 March 21 to 24, 1965, landing at Crater Alphonsus, 3 miles from its intended target. It returned 5814 pictures of the area around Alphonsus.

Ras Algethi a common name for the northern bright star Alpha Herculis, also known as the kneeler's head of Hercules. Ras Algethi is a telescopic double in the large northern constellation Hercules, north of Ophiuchus, and lies 410 light-years from Earth. See TELESCOPIC DOUBLE.

Ras Alhague a common name for Alpha Ophiuchi. Ras Alhague, the head of the serpent charmer, is a 2.07-magnitude A5 star 60 light-years from Earth.

Ras Elased Borealis a common name for Mu Leonis, which is also called Rasales, the eyebrows. Mu Leonis is a star of magnitude 4.10, type gK3, and 155 light-years from Earth.

Ra-Shalom (Asteroid 2100) an Aten asteroid of period 0.76 years. It was discovered by Eleanor Helin in 1978, using the Schmidt camera at Mount Palomar. See ATEN ASTEROIDS.

ray 1. an elemental path of radiated energy;

2. a long, narrow, light-colored streak on the lunar surface originating from a crater. Rays range in length to over 150 kilometers, and several usually radiate from the same crater, like spokes of a wheel. There is a strong tendency for ray systems to be conspicuous only in full sunlight. Further, conspicuous ray systems are not necessarily related to large craters. Many short, plume-like single rays issue from small, bright craters less than 5 miles in diameter. Lunar craters with rays include Clavius, Eratosthenes, Messier, Furnerius, Herschel, Kepler, Plato, and Tycho.

Rayet, Georges Antoine Pons (1839–1906) French astronomer who, with French astronomer Charles Wolf (1827–1918), discovered three small stars, the first in a new class of white or yellowish stars—the so-called Wolf-Rayet Stars—whose spectrum indicates the presence of hydrogen and helium.

Rayleigh scattering the scattering of light by particles smaller than the light's wavelength. This process favors scattering of blue light.

R Coronae Borealis variables the class of variable stars that exhibit irregular and sudden decreases in brightness. The Large Magellanic Cloud contains a few of these stars: W Mensae, the brightest; RY Sagittarii; S Apodis; and UW Cetauri.

R Cygni a Mira variable star discovered in 1852 by N.R. Pogson. R Cygni is found in the Cygnus constellation just south of Nova Cygni, the bright nova that flared up in the area in August of 1975. R Cygni is 5° ENE from Deneb and 1° ENE from 63 Cygni.

reaction force the equal and opposite force that accompanies every force. See NEWTON'S LAWS OF MOTION.

real image an image, formed at the focus of a telescope, that can be photographed.

recovery 1. a procedure whereby a launch vehicle or portions of its systems, or a satellite or portions of it, are retrieved after once having been launched and placed in orbit;

2. the first observation of a periodic comet during a particular approach to the sun.

recurrent nova a star that erupts as a nova every few dozen years. T Pyxidix, RS Ophiuchi, and T Coronae Borealis are recurrent novae.

Reda see TARAZED.

reddening, interstellar the reddening of starlight as the result of the scattering of blue light when the light of a star passes through clouds of gas and dust in space.

red dwarf a type of low-mass, cooler star located at the lower end of the main sequence, spectral type K or M. Surface temperatures range between 2500 and 5000 K. Because a red star does not develop an inert helium core surrounded by a shell of unprocessed hydrogen, it never ignites a hydrogen shell and cannot become a giant. As nuclear reactions in the star convert hydrogen to helium, it slowly contracts, heats up, and moves to the left side of the Hertzsprung-Russell diagram to become a white dwarf. An example is Barnard's Star. See HERTZSPRUNG-RUSSELL DIAGRAM.

red giant a star in the intermediate stage of its evolution. It is very large—a diameter 1 to 100 times greater than that of our sun—and has a comparatively low surface temperature—2000 to 3000 K. Of course,it has a reddish hue. Arcturus in Boötes and Aldebaran in Taurus are examples of red giants.

Red Planet a nickname for Mars, appropriate because its bright orange-red color enables it to be identified easily in the night sky. All the other planets appear yellowish to the naked eye. Mars' red surface coloration is due to oxidized iron minerals.

red shift the displacement of observed spectral lines toward the longer wavelengths of the red end of the spectrum. The term *relativistic red shift* is applied to the Doppler effect caused by the relative speed of recession of an observed body and the gravitational or relativistic shift in which the frequency of light emitted by atoms in the stellar atmosphere is decreased by a factor proportional to the mass-radius relationship of the star.

red shift of galaxies the shift toward longer wavelengths in the light of distant galaxies as they recede from the solar system.

Red Spot a large, usually reddish, gaseous vortex on Jupiter's surface. About 14,000 to 30,000 km in size, it has been observed for several centuries to drift slowly as Jupiter rotates. See GREAT RED SPOT.

red variable any of a group of pulsating stars that fluctuate in brightness with a long period. Their periods are irregular, fluctuating from 3 months to about 2 years. Mira, in the constellation Cetus, is one example.

reentry the event that occurs as a spacecraft, having once been launched, is returned to Earth's atmosphere. It is a 14-minute period starting as a returning spacecraft hits Earth's atmosphere at an altitude of 400,000 feet. In Apollo reentries, the on-board computer swings the spacecraft as it hits the atmosphere so that the spacecraft gains altitude briefly, cutting several thousand mph off the 24,700 mph reentry speed. Friction through contact with the atmosphere causes heating up to 5500° F and chars almost an inch of material off the heatshield of the spacecraft. Communications are blacked out for 4 minutes because the heat prevents passage of radio waves. The drogue deployment and additional landing activities of the Apollo program are no longer used by NASA.

Instead, the reusable Space Shuttle makes an aircraft landing. At the same time, the communications blackout for the shuttle is longer—about 20 minutes—because its reentry glide path is much shallower.

reference star any one of 1535 fundamental comparison stars. Their declinations and right ascensions are used as standard reference points in computing the relative positions of other astronomical bodies.

reflecting telescope a telescope that uses a mirror in the principal stage of forming an image. The major types of reflecting telescopes are the following:

Cassegrain—the telescope contains an auxiliary mirror to reflect the image back through a hole in the main (principal) mirror. This design makes for compactness.

Newtonian—the light is gathered by a parabolic mirror and reflected back up the telescope tube to a plane mirror angled at 45°. That mirror deflects the light to the side of the tube, where the eyepiece is located. The design is widely used.

Schmidt—a wide-angle instrument that has a spherical main mirror and is capped by a correcting plane, which compensates for defects, such as spherical aberration.

Gregorian—the first compound reflecting telescope designed. It has a small concave secondary mirror that is mounted beyond the focal plane and reflects the light back through a central hole in the primary mirror. By the time the required ellipsoidal secondary mirror could be built, in the 18th century, the design was obsolete.

See REFRACTING TELESCOPE.

reflection a process in optical instruments whereby a surface discontinuity—an abrupt change in the shape of the wave—turns back a portion of the incident radiation into the medium through which the radiation approached.

reflection nebula a vast interstellar dust cloud that produces a bluish glow. We see the nebula because it is reflecting light from a nearby star. Reflection nebulae are always fainter than the star that illuminates them, unless the star is hidden from our view by a denser portion of the nebula. Some reflection nebulae are illuminated not by an individual star but by the combined light of the entire galaxy, the Milky Way. The clouds of dust in the Milky Way or surrounding some of the stars in the Pleiades are examples of reflection nebulae. They merely reflect starlight toward us without emitting visible radiation of their own and show the spectrum of the nearby star or stars whose light is being reflected. Reflection nebulae usually look bluish because they are reflecting light from hot stars.

refracting telescope a telescope that uses lenses to gather light and form an image. A convex objective lens forms an image that is then enlarged by an eyepiece. The image is inverted. There are two types of reflecting telescopes:

Galilean telescope—comprising a single long-focus object lens and a powerful diverging lens, which is used as the eyepiece. Galileo's best telescopes—they date from the early 17th century—supplied magnification of about 30 times. Although far from perfect, they made possible the great astronomical discoveries of the 17th century: sunspots, the many satellites of the planets, and the ring around Saturn.

Keplerian telescope—employing a positive (convex) lens in place of the negative lens Galileo used in the eyepiece. This change gave a larger, though still inverted, field of view and higher magnification.

Refracting telescopes suffer from such defects as spherical and chromatic aberrations, which cause blurred images. In addition, large lenses are difficult to manufacture and mount. There are great technical problems in making large lenses that are free of imperfections and impurities, and it is difficult to support large lenses around the edge in a way that reduces image distortions to a minimum. Thus, even the world's largest refracting telescope, at Yerkes Observatory, near Chicago, has a lens diameter of only 102 cm (40 inches).

All the larger refracting telescopes—Royal Greenwich Observatory, Cambridge Observatory, Dearborn Observatory, Lowell Observatory, Lick Observatory, and Meudon Observatory—were built late in the 19th century. The desire for ever-larger apertures to reach ever-farther and fainter objects in space has meant that the major telescopes built in the 20th century have been reflecting telescopes. The surviving large refracting telescopes are mainly used in astronomy for the measurement of stellar positions, proper motion, and parallax. See GALILEO, KEPLER, and REFLECTING TELESCOPE.

refraction 1. the bending of light as it passes from a transparent medium to a medium of different density;

2. a process in which the direction of energy propagation is changed as the result of a change in density within the medium.

Regiomontanus 1. a distorted walled plain in the third quadrant of the near side of the moon, at -28° S and -1° W, between the Purbach and Walter craters. Regiomontanus, 53 × 76 miles in extent, has multiple peaks on its north wall;

2. the name given to German astronomer and mathematician Johannes Müller (1436–1476) for his contributions to geography—Christopher Columbus used some of his astronomical data in navigating to the New World. The Latin form of the name of Königsberg, Müller's birthplace, is *Mons Regius*, hence the name *Regiomontanus* bestowed by Müller's town of birth.

regolith a layer of dust and broken rock created by meteoritic bombardment. Thick layers of regolith cover much of the surfaces of the moon and Mars. Regolith is produced from the underlying solid crust of those bodies by the explosive impact of large and small meteoroids.

Regulus the common name for Alpha Leonis, a bluish-white star of first magnitude that is the brightest star in the northern constellation Leo. Regulus is situated in the handle of the Sickle formation in Leo and the right forepaw of the Lion. Regulus, the Little King, was named by Copernicus. A visual triple star with an orange companion, Regulus lies at a distance of 26 parsecs from Earth. Regulus is also called Kalb and the Royal Star.

Reichenbach a crater in the fourth quadrant of the near side of the moon, at -31° S and +49° E, west of the Stevinus and Snellus craters. Reichenbach is 48 kilometers in diameter.

Reichenbach Valley a crater-chain feature located in the southern uplands of the fourth quadrant of the moon's near side.

relative sunspot number a measure of sunspot activity, computed from the formula $R = k(10g + f)$, where g is the number of sunspot groups, f is the total number of individual spots, and k is a constant depending on the caliber of the observer (usually about 1). It is also called *Wolf number* and *Zurich number*.

relativistic red shift the red shift due to the Doppler effect on objects traveling at speeds near the speed of light.

relativistic speeds speeds approaching the speed of light.

Relay satellites two experimental active-repeater satellites launched by NASA. Relay 1, launched on December 13, 1962, handled 12 simultaneous two-way telephone conversations or one television channel. It provided the first satellite communications link between North and South America and Europe. Relay 2, an improved version, was launched in January of 1964.

representative stars a sample of stars randomly drawn from the total population of stars in space.

reseau a network of fine lines superimposed photographically onto a glass photographic plate to produce the same network on a photograph of a star field.

resolution **1.** the ability of a telescope to separate objects that appear close together;

2. the ability of a telescope to show detail.

resonance an orbital condition in which one object is subject to periodic gravitational perturbations by another, most commonly arising when two objects orbiting a third have periods of revolution that are multiples or fractions of the other.

retardation the difference in the time of moonrise on successive nights. Retardation may exceed an hour, but it can be as little as 15 minutes during the time of the Harvest Moon. The variation is due to the moon's northward or southward motion along the ecliptic.

Reticulum (Ret) the Net, a southern constellation of relatively faint stars between Dordao and Hydrus, just north of the Large Magellanic Cloud. The Net of the star group's name represents not a fishing net but a reticle (derived from the Latin *reticulum*, a little net) used to establish a scale in an eyepiece.

retrofire to ignite a retrorocket. See RETROROCKET.

retrograde loop the apparent backward (westward) motion of planets as seen against the background of stars.

retrograde motion (r) **1.** movement in an orbit in the opposite direction to the movement of the primary—the body being orbited;

2. movement of a space object in orbit in a direction opposite to that of Earth in its revolution around the sun, that is, counterclockwise around the sun;

3. the temporary apparent backward (westward) movement of a superior planet—Mars or Pluto, whose orbits lie beyond that of Earth—across the sky before or after opposition.

retrograde orbit in the solar system, an orbit that carries a moon, planet, or comet in the opposite direction from most other motion in the solar system. Retrograde orbits are clockwise as seen from Earth. Examples include Phobe (Saturn's moon); the planet Uranus; four of Jupiter's moons (Ananke, Carme, Pasiphaë, and Sinope); Triton (Neptune's moon); Venus; and Halley's Comet.

retrograde rotation the movement on an axis spinning from east to west, or clockwise as seen from the north pole (opposite to the spin direction of Earth). Uranus is one example.

retropack a rocket unit built into or strapped to a spacecraft that is designed to provide RETROTHRUST.

retrorocket a rocket fitted on or in a spacecraft or artificial satellite to produce thrust opposed to forward motion.

retrosequence a sequence of events preparatory to, and programmed to follow, the retrofiring for spacecraft reentry. See RETROFIRE.

retrothrust or **reverse thrust 1.** the thrust used in performing a braking maneuver;

2. the thrust applied to a moving object in a direction to oppose the motion of the object.

reverse thrust see RETROTHRUST.

reversing layer the lowest of the three solar atmospheric layers. It is responsible for most of the dark lines in the solar spectrum.

revolution 1. the movement of one body around another, central body; **2.** one complete cycle of the movement of a celestial body, such as a planet or moon, in its orbit, as in a revolution of Earth about the sun.

Rhea (JV) one of the moons of Saturn, discovered in 1672 by French astronomer Jean-Dominique Cassini (1625–1712), the discoverer of 4 moons of Saturn and the dark division in Saturn's rings. Rhea has an icy surface. It has a diameter of 1500 km and orbits Saturn in 4.42 days at a mean distance of 527,000 km.

Rhea Mons a shield volcano in Beta Regio, at latitude +30 N and longitude 250°, in the northern hemisphere of Venus. It rises 4.5 km above the adjacent plain. See SHIELD VOLCANO.

Rheita a 70-km diameter crater in the fourth quadrant of the near side of the moon, located at -37° S and +48° E. Rheita's depth is 14,500 feet, measured from the highest point on the rim, and a multiple mountain ridge to the north rises 3700 feet above the floor. The crater is bordered on the west by Rheita Valley. See RHEITA VALLEY.

Rheita valley a lunar valley 230 miles (340 km) long and 8400 feet in depth. It lies between Mallet C and Rheita in the fourth quadrant of the near side of the moon. See RHEITA.

Rho Cassiopeiae a variable star near Beta Cassiopeiae.

Rho Ophiuchi Dark Cloud the most impressive feature of the summer sky, a chain of star clouds called the *Milky Way in Ophiuchus* and stretching from Cygnus to Sagittarius. The Rho Ophiuchi Dark Cloud lies only a few degrees from the computed position of the actual galactic center. The incredibly rich star fields of this area are mottled and streaked by a profusion of dark, intricately shaped and winding lanes of nonluminous material. The gigantic dark lane, called the *Great Rift* and easily visible to the naked eye, is the same external equatorial dust band that we see in the edge-on external galaxies. Beyond this rift, some 30,000 light-years away, lies the central hub of the galaxy. Although the position of of this hub is said to be in Ophiuchus, the most accurate investigations place it just across the border, in Sagittarius. This position coincides with a strong radio source called Sagittarius A, now believed to be the actual galactic nucleus.

R Hydrae a Mira-type variable star east of Gamma Hydrae in the Hydra constellation. See MIRA.

Riccioli a walled plain inside an old volcanic crater in the third quadrant of the near side of the moon, at -3° S and -75° W, adjoining Grimaldi. Riccioli is oval, with a diameter of 97 miles and a depth of 7500 feet, measured from the highest point of the crater rim. The southern half of the floor is very rough and has a peak near its center. Dark sections of Riccioli's north floor are flooded with lava.

rich cluster any cluster containing over 1000 galaxies, mostly elliptical, scattered over a volume about 3 megaparsecs in diameter. Such a cluster is generally very crowded, with the galaxies more concentrated toward the center. Rich clusters often contain one or more giant elliptical galaxies at their centers. The Coma cluster, in the constellation Coma Berenices, is an example of a rich cluster. It lies over 100 megaparsecs from Earth and contains at least 1000 galaxies. One of the nearest clusters to us, the Virgo cluster, contains over 2500 galaxies and is, therefore, classified as a rich cluster. It contains the giant elliptical galaxy M87. See GLOBULAR CLUSTER and OPEN CLUSTER.

rift valley a long, straight, deep valley produced by the separation of crustal plates. Valles Marineris, called the Grand Canyons of Mars, is the major canyon system of Mars and may be a huge rift valley associated with expansion and crustal tension. The linear canyons are about 150 kilometers wide.

Near the Beta Regio region on Venus are low areas that contain basins and possible rift valleys dropping as much as 3 km below the reference level of the plains. There are also parallel valley-like features northwest of Ishtar Terra, a plateau region in the northern hemisphere of Venus. Earth's Red Sea Rift and Mid-Atlantic Ridge are also rift valleys.

rift zone an area in which the crust of a planet or moon is being torn apart by internal forces. Rift zones are generally associated with the injection of new material from the mantle and with the slow separation of tectonic plates.

Rigel the common name for the very brilliant star Beta Orionis, a massive, remote bluish-white supergiant in the Orion constellation on the celestial equator. Rigel, also called Algebar, is the seventh brightest star in the sky—its luminosity is over 50,000 times that of the sun. Because it stands on the equator at 0°, it is visible from most parts of Earth. Its distance from Earth is 270 parsecs.

right ascension (R.A.) the angle of an object around the celestial equator, measured in hours, minutes, and seconds eastward from the vernal equinox.

rill or **rille** any of the elongated, straight or sinuous trenches or valleys seen on the moon. Alpine Valley, Cauchy Fault, Hadley Rille, Lee Lincoln Scarp, Posidonius, Schrodinger Canyon, and the Straight Wall are examples of lunar rills.

rille see RILL.

ring galaxy a galaxy that resembles a ring about a bright nucleus. Ring galaxies are believed to have been formed as a result of a head-on collision of two galaxies.

Ring Nebula (NGC 6720 & M57) a planetary nebula whose hollow sphere has the shape of a ring. Located in the constellation Lyra, some 700 parsecs away, the Ring Nebula appears as a glowing disk resembling Uranus as seen through a large telescope. The Ring is easily located, standing about 45% of the distance from Beta to Gamma Lyrae and slightly south of a line joining them. Probably the best-known planetary nebula in the heavens, the Ring was discovered in 1779 by the French astronomer Antoine Darquier, of Toulouse.

ring system a system of huge numbers of individual small particles orbiting a planet in its equatorial plane. Jupiter, Saturn, Uranus, and Neptune have ring systems. Three credible origins have been suggested for the phenomenon: (a) It is the debris of a former satellite. (b) It was produced when a body passed within the Roche limit and fragmented due to the tidal stress that resulted. (c) It formed from the same material that produced the planetary satellites, but the material never accreted inside the Roche limit and was left stranded. See ROCHE LIMIT.

Ring Tail Galaxy (NGC 4038) a spiral galaxy of rather peculiar structure—it resembles an inverted question mark—sometimes regarded as a gravitationally interacting pair of galaxies or an actual collisional system resulting from a collision of two galaxies. It is located west southwest from Gamma Corvi. Like many other peculiar galaxies, the Ring Tail is a source of radio radiation, first detected in 1957.

Riphaean Mountains a conspicuous mountain range in the Mare Nubium, at -8° S and -27° W, in the third quadrant of the near side of the moon.

rising the daily appearance on the observer's horizon of a planet, star, or moon, resulting from the rotation of Earth. The celestial body disappears from view below the horizon during the next 24 hours. At intermediate latitudes, circumpolar stars never set, and some—in the corresponding area about the opposite pole—never rise.

R Leonis one of the brightest of the long-period variables known: the average period for R Leonis is 312 days. This star is the fourth of its type to be discovered—the others are Omicron Ceti, Chi Cygni, and R Hydrae. It was discovered in 1782, by J.A. Koch, of Danzig. A pulsating red giant of the Mira class, R Leonis sometimes rises to 5th magnitude at maximum and usually declines to 10th or fainter at minimum. It is noted for the peculiar intensity of its red light, which is best described as a rosy scarlet with a touch of purple. R Leonis, in the Leo constellation, is located 5° west of Regulus and 600 light-years from Earth. The actual luminosity of the star at maximum appears to be in the range of 200 to 260 times that of the sun, and the absolute magnitude at peak brightness approaches -1.

R Leporis a Mira-type variable star in Lepus. It was first seen, in the Lepus constellation, by English astronomer John Russell Hind (1823–1895) and is so red that it is called Hind's Crimson Star. The color of the star is an intense smoky red, described by various observers as resembling a glowing coal or an illuminated drop of blood. R Leporis is about 1500 light-years from Earth. Its magnitude varies from 5.9 to 11, and its period averages 432 days. At maximum the star may rise to nearly naked-eye visibility.

R Monocerotis (NGC 2261) a variable star in the southern constellation Monoceros, east of Orion and northwest of the Rosette Nebula. R Monocerotis has a magnitude of 10 to 12, an irregular period, and a luminosity 15 times that of the sun. It is enveloped by Hubble's Variable Nebula, the first object to be photographed with the 200-inch reflecting telescope at the Palomar Observatory. R Monocerotis was discovered in 1783 by English astronomer William Herschel (1738–1822). Hubble's Variable Nebula is rather comet-like in form, and R Monocerotis is located near the nebula's southern tip. The star, very often difficult to observe and often lost in the bright bluish glow of the nebula, is a strong emitter of infrared radiation. It is thought that R Monocerotis may be a protoplanetary system—a star embedded in a dense cloud of a nebula. See HUBBLE'S VARIABLE NEBULA.

Roche limit or **tidal stability limit** the minimum distance possible between a planet and a satellite that holds itself together by its own gravity. Below this distance, a moon orbiting a planet or other celestial body would be disrupted by tidal forces, or the moon would not have formed in the first place.

The Roche limit is approximately 2.5 planetary radii from the center, and tides at lesser distances are stronger than the mutual gravitational attraction between the two adjacent orbiting objects. Fragments are not likely to accrete, or assemble themselves, into a larger object below the Roche limit. If the orbit of an existing satellite brings it within its planet's Roche limit, tidal forces will pull the satellite apart.

Roche lobe the volume of space a star controls gravitationally within a binary system.

Roche surface the outer boundary of the volume of space that a star's gravity can control within a binary system.

rocket a vehicle or projectile powered by an engine that develops thrust by its reaction to the jet of hot gases it produces. (The term also refers to the rocket engine itself.) The principle of operation of a rocket engine stems directly from Newton's Third Law of Motion: For every action there is an equal and opposite reaction.

Rocketry appears to have been invented by the Chinese for use as the so-called fire arrows they directed at the Tartars during the siege of Kaifeng. From the 13th century on, there is mention in military histories of the martial use of rockets—they were used, for example, by the British in the War of 1812. In 1926, American rocket scientist Robert Goddard (1885–1945) launched the first liquid propellant rocket. In 1944 and 1945, V-2 missiles developed by German rocket scientist Wernher von Braun (1912–1977) were launched against England and targets on the Continent. These 46-foot long rockets, with a range of 200 miles, were the vehicles from which modern space travel developed. Examples of rockets used as launch vehicles by NASA include the Redstone, Atlas, Titan, and Saturn V.

rocket propellant (RP) any agent used for consumption or combustion in a rocket or spacecraft and from which the vehicle derives its thrust. Typical liquid rocket propellants are the fuel dimethyl hydrazine and the oxidizer nitrogen tetroxide. These liquids ignite on contact and are used with catalysts, substances that change the rate of a chemical reaction but do not themselves undergo change. See OXIDIZER.

rocketry the science of rocket design, including theory, research, development, experimentation, and application. See ROCKET.

Roemer, Olaus (1644–1710) Danish astronomer who, in 1675, determined the finite velocity of light through his observations of the time variations in the eclipse of Jupiter's satellites. He later devised the first practical transit instrument.

roll **1.** the rotational or oscillatory movement of a spacecraft about the longitudinal axis of the body;

2. the act of rolling;

3. the amount of this movement, that is, the angle of roll, indicating the position or orientation of a spacecraft, expressed in terms of its axes and a line or plane of reference.

The three axes of a space vehicle are the lateral, vertical, and longitudinal axes. Rotations of the vehicle relative to these are called, respectively, pitch (up and down movement), yaw (side-to-side movement), and roll (spinning movement or rotational movement about the longitudinal axis).

roll axis the longitudinal axis through a spacecraft about which the body can roll.

rolling plains the type of terrain found on about 65% of the surface of Venus. These upland rolling plains have elevations that lie within about 1000 meters of the average planetary radius. Radar studies reveal that they contain many circular features that range from 20 to 800 km across. Depending on their precise forms, as indicated by radar, some are thought to be impact craters, and others appear to be volcanoes.

Rook Mountains or **Montes Rook** a mountain range on the moon's far side, located at -10° S and -93° E, forming the north border of Mare Orientale.

Rosette Nebula a relatively large but difficult to locate emission nebula in the southern constellation Monoceros, east of Orion. The Rosette Nebula is a complex, wreath-shaped nebula of gas and dust enclosing, in its central zone, a cluster of very bright stars known as NGC 2244. The brightest member, 12 Monocerotis, is a yellow giant of magnitude 5.85. The distance from Earth of the Rosette is about 2600 light-years, giving the cloud an actual diameter of some 55 light-years. The Rosette appears to be one of the most massive nebulae known, with a mass of about 11,000 suns.

Ross 614 a faint but notable binary system, found in the southern constellation Monoceros, about 2° north of the coarse star cluster NGC 2232, and containing two of the smallest stellar masses yet discovered. The star was first detected, in 1927, by American astronomer F.E. Ross, working at the Yerkes Observatory. Ross 614 is a red dwarf with a visual magnitude of 11.1. Lying at a distance of 13.1 light-years from Earth, this is one of the 25 nearest stars known. Ross has an estimated diameter of about a third that of the sun. With a mass of 0.08 that of the sun, Ross 614 B (the companion star) has about 80 times the mass of Jupiter, and a luminosity 1/63,000 that of the sun.

Rotanev the common name for the star Beta Delphinus, a dF3 star, magnitude 3.72. This yellow-white star is located in the small northern constellation Delphinus, between Pegasus and Aquila, at 96 light-years from Earth.

The name Rotanev was given to the star in 1814 by the Italian astronomer Niccolo Cacciatore, assistant to the great astronomer Giuseppe Piazzi at Palermo Observatory. The Latinized form of Cacciatore, meaning hunter, is Venator. Spell Venator backwards and you have Rotanev, making Cacciatore the only person to name a star after himself and get away with it. For an additional example of Cacciatore's interesting practice of naming stars, see DELPHINUS.

rotation 1. the movement or path of a planet or other celestial object on its axis;

2. one complete turn of a planet or other celestial object. All stars (suns) rotate, but their rates of rotation vary. Our sun rotates on its axis every 28 days.

Rover see LUNAR ROVING VEHICLE.

Rowton meteorite the only iron meteorite known to have fallen on England, in 1876. It weighs 3.5 kg (7 pounds, 11 ounces).

Royal Star the very bright star Regulus, in the northern constellation Leo (the Lion), between Cancer and Virgo. The Royal Star marks the Lion's heart, where Ptolemy located it. See REGULUS.

r-process reactions the rapid reactions believed to occur inside supernovae, in which heavy elements are formed as atomic nuclei capture neutrons.

RR Lyrae star or **short-period cepheid** or **cluster variable** one of a group of pulsating variable stars in the halo of the Milky Way that have periods between 1.2 and 30 hours. All these stars have approximately the same luminosity, making them useful for measuring celestial distances.

Rucha a common name for Delta Cassiopei, a type A5V star, 43 light-years from Earth. It may possibly be an eclipsing binary. Rucha also is called Ruchbah and Ksora.

Rule the common name for the southern constellation Norma, in the Milky Way between Lupus and Ara. In old star maps the constellation was shown as *Norma et Regula*, as a reflection of its appearance—a draftsman's set-square and rule—and its location, next to the Compasses (Circinus constellation) and a builder's level (Triangulum Australe constellation).

Rümker a semi-ruined crater—its appearance damaged by meteorite impacts—on the Sinus Roris, in the second quadrant of the face of the moon, at +40° N and -57° W. Its diameter is about 40 kilometers. The lunar crater is also called Rümker Plateau.

runaway star a young star that is traveling rapidly away from a region of recent star formation. This type of star could have originated through its ejection from a nearby binary system when its companion star underwent a supernova explosion. Examples of runaway stars include AE Aurigae, 53 Arietis, Mu Columbae, and Barnard's Runaway Star.

Runaway Star, Barnard's a faint red dwarf in the large constellation Ophiuchus, south of Hercules. It is famous for having the greatest apparent motion—proper motion—of any known star. It was discovered in 1916 by American astronomer Edward Emerson Barnard (1857–1923) through a comparison of photographic plates. Its magnitude is 11.3 and its luminosity is about 1/2500 that of the sun. This fairly cool star has a surface temperature of about 3200 K. At a distance of 6 light-years from Earth, it is the second nearest star to our solar system. Only the Alpha Centauri triple star system is closer. See BARNARD'S STAR.

rupes the ridges or cliffs found on planetary surfaces, for example, Argyre Rupes and Olympus Rupes on Mars, and Adventare Rupes and Santa Maria Rupes on Mercury.

Russell-Vogt theorem the theory that the equilibrium structure of a star is determined by its mass and chemical composition.

RV Tauri variables a small group of highly luminous, pulsating variable stars that have enormous atmospheres of gas that emit infrared radiation. Most are yellow or orange supergiant stars. Examples include RV Tauri, R Sagittae, and R Scuti.

RW Aurigae variables a subclass of very young stars, also called *nebular variables* and *T Tauri stars*. Almost all these variables are yellow dwarfs, and very few are brighter than 10th magnitude at maximum.

S

Sabaea Terra or **Terra Sabaea** a dark surface feature, 2200 km in diameter, on Mars, in an area of heavily cratered terrain at latitude 0° to -20° and longitude 3° to 348°, in the southern hemisphere, near the Martian equator. The area is also called *Sinus Sabaeus*.

Sabik the common name for the white-green star Eta Ophiuchi, situated in the Water Jar of the large equatorial constellation Ophiuchus, south of Hercules. Sabik, meaning the receding one, is a close double, both components being whitish green, 69 light-years from Earth. Sabik's luminosity is about 40 times that of the sun, and its orbital period is 84 years.

Sabine a 31-km crater on Mare Tranquillitatis, at +2° N and +20° E, in the 1st quadrant of the moon's near side. Sabine has an almost identical twin crater, Ritter, which is close by.

Sadalachbia the common name for the white star Gamma Aquarii, in the large southern constellation Aquarius, near the celestial equator, between Pisces and Aquila. This star has a magnitude of 3.97 at a distance of 86 light-years from Earth.

Sadalmelik or **Sadal Melik** a common name for the brightest star, magnitude 2.93, in Aquarius. This red star, 1080 light-years from Earth, and also called Alpha Aquarii, is situated on the right shoulder of Aquarius, near the celestial equator, between Pisces and Aquila.

Sadalsud the common name for the star Beta Aquarii, situated in the left shoulder of the southern constellation Aquarius, near the celestial equator, between Pisces and Aquila. This pale yellow star was aptly named—Sadalsud means luckiest of the lucky—by early astronomers, who took its rising to signify that winter had passed. Sadalsud, 1100 light-years from Earth, is a supergiant with a magnitude of 3.07.

Sadr or **Sador** the common name, meaning hen's breast, for the yellow-white star Gamma Cygni, magnitude 2.23. This star, 815 light-years from Earth, is part of the northern constellation Cygnus, the Swan, lying in the Milky Way, between Draco and Pegasus. Cygnus X-1 lies nearby.

Sagitta (Sge) the Arrow or Cupid's Arrow, a faint but distinctive northern constellation between Aquila and Cygnus. Although the stars of Sagitta are not bright—it is the third smallest constellation in the sky and has no stars brighter than 4th magnitude—the pattern is easy to locate and does suggest an arrow. Sagitta can be found by looking just north of Altair.

Sagittarius (Sgr) the Archer, a zodiacal constellation in the Southern Hemisphere, between Scorpius and Capricorn. The name Archer dates from Mesopotamian mythology, and its bright stars include Rukbat (Alpha Sagittarii, the archer's knee) and Arkab (Beta Sagittarii, the tendon). The star group also contains many nebulae and deep-sky objects, including the Omega Nebula, Lagoon Nebula, Horsehead Nebula, and the Trifid Nebula.

Sagittarius A a powerful radio source located at the core of the Milky Way—its brightest part, beyond which lies the center of our galaxy—in the large southern constellation Sagittarius.

Sagittarius B2 a dark cloud of gas and dust near the center of the Milky Way, in the same part as Sagittarius A.

Saiph the Sword, a common name for Kappa Orionis and hardly appropriate for its position in Orion's right foot. It is a blue-white star of magnitude 2.05, found in the equatorial constellation Orion, near Taurus, and 1826 light-years from Earth. See ORION.

Sakigake a probe launched in 1985 by Japan's Institute of Space and Astronautical Science (ISAS) to fly by Halley's Comet on March 11, 1986, as well as to study solar wind and cometary interaction.

Salyut a series of USSR space stations. Salyut 1 was launched in April of 1971, and the program ended with Salyut 7 eleven years later. In addition to serving as platforms for terrestrial and astrophysical observations, the Salyuts were used to perform medical, biological, and technological experiments. The Salyuts were operated by cosmonauts from countries affiliated with the USSR as well as by USSR cosmonauts.

There were crews aboard Salyuts for a total of about 2 years, boarding the space stations from Soyuz spacecraft through a docking port at each end of the 15-meter, 19-ton structures. Cargo and fuel were ferried to the station by a series of unmanned Progress spacecraft, which were designed to carry 1 ton of fuel and 1.3 tons of cargo and dock with Salyut 6 and 7. Reloaded with discarded articles and undocked, the Progress craft were destroyed on reentry into Earth's atmosphere. Salyut 6 flights included 5 endurance missions for crews, lasting from 75 days to 185 days. Salyut 7 had three manned missions, the longest of which lasted for 238 days. See SOYEZ.

S Andromedae a supernova that was observed in 1885 in the Andromeda Galaxy and was visible to the naked eye. It was the first extragalactic supernova to be detected.

Sappho a large volcanic crater on Venus that is about 250 km across. It is located on an elevated region of highlands at 13° N and 27° W, northwest of Aphrodite Terra and southeast of Maxwell Montes and Ishtar Terra.

Sargas the common name for the red star Theta Scorpii, situated in the tail of the Scorpion. With a magnitude of 1.87, Sargas is the southernmost of the bright stars in the southern constellation Scorpius, which lies between Sagittarius and Libra. See ANTARES.

Sarin the common name for the star Delta Herculis. Sarin is a white star with an apparent magnitude of 3.2, in the northern constellation Hercules, near Lyra and Corona Borealis.

saros or **saros cycle** an eclipse cycle of about 18 years—6585.32 days, almost the same length as 223 synodical months. At the end of each saros, the sun, moon, and line of nodes return to approximately the same positions relative to Earth that they held about 18 years earlier, giving a general indication of the time when an eclipse is due and that another series of eclipses will begin that closely resembles the series just completed. Each time a new saros begins, the eclipses occur about 115° west from where they were at the start of the previous saros. See LINE OF NODES, ECLIPSE, and SYNODIC PERIOD.

saros cycle see SAROS.

satellite (artificial) a man-made object or spacecraft that revolves about a spatial body, such as Explorer I orbiting Earth. NASA divides its satellites into major categories: (a) *scientific satellites*, which carry instruments to measure magnetic fields, space radiation, or solar characteristics, or carry telescopes for particular uses—Explorer, Skylab, Mariner, etc. (b) *application satellites*, which forecast weather, survey Earth resources, or extend communications—Tiros, Nimbus, Telstar, and Landsat.

satellite (natural) an attendant body that revolves about another body, called the *primary*, for example, a moon or other celestial body that orbits a planet or sun.

satellite galaxy a small galaxy that lies close to a larger galaxy.

satelloid a vehicle that revolves about Earth or other celestial body, but at an altitude so low that it requires sustaining thrust to withstand the attraction of gravity and therefore remain in place.

Saturn the second largest planet in our galaxy and the sixth planet from the sun. Saturn has the largest known ring system and, with at least 23 moons, the largest known satellite system. Because Saturn spins so fast, it is flattened at its poles. Its atmosphere has hydrogen, methane, and helium as major constituents and contains regions of belts and zones. The planet emits radio waves, and thick and constantly moving clouds completely envelop the planet. Ovals resembling Jupiter's large storm areas are visible. Strong, high-speed winds blow, especially at the equator, and auroras occur near the poles. Saturn was visited by Pioneer 1 and Voyager 1 and 2. See PIONEER PROBES, SATURN'S ATMOSPHERE, and VOYAGER.

Saturnian system the planet Saturn and its moons. See SATURN'S SATELLITE SYSTEM.

Saturn Nebula (NGC 7009) a small but bright planetary nebula found in the southern constellation Aquarius, near Pisces and Aquila. The nebula has handle-like protuberances give it an appearance resembling that of Saturn.

saturnographic referring to positions on Saturn measured in latitude from Saturn's equator and in longitude from a reference meridian.

Saturn rockets a group of large United States rockets designed for manned spaceflights.

Saturn 1—10, liquid propellant, height 58 meters, weight 528,440 kg with payload, length 25 meters, diameter 6.6 meters. All 10 flights, 1961 to 1965—designed to test the rocket's performance and study the effects of micrometeoroids on the spacecraft—were completed successfully.

Saturn 1 Uprated, liquid propellant, height 68 meters, weight 589,676 kg plus payload of up to 18,143 kg, length 24 meters, diameter 6.6 meters. Saturn 1B, 1966 to 1975, was developed to test Apollo hardware in orbit. Four tests were flown between 1965 and 1968. Saturn 1B also launched Skylabs 2, 3, and 4 in 1973 and the Apollo-Soyuz Test Project in 1975.

Saturn V, liquid propellant, height 111 meters with payload, weight 2,766,942 kg plus payload of up to 129,275 kg, length 42 meters, diameter 10 meters. Saturn V, 12 successful flights from 1967 to 1973, was the launch vehicle developed for the Apollo lunar missions. It was last used on May 14, 1973, to lift the unmanned Skylab space station into Earth orbit. See Fig. 78.

Saturn's atmosphere similar in many ways to Jupiter's atmosphere—it has belts, zones, and spots—but lacks the color contrast observed in Jupiter. Its cloud layers lie deeper in its atmosphere than do Saturn's. Voyager 1 and Voyager 2 detected a few circulating ovals, storms in high-pressure regions of Saturn's atmosphere. The ovals circulate in a direction opposite to the direction of low-pressure storms on Earth.

The major gases of Saturn's atmosphere are helium, hydrogen, and methane. Saturnian winds range from about 50 mph in the westward direction to nearly 100 mph in the eastward direction. Saturn's three

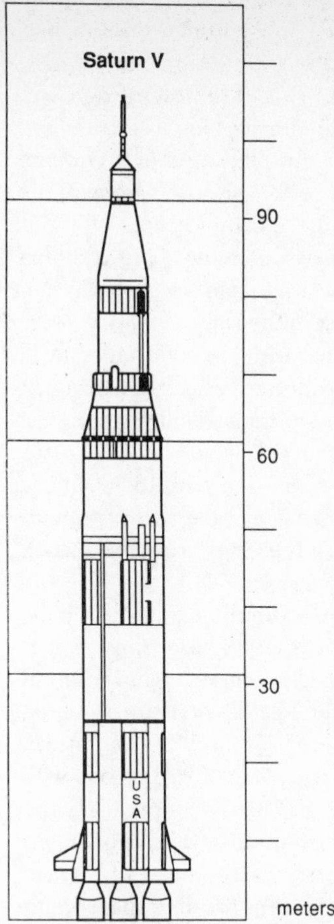

Fig. 78. **Saturn V rocket.** This imposing rocket, standing over 100 meters tall with payload, is one of the large rockets used for manned NASA spaceflights. See the entry for Saturn rockets.

cloud layers—in order from top to bottom—are composed of ices of ammonia, ammonium hydrosulfide, and water, and they are farther apart than Jupiter's. The is because Jupiter has a stronger gravity.

Saturn's guardian satellites also referred to as coorbital satellites and as new satellites, a number of minor satellites of Saturn, at present thought to number as many as fifteen. Voyager 1 photographed six tiny moons that had never been seen before. Voyagers 1 and 2 did not obtain quality images of any of Saturn's guardian satellites, but showed enough detail to enable scientists to learn that they have rough surfaces, are irregular in shape, and are heavily cratered. Satellites 10 and 11, called the coorbitals, share an orbit 91,000 km above Saturn's cloud tops. Little is known about satellites 12 through 15, aside from their orbits and periods. Satellite 12 orbits at the same distance from Saturn as Dione, at a point about 60° ahead of Dione. Satellites 13 and 14, outside and inside the thin F ring, respectively, appear to herd this ring between them. Satellite 15 appears to limit the outer edge of the A ring in a similar manner. See DIONE, SATURN'S RING SYSTEM, and SATURN'S SATELLITE SYSTEM.

Saturn's magnitude Saturn is not of equal brightness at every opposition. Much depends on the angle at which the ring system is presented, since the rings have an albedo higher than that of the globe. When the rings appear wide open to observers on Earth, the magnitude attains -0.3, making Saturn brighter than any star apart from Sirius and Canopus. When the rings are seen edge-on, the opposition magnitude is only +0.8. See ALBEDO.

Saturn's ring system a system of innumerable icy particles orbiting Saturn, with an overall diameter of 273,000 km. The rings are tilted at nearly 27° to Saturn's orbital plane. Four rings are now recognized: ring D (innermost and faintest), ring C (the Crepe ring, so called because of its milky transparency against the blackness of space and because it appears to be a dusky veil when seen against the globe of the planet), ring B (brightest), and ring A (outermost and second brightest). (The last three of these rings are discussed below.) The 2600-km gap between rings A and B is called *Cassini's division*. *Encke's division* in ring A is a ripple rather than a true break in the rings.

Saturn's A ring the outermost ring, measuring 169,000 miles from one side to the other. It is bright, though not as reflective as ring B. Within it is Encke's division, which seems to be a genuine gap, even though it is much less prominent than Cassini's division.

Saturn's B ring located inside Cassini's division and 16,000 miles wide. It is the brightest of the rings and has a reflective power, or albedo, greater than that of Saturn. Where the rings cross the planet, they produce a strong shadow.

Saturn's C ring 10,000 miles wide and extending to within 9000 miles of the planet's surface. The Crepe ring, or Dusky ring, as it is called, is transparent and may be seen as a hazy, darkish band where it crosses the disk. See ENCKE'S DIVISION and CASSINI'S DIVISION.

Saturn's satellite system the main group of 17 satellites of Saturn, which include a wide variety of objects—from Titan, a large moon with a substantial, haze-filled atmosphere; to Enceladus, which has the highest albedo of any object in the solar system; to several tiny moons invisible from Earth. All of the moons except Phoebe have a prograde orbit. Mimas, the closest major satellite to Saturn, has an impact crater covering more than a quarter of the 380-km diameter of the entire moon. Nowhere else in the solar system has such a disproportionately large feature been seen. See ALBEDO, TETHYS, MIMAS, ENCELADUS, DIONE, and RHEA.

scan see RADAR SCAN.

scanner a radar mechanism for directing a searching radar beam through space and imparting target information to an indicator. See RADAR.

scanning the motion of a radar antenna assembly when searching for a target.

scarp 1. a steep descent or slope, especially the lines of cliffs found on Mercury, Earth, Mars, and the moon;

2. a lunar escarpment or cliff extending along the edge of a plateau.

Typical lunar scarps include the Straight Wall, the Apennine Scarp, and the Altai Scarp. See ALTAI SCARP, APENNINES, and STRAIGHT WALL.

scattering the phenomenon of random deflections experienced by light waves passing through an irregular medium. Scattering in Earth's atmosphere is the explanation for why stars appear to twinkle.

Sceptrum also called 53 Eridani. Sceptrum is an orange star in the southern constellation Eridanus, near Orion, and has an apparent magnitude of 4.0.

Scheat the common name, meaning shoulder of the winged horse, for the star Beta Pegasi, situated in the left foreleg of the northern constellation Pegasus, near Aquarius and Andromeda. Scheat is an orange M2II-type star, varying between 2.4 and 1.7 magnitude and lying 210 light-years from Earth.

Schedar or **Schedir** the common name, meaning breast, for the star Alpha Cassiopei. Schedar is a K0II orange giant, magnitude 2.22, and is one of the two brightest stars in the northern constellation Cassiopeia, near Cepheus and Camelopardalis. Schedar is 147 light-years from Earth.

Scheddi see DENEB ALGEDI.

Schedir see SCHEDAR.

Schiaparelli, Giovanni (1835–1910) Italian astronomer who discovered Hesperia (Asteroid 1861), observed numerous double stars, and studied the terrestrial planets, especially Mars. In 1877 he remarked upon the so-called canali. His Mars work was epoch-making, earning from astronomer Percival Lowell the epithet *Columbus of a new planetary world*. Schiaparelli made pioneer observations of Uranus and observed certain markings on Mercury and Venus. See PERCIVAL LOWELL and MARTIAN CANALS.

Schickard a walled plain, 134 miles in diameter, in the 3rd quadrant of the moon's near side, at -44° S and -53° W. Schickard is one of the largest plains on the moon's surface.

Schirra, Walter M., Jr. (1923–) American astronaut who flew aboard Mercury 8 (1962), Gemini 6 (1965), and Apollo 7 (1968). His 6-orbit flight aboard Mercury 8 proved to be the smoothest of any flight in the Project Mercury program.

Schrodinger a lunar walled plain near the great Schrodinger Valley and not visible from Earth because it is on the far side of the moon, at 75° S and 133° E. It was first photographed by the Orbiter unmanned probes.

Schrodinger Valley a great valley at 47° N and 133° E on the far side of the moon—therefore not visible from Earth.

Schroter effect a difference of at least a day or two often observed between the theoretical and observed phases of Venus when it is at dichotomy (half-phase). This phenomenon is probably due to the effects of the atmosphere of Venus. It was first observed in the 1790s by German amateur astronomer Johann Hieronymus Schröter (1745–1816).

Schroter Valley a great winding valley extending 120 miles long, 2 to 5 miles wide, and 500 to 4500 feet deep from the crater Herodotus, at +2° N and -7° W in the 2nd quadrant of the moon's near side.

Schubert a 160-km diameter crater south of Chekhov, in the southern hemisphere of the planet Mercury. See CHEKHOV.

Schwarzschild limit the computed maximum density for a celestial body to exist in its present form. If density exceeds this limit, the body will collapse and become a black hole. See BLACK HOLE.

Schwarzschild radius the radius of a collapsing celestial body at which it will become a black hole. See BLACK HOLE.

Schwassmann-Wachmann 1 a comet noted for its nearly circular orbit between Jupiter and Saturn as well as for its sudden brightenings.

scientific notation a method for expressing very large or very small numbers by using powers of 10. For example, 6 trillion miles may be written as 6×10^{12} miles, and 1/100 as 10^{-2}.

scintar any radio source that shows the effects of interplanetary scintillation. This property distinguishes quasars and radio stars from radio galaxies and nebulae.

scintillation the rapid variation in apparent position, brightness, or color of a distant luminous object viewed through the atmosphere, for example, the twinkling of the stars and to a lesser extent of planets due to the uneven refraction of light in areas of different density in Earth's atmosphere. The changes in density are related to effects of weather.

Scorpio see SCORPIUS.

Scorpius or **Scorpio** (Sco) the Scorpion, a conspicuous zodiacal constellation in the Southern Hemisphere between Sagittarius and Libra. The sun appears in Scorpius each year from about November 23 to November 30. In early astronomy Scorpius was the largest constellation. Later on, Libra was formed from its claws. The brightest star of Scorpius is Antares (Alpha Scorpii), a red supergiant of the first magnitude. The other stars of Scorpius include Acrab (Beta Scorpii, a trinary), Dschubba, Lesath, and Shaula.

Scorpius X-1 the first cosmic X-ray source to be discovered. It was discovered during the journey of a sounding rocket—one that breaks through the atmosphere into space for only a few minutes—from

White Sands, New Mexico, in June of 1962.

scrub to cancel or postpone, for example, a scheduled spacecraft launch or part of a space mission.

Sculptor (Scl) a southern constellation between Phoenix and Cetus, originally called *l'Atelier du Sculpteur*, meaning the sculptor's workshop. It contains no very bright stars but can be located by first finding Fomalhaut, then looking eastward. The constellation Sculptor was named by French astronomer Nicolas de Lacaille during 1751 and 1752. See FOMALHAUT.

Sculptor galaxy or **Sculptor-type system** a very small elliptical galaxy discovered in 1976 as a new member of the so-called Local Group of galaxies, the cluster of galaxies of which our own Milky Way is a member. The Sculptor galaxy lies at a distance of 85 kpc, in the southern constellation Sculptor.

Scutum (Sct) the Shield, a small, faint southern constellation, the 5th smallest in the sky, introduced by Polish astronomer Johannes Hevelius in 1684 under the name Scutum Sobiescianum, or Sobieski's Shield. Scutum, which contains a small, very bright star cloud, lies just north of Sagittarius and east of Aquila. The constellation was considered to be the coat of arms of John Sobieski III (1624–1696), the king of Poland who defeated the Turks in 1683. Scutum contains a cluster of stars called the Wild Duck cluster, because its fan shape suggests a flight of ducks.

sealed cabin the occupied space of a spacecraft characterized by walls designed to prevent gaseous exchange between the inner atmosphere and its surrounding atmosphere and containing its own mechanism for maintenance of the inside atmosphere.

Sea of Humors see MARE HUMORUM.

Sea of Showers see MARE IMBRIUM.

seas see LUNAR MARIA, MARIA.

season any one of the four divisions of the year with climatic changes influenced by the tilt of Earth's axis.

seasonal changes on Mars the changes in shape and darkness of the dusky patches on Mars from summer to winter and year to year. These changes formerly were thought to indicate Martian vegetation, but are now known to result from the blowing of dust deposits on the planet surface.

second a celestial body revolving around another body, its *primary*. An example is the moon revolving around Earth.

secondary atmosphere the gases outgassed from a planet's interior. They are usually rich in carbon dioxide. See OUTGASSING.

secular perturbations the changes in the orbit of a planet or satellite that operate in extremely long cycles.

seeing the viewing quality or steadiness of the images obtained in astronomical observations. For example, if the stars are twinkling a lot, the observation is termed "poor seeing." In "good seeing," the sky will appear steady. *Seeing* is also called *astronomical seeing* and *seeing conditions*.

Segin the common name for Epsilon Cassiopei, a blue-white star of magnitude 3.37. Segin, in the W-shaped northern constellation Cassiopeia, between Cepheus and Camelopardalis, is 520 light-years from Earth.

seismic waves the vibrations that travel through the interior of Earth due to seismic quakes.

seismology 1. the study of earthquakes and the conditions that produce them, and of the internal structure of Earth;

2. the study of small changes in the radial velocity of the sun as a whole.

seleno- a combining form from the Greek word meaning moon.

selenocentric relating to the center of the moon.

selenographic 1. pertaining to the physical geography of the moon;

2. referring to the positions of the moon measured in latitude from the moon's equator and in longitude from a reference meridian.

selenology the branch of astronomy that deals with the moon, its magnitude, motion, etc.

Seleucus a terraced walled crater about 51 km in diameter, on Oceanus Procellarum, in the second quadrant of the face of the moon, at +21° N and -67° W. Its central hill is 7500 feet high.

semidiameter 1. the radius of a closed figure;

2. half the angle at the observer that is subtended by the visible disk of a celestial body.

semidiurnal having a period of, occurring in, or related to approximately half a day.

semimajor axis one-half the longest diameter of an ellipse.

semiminor axis one-half the shortest diameter of an ellipse.

semiregular variable a pulsating giant star or supergiant star.

separation 1. the angular distance (measured in degrees, minutes, and seconds of arc) between components of a double star;

2. the action of a fall-away section or companion body as it casts off from the remaining body of a spacecraft;

3. the action of the remaining spacecraft as it leaves a fall-away section behind it.

separation velocity 1. the velocity at which a space vehicle is moving when some part or section is separated from it;

2. the velocity of a space probe or satellite at the time of separation from the launch vehicle.

September equinox 1. the time when the sun crosses the plane of Earth's equator, making day and night of equal duration all over Earth and occurring about September 22;

2. also called *autumnal point*, the position of the sun at the time of the autumnal equinox.

Serpens (Ser) the Serpent, a constellation thought to represent a huge snake held by the constellation Ophiuchus. It consists of two parts separated from one another, *Serpens Caput*, the head, and *Serpens Cauda*, the tail. Ophiucus, the Serpent Bearer, lies on the celestial equator, between the head and the tail. Serpens contains the Eagle Nebula, and its brightest star is the giant K2 star Unakalhai, Alpha Serpentis, the serpent's neck. See OPHIUCHUS.

Serpentarius an obsolete name for the Ophiuchus constellation.

SETI the search for extraterrestrial intelligence, usually applied to searches for radio signals from other civilizations.

Seven Sisters see PLEIADES.

Sextans (Sex) the Sextant, a small equatorial constellation just south of Regulus, between Hydra and Leo. Sextans was named by astronomer Johannes Hevelius (1611–1687) to commemorate his large sextant, used by him from 1658 to 1679, to chart the heavens. His sextant was destroyed in a fire.

sextant a double-reflecting astronomical instrument used for measuring angular distances, especially the altitudes of celestial bodies.

sextant altitude the altitude of a celestial body as actually measured with a sextant.

Seyfert galaxy any of a group of spiral galaxies having bright, compact nuclei. They characteristically have broad emission lines, suggesting the presence of very hot gases in violent motion at their centers. The nearest bright Seyfert to Earth is NGC 4151. See BARRED GALAXY.

shadow darkness or shade in a region, caused by an obstruction between a source of light and the region, for example, when the moon stands between the sun and Earth, preventing part of the sun's light from reaching a region on Earth. The darkest part of a shadow, in which light is completely cut off, is called the *umbra*. The lighter part surrounding the umbra, in which the light is only partly cut off, is called the *penumbra*. See Fig. 65.

shadow bands the light and dark bands that appear to sweep across the surface of Earth in the minutes before and after totality during a solar eclipse. These bands are caused by irregularities in Earth's upper atmosphere. See TOTALITY.

Sham a common name for the blue-white star Alpha Sagittarii, the brightest star in the southern constellation Sagittarius, near Scorpius and Capricornis. Sham, 250 light-years from Earth, is a B9 star with an apparent magnitude of 4.11.

Shaula the common name for the star Lambda Scorpii, part of the southern constellation Scorpius, near Libra and Sagittarius. Shaula is a B1V star, 325 light-years from Earth, and has a magnitude of 1.62.

Shedir a common name for the orange star Alpha Cassiopeiae. See SCHEDAR.

Sheliak the common name for Beta Lyrae, in the northern constellation Lyra, between Cygnus and Hercules. Sheliak, an eclipsing binary of magnitude 3.38–4.36, lies 1300 light-years from Earth.

shell galaxies any of the elliptical galaxies around which lie extremely faint, incomplete rings of light.

shell star a hot main sequence star showing bright emission lines superimposed on its normal emission spectrum and thought to be caused by a sphere or shell of gas around the star.

Shepard, Alan (1923–) astronaut, the first American in space. He made the first manned Mercury flight (suborbital) in 1961. Shepard later commanded the Apollo 14 lunar landing in 1971. See APOLLO SPACECRAFT.

shepherd satellite **1.** an informal term—along with *shepherd moon* and *guardian moon*—for a satellite that is thought to maintain the structure of a planetary ring through its close gravitational influence;

2. either of the two Saturn satellites, Prometheus and Pandora, that orbit just inside and outside of the F ring;

3. either of the two shepherd moons, Cordelia and Ophelia, situated on either side of the E ring in the Uranian system.

Sheratan the common name for the white star Beta Arietis, found in the northern constellation Aries, near Taurus and Pisces. Sheratan is Arabic for sign. It marked the vernal equinox at the time of the Greek astronomer Hipparchus (2nd century BC), who discovered the precession of the equinoxes. Sheratan, magnitude 2.65, is 52 light-years from Earth. See PRECESSION.

Shield the common name for the constellation Scutum. See SCUTUM.

shield volcano a type of broad volcano built up through the repeated nonexplosive eruption of fluid basalts to form a low dome or shield shape, often with a large caldera at the summit. Examples include the

Hawaiian volcanoes on Earth and the Tharsis volcanoes on Mars. See CALDERA and THARSIS RIDGE.

Ship the common name for the constellation Argo. See ARGO.

shock wave or **shock** a surface or region of abrupt change in pressure or density moving as a wave front at or above the velocity of sound through which a fluid undergoes a marked decrease in velocity accompanied by a marked increase in pressure, density, temperature, and entropy. See ENTROPY.

shooting star another name for meteor. The phenomenon is actually caused by a meteor falling through Earth's atmosphere.

shoran *acronym for sho*rt-*ra*nge *n*avigation, a precise electronic position-fixing system used to determine the position of an aircraft. Aboard the aircraft are a pulse transmitter and receiver, and two transponder beacons are positioned at fixed points on Earth. The time it takes for signals to be sent from the transmitter and return to the receiver enables a navigator to determine the aircraft's position.

short-period cepheid see RR LYRAE STAR.

short-period comet any comet with a revolution period of less than 200 years. The comets or bits of these comets lie completely within the solar system. Examples are ENCKE COMET, HALLEY'S COMET, and GIACOBINI-ZIMMER COMET.

shower (of meteors) numerous meteors that appear to radiate during the same time period from a given point in the sky. Such showers usually occur when the Earth passes through collections of meteoric material left in the path of a comet. See also METEOR SHOWER.

shutdown the process of decreasing engine thrust to zero when a vehicle has reached the desired speed.

shuttle see SPACE SHUTTLE.

Sickle of Leo the crescent-shaped star pattern in Leo, whose brightest star is Regulus. Leo, a northern constellation, is near Cancer.

sidereal relating to or measured with reference to the stars.

sidereal hour angle (SHA) the angular distance (0° to 360°) west of the vernal equinox at which a celestial body lies.

sidereal month the average period of revolution of the moon with respect to the stars, a period of 27 days, 7 hours, 43 minutes and 11.5 seconds, or approximately 27-1/3 days. See Fig. 79 and SYNODICAL MONTH.

sidereal period the time taken by a planet or satellite to complete one revolution about its primary—the celestial body nearest the center of a mass of orbiting bodies—as seen from the primary and as referred to a fixed star. Specifically, the interval between two successive returns of

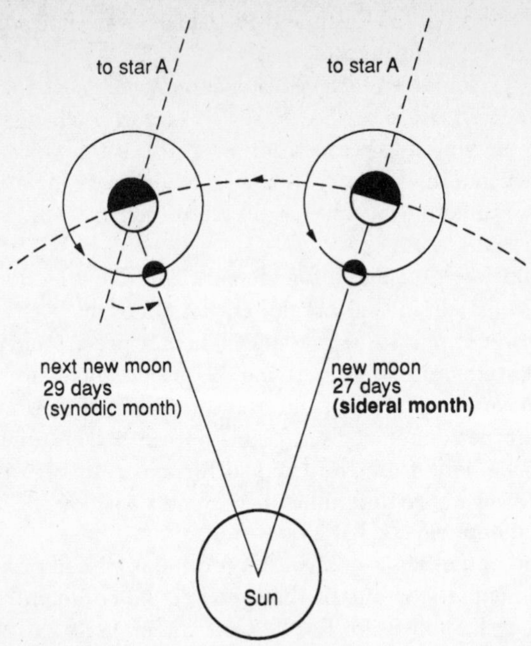

Fig. 79. **Sidereal month.** This depiction of the period of revolution of the moon is shown side-by-side with a depiction of the period of revolution in a *synodic month.*

an Earth satellite in orbit to the same geocentric right ascension. See PRIMARY BODY.

sidereal time time reckoned by the stars; specifically, the hour angle of the vernal equinox, which is equal to the right ascension of objects on the observer's meridian, and thus time based on the rotation of Earth relative to the vernal equinox. Sidereal time may be designated as local or Greenwich, depending on whether the local meridian or the Greenwich meridian is used as the reference.

sidereal year the period of one apparent revolution of Earth around the sun, with respect to the stars, averaging 365 days, 6 hours, 9 minutes, and 9.55 seconds.

siderite an iron-nickel meteorite, also called *iron meteorite*. See METEORITE.

siderolite an old name for a stony-iron meteorite. See STONY-IRON METEORITE.

Sigma Octantis the south polar star, a dim white star in the constellation Octans. It lies within 7° of the south celestial pole.

Sikhote-Aline meteorite the largest observed meteorite fall. This iron meteorite fell in eastern Siberia in 1947. The smoke trail accompanying the meteorite persisted for several hours after the fall and was dense enough to totally obscure the sun or reduce it to a dull red ball in the sky. It has been estimated that the dust cloud contained 200 tons of material, whereas the weight of meteorite fragments collected was 70 tons. At high impact velocities—4 km per second—a meteorite striking soft earth tends to break up, and the fragments and earth produce a crater whose size considerably exceeds the size of the meteorite. The greater the impact speed, the larger the crater produced. The only observed case of the formation of an impact crater is the Sikhote-Aline shower. In the dispersion ellipse of this shower, 122 such craters were found, of which 17 were from 10 to 26.5 meters in diameter.

singularity 1. the mathematical representation of a black hole, the theoretical point at which space and time are infinitely distorted;

2. the object of zero radius into which the matter in a black hole is believed to fall.

Sinope a satellite of Jupiter discovered by American astronomer Seth B. Nicholson (1891–1963) in 1914. Sinope's revolution period is 758 days, and its mean distance from Jupiter is 23,370,000 km (14,521,000 miles).

sinous rille a narrow, winding valley on the moon caused by ancient lava flows along narrow channels.

sinus an apparent lunar bay, usually in a mare. Three examples are Sinus Aestuum, Sinus Iridum, and Sinus Roris.

Sinus Aestuum the Bay of Heats, a lunar feature at +12° N and -9° W, in the 2nd quadrant of the moon, east of the Copernicus Crater and southwest of the Apennine Mountains.

Sinus Iridum the Bay of Rainbows, a lava-flooded lunar bay in the 2nd quadrant of the moon, at +45° N and -32° W, in Mare Imbrium.

Sinus Magaritifer the dark markings on Mars seen in the planet's southern hemisphere at longitude 12° to 45°, latitude -2° to -27°. Sinus Magaritifer has two large regions of dark, broken terrain: Magaritifer Chaos, diameter 430 km; and Magaritifer Terra, diameter 1924 km.

Sinus Medii the Central Bay, a small, dark, irregular plain, 100 miles by 200 miles in area. This lunar feature is near the apparent center of the moon's disk as seen from Earth.

Sinus Roris the Bay of Dews, a mare in the 2nd quadrant of the moon, forming a rectilinear part of Oceanus Procellarum at +54° N and -46° W.

Sinus Sabaeus 1. the current designation for Mars' quadrant MC-20, which borders the equator in the southern hemisphere, longitude 0° to 200° and latitude 0° to -30° S;

2. an old name for Sabaea Terra. See SABAEA TERRA.

Sirenum Terra or **Terra Sirenum** once called Mare Sirenum, one of the most conspicuous dark features seen on the surface of the southern hemisphere of Mars, at longitude 120° to 180° and latitude 3° to -80° S. Its diameter is 4912 km.

Sirius the Dog Star, also called Canicula, a white main-sequence visible binary star that is the brightest-appearing star in the heavens. Located in the southern constellation Canis Major, Sirius in classical mythology was a dog that was changed into a star. Its companion, Sirius B, was the first white dwarf to be discovered. The distance of Sirius from Earth is 2.67 parsecs.

Sirius B the dim white dwarf companion star to Sirius.

Sirsalis a double crater near Oceanus Procellarum, in the 3rd quadrant of the moon, at -13° S and -60° W. The crater is 32 km in diameter and 5300 feet deep.

Sisyphus (Asteroid 1866) an Apollo asteroid, diameter 9 km, perihelion distance 0.87 AU, and aphelion distance 2.92 AU. Its cometlike orbit crosses Earth's orbit. See APOLLO GROUP.

Situla the common name for Kappa Aquarii. This dim orange star in the southern constellation Aquarius is situated just above the star Albali (E Aquarii) and has an apparent magnitude of 5.3.

61 Cygni a binary star in Cygnus, northwest of Gienah, the left wing of the Swan. It was the first star to have its parallax measured, by Prussian astronomer Friedrich Bessel (1784–1846). This fifth-magnitude star lies 11.1 light-years from Earth. Italian astronomer Giuseppi Piazzi (1746–1826) called 61 Cygni the Flying Star because of its abnormally large proper motion. See PROPER MOTION.

Skat the common name for Delta Aquarii, the right leg of the southern constellation Aquarius, near Pisces and Aquila. Skat, a white star, has an apparent magnitude of 3.5. Skat is 84 light-years from Earth.

Skjellerup-Maristany Comet or **Skjellerup Comet** (1927 IX) a comet that reaches magnitude -6 in the month of December. Skjellerup glows with an intense yellow light, at maximum brilliance outshining Venus. It has a period of 36,500 years and a perihelion distance of 0.17 AU.

Skylab a United States Earth-orbiting manned space station in use from May 25, 1973, to February 8, 1974. Skylab proved that humans could live and work in weightless conditions for extended periods of time. The missions were called Skylab 2, 3, and 4. The crews were, for Skylab 2: Charles Conrad, Jr., Joseph P. Kerwin, and Paul J. Weitz; for Skylab 3: Alan L. Bean, Owen K. Garriott, and Jack R. Lousma; and for Skylab 4: Gerald P. Carr, Edward G. Gibson, and William R. Pogue.

The orbiting workshop was powered from solar panels. Scientist astronauts observed a wide range of solar conditions over a 9-month period. More than 180,000 photographs and 40,000 Earth resources pictures were taken with the ATM. In addition to photographing the sun, the ATM and a far-ultraviolet camera were used to view Kohoutek in 1973.

NASA scientists projected that Skylab would remain in orbit for 10 years. On July 11, 1979, however, it fell into the Indian Ocean. Fragments of Skylab landed in western Australia. See Fig. 80 and KOHOUTEK.

slope angle the angle in the vertical plane between the flightpath of a spacecraft and the horizontal.

Small Magellanic Cloud (SMC) a small galaxy, one of two close neighboring galaxies. (The Large Magellanic Cloud is the other.) Both are naked-eye objects but, being close to the south celestial pole, the galaxies are visible only from the Southern Hemisphere. The Small Magellanic Cloud was first recorded in 1519 by Portuguese navigator Ferdinand Magellan (1480?–1521). Its alternative name is Nubecular Minor.

SNC meteorite one of a class of basaltic meteorites now believed by many planetary scientists to be impact-ejected fragments from Mars.

Sobkou Planitia a plain the 2nd quadrant of Mercury that lies approximately 1000 miles east of the Caloris Basin and 1000 miles northwest of Heemskerck Rupes, at latitude +39° N and longitude 128°.

soft landing the act of landing on the surface of a planet or moon without a jarring impact that would otherwise damage the space vehicle.

sol the modern term for the rotation period of the planet Mars, which is 24 hours, 37 minutes, and 22.6 seconds.

Sol the ancient Roman god personifying our sun.

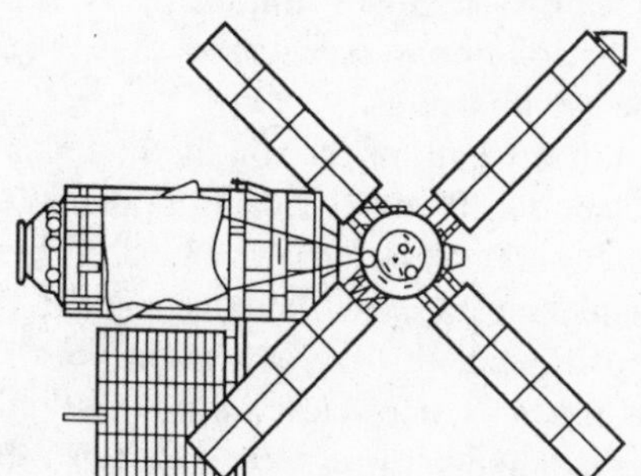

Skylab 1973 - 1979
Length: 29.3 m
Weight: 78 tons
Ship's complement: 3
Propulsion: chemical

Fig. 80. **Skylab.** A United States space station, shown with its equipment fully deployed. See entry.

solar pertaining to the sun or caused by the sun, as in *solar radiation*.

solar activity 1. any type of variation in the appearance or energy output of the sun;

2. the appearance of sunspots, faculae, prominences, and flares of the sun. See FACULAE.

solar apex the point on the celestial sphere near Vega toward which the solar system is traveling relative to the visible stars.

solar cell a photovoltaic cell that converts sunlight into electrical energy.

solar chromosphere the layer of the sun's atmosphere 6000 miles above the photosphere. When the moon passes in front of the sun during a total solar eclipse, the sun's atmosphere flashes into view, and for a few moments observers on Earth can see the red chromosphere and the corona. The chromosphere has a density between 1/1000 and 1/10,000 that of the photosphere.

solar constant the average rate at which radiant energy, 1.94 calories per minute per square centimeter, is received at Earth's surface.

solar core the sun's central region of high-pressure gases, where nuclear energy is produced.

solar corona the sun's outer atmosphere, characterized by extreme temperatures, as much as 3,500,000° F. It is only visible during a total eclipse.

solar cosmic rays the cosmic rays that are thought to originate in the sun.

solar cycle the periodic increases and decreases in the number of sunspots, flares, and other solar activity. The cycle has a period of about eleven years.

solar day 1. the 24-hour period between a midnight and the next midnight;

2. the time interval between two successive transits by the sun of the meridian directly opposite that of an observer, or the time it takes for one complete rotation of the sun on its axis.

solar eclipse the obscuration of the light of the sun by the moon. Solar eclipses occur because the moon—400 times smaller in diameter than the solar photosphere—is also 400 times closer to Earth. Therefore, the sun and the moon subtend almost exactly the same angle in the sky, about 1/2°. The moon's position in the sky at certain points in its orbit—at the time of a new moon—comes close to the position of the sun. Since the lunar orbit is inclined with respect to Earth's orbit, the moon usually passes above or below the imaginary line joining the sun and Earth. Occasionally, however, the moon passes close enough to the sun-Earth line that the moon's shadow falls on the surface of Earth.

The lunar shadow barely reaches Earth's surface during a total solar eclipse. As the moon moves through space in its orbit, and as Earth rotates, the lunar shadow sweeps across Earth in a band as wide as 300 km. Only observers within this narrow band can see a total eclipse. Outside the band of totality, observers within a wide area see only a partial eclipse. When the sun, moon, and Earth are not precisely aligned, the umbra—the darkest part of the shadow—misses Earth completely, but Earth will then be in the penumbra—the intermediate part of the shadow. For astronomers, as long as even a slight portion—as little as 1%—of the sun's photosphere is visible, partial eclipses are not of much value, because under such conditions observers cannot see the faint outer layers of the sun.

A solar eclipse occurs somewhere in the world every year and a half. The band of totality, however, usually does not cross populated areas of Earth, forcing astronomers to travel great distances to carry out their observation. An exceptionally long total eclipse was visible for as much as 6 minutes and 54 seconds from Hawaii and Mexico on July 11, 1991. The next total eclipse visible in the continental United States is expected in 2017. See Fig. 81.

solar faculae the bright surface of the sun's photosphere. See FACULAE.

solar flare an explosive eruption in the outer part of the sun's atmosphere. Such flares are estimated to reach temperatures of millions of degrees and are seen by the observer as sudden and brief brightenings of the solar atmosphere in the vicinity of a sunspot. Solar flares send out electrified particles that reach Earth as magnetic storms and auroras. Solar flares are not to be confused with prominences, which are masses of glowing gas, chiefly hydrogen, above the sun's bright surface. See PROMINENCES.

solar granulation the patchwork pattern of bright areas with dark borders observed on the sun. What are seen as a solar granulation are the tops of rising currents of hot gas in the convective zone.

solar mass the astronomical unit of mass, equal to the mass of the sun, 1.9891×10^{30} kilograms. See TARANTULA NEBULA.

Solar Maximum Mission (SMM) a 5100-pound satellite, managed by Goddard Space Flight Center, that was placed into Earth orbit on

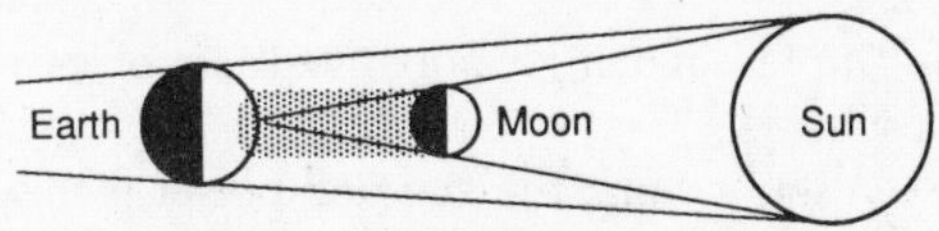

Fig. 81. **Solar eclipse.** See entry.

February 14, 1980, and is believed to be operating still. SMM is a solar observatory, approximately 13 feet in length and 7 feet in diameter. Two fixed solar paddles supply power to the spacecraft during daylight orbits, and 3 rechargeable batteries supply power at night. SMM is the first satellite designed specifically to study flares, the most violent aspect of solar activity.

Its mission was planned to coincide with the solar maximum period, the peak of the 11-year sunspot cycle, in order to provide scientists with observations of solar flares over a wide band of wavelengths, from visible light to the gamma ray region of the spectrum. One of the important results of SMM was the discovery of the variability of the solar constant.

In 1980, the observatory developed control problems, so in April of 1984, SMM was maneuvered into the bay of a Space Shuttle Challenger. Mission specialists George D. Nelson and James Van Hoften—tethered to cables along the orbiter payload bay—in 45 minutes removed the faulty module and replaced it with a new one. Solar Max was still operating normally in 1990–1991, the most recent solar maximum period.

solar motion the rotation of a sun (star) on its axis.

solar nebula the cloud of gas and dust from which a star system is formed.

solar parallax the angle at the sun subtended by the equatorial diameter of Earth.

solar penumbra the gray area surrounding the dark umbra of a sunspot.

solar plages the bright regions in the sun's atmosphere occurring mostly in the vicinity of sunspots.

solar prominence an eruption in the sun's corona of a flamelike tongue of high-density, relatively cool gas from the sun's chromosphere. It can be seen during a solar eclipse.

solar proton the protons emitted by the sun during solar flares.

solar radiation the total electromagnetic radiation emitted by the sun.

solar radio burst a sudden increase in the flux from the sun at radio frequencies.

solar radio waves the radiation at radio frequencies originating in the sun or its corona.

solar spicules the fast-moving, short-lived jets of gases in the sun's upper chromosphere.

solar system 1. a star system, the star and planet family along with its satellites, comets, meteors, and asteroids;

2. the sun and other celestial bodies within its gravitational influence.

solar system dust rings three narrow dust bands near the ecliptic. The bands lie at the distance of the asteroid belt and represent collisional debris from three prominent asteroid families: Apollo, Hidalgo, and Amor.

solar wind the outstreaming of ionized gas, composed mostly of protons and electrons, which fills our solar system. Velocity is 125 to 560 miles per second away from the sun. The pressure of this stream causes the reversal of cometary tails and the production of similar planetary tails behind Earth and other celestial bodies.

solar year 1. a lunar year, a division of time equal to 12 lunar months; **2.** a division of time equaling about 365 days, 5 hours, 48 minutes, and 46 seconds—the time between a vernal equinox and the next vernal equinox.

Solis Planum a dark, extremely large plateau, diameter 1000 km, once called Solis Lacus, seen south of Tharsus Ridge on Mars at longitude 98° to 88° and latitude -20° to -30°.

Solitary Star see MUFRID.

solstice either of the two times of the year when the sun has no apparent northward or southward motion, at the most northern or most southern point of the ecliptic. The summer solstice, when the sun is at its zenith at the tropic of Cancer, occurs about June 22. The winter solstice, when the sun is over the tropic of Capricorn, occurs about 22. See ECLIPTIC.

Sombrero Galaxy (M104 or NGC 4594) the Spiral Hat Galaxy, a spiral galaxy in the constellation Virgo, on the border of Corvus—latitude -12°—that has a large bright nucleus and is crossed by a thick, dark line of material. Its distance is 11 megaparsecs.

sonic speed 1. acoustic velocity, the speed of sound; **2.** the speed of a body traveling at a Mach number of 1.

source a location or device from which energy emanates as a heat source, sound source, etc.

south celestial pole the point on the celestial sphere directly above Earth's South Pole.

Southern Birds the name given to the five southern constellations: Apus, the Bird of Paradise; Columba, the Dove; Corvus, the Crow or Raven; Grus, the Crane; and Pavo, the Peacock.

Southern Cross see CRUX.

Southern Lights see AURORA.

South Tropical Disturbance a dark elongated band in the cloud surface of Jupiter at about the same latitude as the Great Red Spot. It was first seen in 1901 as a dark spot and it then spread rapidly. It has at times exceeded 180° of longitude in length and, like the Red Spot, appears and disappears intermittently.

Soviet Mountains a purported lunar mountain range, said to have appeared in photographs made by Lunik 3 (USSR) in 1959. Astronomers do not believe the mountain range exists.

Soyuz (union) any of a third generation of manned spacecraft of the USSR. Unlike Apollo, it was intended only for Earth orbit missions up to an altitude of about 1300 meters, about 800 miles. The first trial flight of Soyuz 1, in April of 1967, ended in disaster when deployed parachutes tangled after reentry and cosmonaut Valentin Kamarov was killed. Soyuz 2 and 3 were involved in docking experiments, and Soyuz 4 and 5 achieved the first Russian docking of two spacecraft and a transfer of crew, in January of 1969. As a result of this success, Soyuz spacecraft were later used to ferry cosmonauts to and from the Salyut space station, and an unmanned Soyuz, the so-called Progress, was used to ferry fuel and supplies to and from Salyut.

Soyuz—overall length estimated at 34 feet, including the 9-foot docking probe—has two habitable compartments, with a total volume estimated at 318 cubic feet. The orbital compartment, carried on the nose, is spherical and provides living and sleeping quarters. Soyuz 7 carried three men, but it could probably accommodate seven. Solar panels, folded during launch, are extended in orbit to replenish the craft's batteries. In June of 1970, Soyuz 9 set a new endurance record of nearly 18 days in Earth orbit. Upgraded versions of Soyuz, called Soyuz T and Soyuz TM, have been used for ferrying cosmonauts since 1980. See SALYUT.

space 1. the part of the universe lying outside the limits of Earth's atmosphere;

2. the volume in which move all celestial bodies, including Earth.

space-air vehicle or **aerospace vehicle** a vehicle that can be operated either within or above the sensible atmosphere.

space capsule a container used for carrying out an experiment or operation in space. The designation applied originally to Mercury and Gemini spacecraft or to any other small, pressurized cabin suitable for containing men or animals in orbital flight. When the larger Apollo and Soyuz spacecraft came into use, the expression *space capsule* fell out of favor.

space coordinates the three-dimensional system of Cartesian coordinates, enabling a point in space to be located by three magnitudes, indicating distance from three planes that intersect at a point.

spacecraft a device, manned or unmanned, that is designed to be placed into an orbit about Earth or into a trajectory leading to another celestial body.

space docking the temporary joining together in space of two independently launched spacecraft.

Spacelab (ESA) a reusable international orbital space station developed by the European Space Agency (ESA). The first mission of Spacelab, Spacelab 1, was launched on November 28, 1983, aboard the Space Shuttle Columbia. This was the first time six persons flew into space aboard a single vehicle. Five were citizens of the United States, and the sixth was a German citizen. This 10-day flight was a joint NASA-ESA mission, during which 70 investigations in 5 different scientific disciplines were conducted.

Spacelab is Europe's contribution to the NASA Space Transportation System (STS). It consists of a cylindrical module in which astronauts and civilian scientists, called *payload scientists*, are intended to work in a shirtsleeve environment. A series of unpressurized pallets will support experiments requiring direct exposure to space. The hatch between the Shuttle cabin and the cylindrical work module is left open during a mission, affording shared pressure and common air. Spacelab is expected to be used by scientists of countries around the world. It is expected to be made available to research insitutes, scientific laboratories, industrial companies, government agencies, and individual scientists. While many of its planned missions are government sponsored, Spacelab is also intended to serve commercial customers. See Fig. 82.

space medicine a branch of aerospace medicine concerned specifically with the health of persons who make, or expect to make, flights into space.

space polar coordinates or **spherical coordinates** a system of three coordinates by which means of which a point on the surface of a sphere is located in three dimensions.

space probe another name for a planetary probe or spacecraft, such as Mariner or Pioneer.

Fig. 82. **Spacelab.** Spacelab I, launched in 1983, consisted of a cylindrical module in which astronauts and scientists worked on experiments. Carried in the cargo bay of the Space Shuttle Orbiter, Spacelab served as a center for conducting scientific investigations deemed to be impossible on Earth.

space reddening the observed reddening, or absorption of shorter wavelengths, of the light from distant celestial bodies due to scattering by small particles in interstellar space.

space shuttle the Space Transportation System (STM) built for NASA, and the world's first true aerospace vehicle. This reusable spacecraft is a winged and reusable orbiter resembling a jetliner in size (125 feet long) and appearance. It delivers people and equipment to Earth orbit for a mission, makes pickups, and then returns home. As required by its missions, the shuttle may stay in space for a few days or weeks. Its velocity in orbit is about 17,500 miles (28,000 km) per hour, circling Earth every 90 minutes. Upon reentry, the astronauts maneuver the shuttle like a glider in the air. They bring it to a landing at a ground speed of about 215 (135 km) per hour on a runway.

After an exhaustive series of tests, beginning in 1976, the Space Shuttle was declared operational in 1982 and ready to undertake operational missions:

STS-5 Columbia—November 11 to 16, 1982. The first operational flight, with mission specialists aboard, who were trained in satellite deployment and extravehicular activities. Deployed two communications satellites from the cargo bay.

STS-6 Challenger—April 4 to 9, 1983. Originally scheduled for a January 1983 launch, it was delayed to correct a variety of technical problems. Began placement of the Tracking and Delta Relay Satellite System (TDRSS), a high-capacity system providing communications between numerous spacecraft and Earth. Conducted three experiments in the cargo bay: artificial snow formation, a packaged seed collection, and composite metals.

STS-7 Challenger—June 18 to 24, 1983. Sally K. Ride became the first American woman in space. Deployed a German shuttle pallet satellite (SPAS), which is intended for use in a test of the Canadian RMS deployment and retrieval capabilities. Deployed Canadian and Indonesian communications satellites. Performed 10 experiments: forming metal alloys in microgravity, operating heat pipes, use of a remote sensing scanner, and various others, including one on the effect of space on the social behavior of ant colony.

STS 51-L/Spartan-Halley Challenger—a planned six-day mission with Francis R. Scobee, Michael J. Smith, Ellison S. Onizuka, Judith Resnick, Ronald E. McNair, Gregory Jarvis, and Christa McAuliffe, a teacher from New Hampshire, aboard. The mission proved to be a disaster. Challenger had been scheduled for launch at 9:36 Eastern Standard Time on the morning of January 26, 1986, but was delayed for 24 hours because bad weather was predicted. On the next day, a countdown delay of approximately 2 hours was required because of a problem with the removal of the crew hatch door lock. On January 28, the liftoff was delayed approximately 2 hours to allow the weather to warm up and to remove ice from the craft. Liftoff occurred at 11:38 Eastern Standard Time. Challenger exploded 73 seconds later, killing all seven crew members. See Fig. 83.

space station an orbiting space laboratory in which people can live and work. Skylab (U.S.) and Salyut (USSR) are examples. See SKYLAB and SALYUT.

space telescope see HUBBLE SPACE TELESCOPE.

space velocity the velocity of a star with respect to the sun—toward or away from it. See RADIAL VELOCITY.

spacewalk or **extravehicular activity** (EVA) any human activity carried out in space outside a spacecraft. The first spacewalk was accomplished by cosmonaut Alexei Leonov (Voskhod 2 spacecraft) on March 18, 1965. NASA's EVA experience began with astronaut Edward White's 20-minute spacewalk in June of 1965, during the Gemini flights. In November of 1969, astronauts Charles Conrad and Alan Bean spent 14 hours on the moon. Astronauts wear an extravehicular mobility unit (EMU) outside their spacecraft. It includes all the equipment needed for working outside the ship or on the lunar surface. In addition, there is a portable life support system in a backpack, which enables an astronaut to operate independently of the ship for up to 4 hours. See EVA, EXTRAVEHICULAR MOBILITY UNIT, and PORTABLE LIFE SUPPORT SYSTEM.

spectral class see SPECTRAL TYPE.

spectral line a bright, or dark, line found in the spectrum of some radiant source.

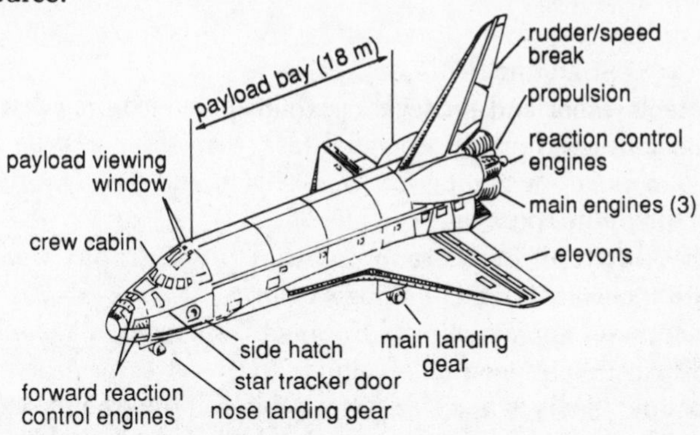

Fig. 83. **Space Shuttle Orbiter.** See entry for space shuttle.

spectral type or **spectral class** one of several temperature classes in the order OBAFGKM, signifying decreasing temperature from O to M, into which over 99% of the approximately 250,000 known stars are placed. (There are four additional classes: W, N, R, and S.) Stars are classified according to their spectra, that is, their physical and chemical characteristics as revealed by use of a spectroscope. The system of classification is called the Harvard system. Each spectral class is subdivided by 10 numerals, ranging from 0 to 9 (for example, B1, A5, and G0 to accommodate small differences in spectral lines within a major class.

Major Spectral Classes

Class	Color	Temp. °F	Example
O	blue-white	60,000	
B	blue-white	40,000	Spico
A	white	20,000	Sirius
F	yellow-white	12,000	Procyon
G	yellow	10,000	Alpha Centauri
K	orange-yellow	7,000	Aldebaran
M	orange-red	5,000	Mira

Luminosity Classes of Stars

Class	Star Type
0	extremely luminous super supergiants, present in small numbers in the Magellanic Clouds and the Milky Way
Ia	luminous supergiants
Ib	supergiants of lower luminosity
II	bright giants
III	ordinary giants
IV	subgiants
V	dwarfs
VI	subdwarfs

spectrograph a spectroscope with a photographic recording device. The instrument breaks light into parallel rays, then disperses the light by means of a prism or grating into a spectrum and, finally, produces a photograph of the spectrum. See Fig. 84.

spectroheliograph an instrument that photographs the sun in monochromatic light (light of a single color).

spectroscope an apparatus used to effect dispersion of radiation and visual display of the spectrum obtained.

spectroscopic binary star a star system in which the true binary nature of the system is revealed by the periodic shifting of spectral lines. Such a system cannot be separated optically.

spectroscopic parallax a method for indirectly determining, from stellar brightness, the distance to a star, sometimes called the parallax. In spectroscopic parallax, the absolute magnitude of a main-sequence star is deduced from the spectral type of the star by using the Hertzsprung-Russell diagram. This, together with the apparent magnitude, gives the distance modulus, hence the distance. See HERTZSPRUNG-RUSSELL DIAGRAM.

spectrum any series of energies arranged according to wavelength or frequency.

speed of light (c) the speed at which light travels in a vacuum: 186,000 miles per second, or 300,000 km/sec.

speed of sound the speed at which sound waves travel: 1116.45 feet per second.

spherical aberration a defect in the shape of a telescopic lens, causing the light passing a spherical lens near its edge to be converged more than light passing the center of the same lens. Spherical aberrations cause the image to blur.

spherical coordinates or **space polar coordinates** a system of coordinates by which a point on the surface of a sphere is located in three dimensions by (1) its distance from a fixed point at the center, called the pole; (2) the colatitude, or angle, between the polar axis—a reference line through the pole—and the radius vector—a straight line connecting the pole and the point; (3) the longitude, or angle, between a reference plane through the polar axis and a plane through the radius vector and the polar axis also called space polar coordinates.

spheroid or **ellipsoid** or **ellipsoid of revolution** a solid shape resembling a sphere. A spheroid can be formed by rotating an ellipse about one of its axes. If the shorter axis is used as the axis of revolution, an *oblate spheroid* (or minor axis) results. If the longer axis is used, a *prolate spheroid* (or major axis) results. Earth is approximately an oblate spheroid.

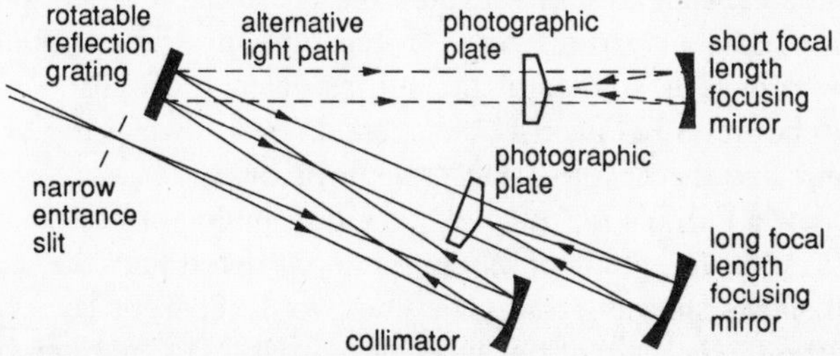

Fig. 84. **Spectrograph.** The path of the light entering the instrument can be followed all the way to the photographic plate that records the image.

Spica Alpha Virginis or Azimech, a bright blue-white star of magnitude 2.76, one of the brightest in the equatorial constellation Virgo, near Leo and Libra. Spica is an eclipsing binary 65 parsecs from Earth.

spicules the bright spikes, or jets, of hot material seen extending into the chromosphere of the sun from below.

Spider the nickname that US astronauts used for the Apollo lunar module.

spin the angular momentum of a rotating body, which is the product of its linear momentum (mass times velocity) and the perpendicular distance from the axis of rotation to the line of motion.

spin axis the axis of rotation of the rotor of a gyroscope in a spacecraft.

spin rocket a small rocket that imparts spin to a larger rocket vehicle or spacecraft.

spin stabilization directional stability of a spacecraft achieved by the action of gyroscopic forces that result from spinning the body about its axis of symmetry.

spiral arms the curved, armlike structures of a galaxy that surround the nuclei of certain galaxies.

spiral galaxy a flattened galaxy comprising a central nucleus and a system of arms that spiral out from the nucleus.

spiral nebula a galaxy of stars (not a nebula at all, as formerly believed) in the form of a spiral. With advent of improved telescopes, some of these so-called nebulas were found to be galaxies, but some of the old names persist. For example, modern astronomers use the name Andromeda Galaxy for what has long been known as the Great Nebula in Andromeda, a designation still encountered.

spoke a radial feature in the rings of Saturn.

sporadic meteor a meteor that does not appear to be associated with a known shower of meteors.

Sporer, Gustav Friedrich Wilhelm (1822–1895) German astronomer and mathematician who investigated the distribution of sunspots, the rotation period for various zones of the sun, and the position of the sun's equator. His studies of the sun revealed a scarcity of sunspot sightings between 1645 and 1715, a period now known as the Maunder minimum. See also MAUNDER BUTTERFLY DIAGRAM.

Sporer's law a formula for describing the distribution of sunspots during the solar cycle. The phase of the sunspot cycle determines the mean latitude of all the sunspot groups. In other words, Sporer's law expresses the variation in latitude of the zones of sunspots. At minimum, the first groups of the new cycle appear at +30° to -40°. Thereafter, the latitude range moves progressively toward the sun's equator until, by the next minimum, the mean latitude is at about the 5° mark, north or south of the equator. This latitudinal progression is known as Sporer's law.

SPOT (*Système* P*robatoire d'Observation de la* T*erre*) an operational high-resolution remote sensing satellite system designed by a French company and first launched in February of 1986.

spring tides the most extreme tides produced when the moon, sun, and Earth are aligned, that is, when the moon is new or full.

Sputnik (a Russian word for satellite or traveling companion) any of a series of 10 Soviet unmanned satellites. Little accurate information has been made public on the Sputnik program.

Sputnik 1—a 58-cm sphere intended as a test vehicle, weight 84.6 kg (186 pounds), launched October 4, 1957, orbited Earth in 96 minutes. It transmitted radio signals at 0.6-second intervals. It burned up in the atmosphere after 92 days.

Sputnik 2—launched November 3, 1957. It carried the dog Laika.

Sputnik 3—launched May 15, 1958.

Sputniks 4, 5, and 6—tested the Vostok reentry capsules. Sputnik 5 made the first successful return of dogs, Belka and Strelka, from space.

Sputniks 7 and 8—associated with the Venus space probe.

Sputniks 9 and 10—Vostok test flights, later called Cosmos.

SS Cygni star see U GEMINORUM STAR.

SS433 a bizarre star that first attracted attention in June of 1978 as a result of peculiarities in its spectrum. SS433 lies at the center of a supernova remnant called W50. One hypothesis is that SS433 is a binary star system made up of a hot massive star and a neutron star, orbiting each other every 13.1 days. See NEUTRON STAR.

Stadius a lunar ghost crater—most of the crater wall is reduced to low ridges—44 miles in diameter. The low-walled crater is west of Copernicus, in the 2nd quadrant of the moon at +11° N and -14° W.

stage an independent section of a rocket that may be designed to fall away when its fuel is exhausted, so that subsequent stages have less weight to lift. Manned Saturn rockets, for example, need only two stages for Earth orbit missions, but three for lunar and planetary flights.

staging the separation of a burned-out stage from the remainder of a space vehicle. With both the 2-stage Saturn 1B and the 3-stage Saturn 5, first-stage separation occurs at about 36 miles altitude. Eight small retrorockets—they thrust in the opposite direction to that of travel—slow the burned-out stage so that it separates cleanly from the main vehicle. On Saturn 5, second-stage separation is at about 114 miles altitude, again assisted by 4 retrorockets mounted just below the separation point.

star a sun, a self-luminous gaseous body that produces energy through nuclear reactions within its core. Stars are distinguished from planets or satellites, which shine by reflected light. Stars are classified by their spectra, designated by letters, sometimes with numerical subdivisions. For example, the sun is a G1-type star.

The seven main types of stars with their principal spectral characteristics are, in order of decreasing temperature: O—He II absorption; B—He I absorption; A—H absorption; F—Ca II absorption; K—bands developing; G—strong metallic lines; and M—very red. The letters P, W, Q, R, N, and S are used to designate comparatively rare types of stars that do not fall into the main series. See ABSORPTION LINE and ABSORPTION SPECTRUM.

starburst galaxy a bright blue galaxy in which many new stars are forming. It is believed that starburst galaxies are caused by collisions between galaxies.

star cloud one of several regions of the Milky Way in which great numbers of stars are seen to be so close together that they appear as a luminous cloud.

star cluster a group of stars that are physically close together in space.

star legends It has been said that the sky is a mythological picture book, and certainly most of the wonderful old stories are commemorated there. For example, all the characters of the Perseus tale are displayed, including the sea monster, though nowadays it is better known as Cetus, a harmless whale. Orion, the Hunter, sinks below the horizon just as his killer, the Scorpion, rises. Hercules lies in the north, together with one of his victims, the Nemaean lion Leo. Argo Navis, the largest of all constellations, reminding us of the ship that carried Jason and the Argonauts in quest of the Golden Fleece, was too vast to be left untouched by the astronomers. As a result, we now have Carina, the ship's keel; Puppis, the poop; and Vela, the sails.

star map a map showing the positions and magnitudes of stars, designed to be held above the observer's head during stargazing.

star nomenclature see STELLAR NOMENCLATURE.

star streaming those stars that move in parallel groups (star streams) in their passage around the galaxy. The closest streaming to Earth is associated with the Hyades star cluster.

star system see SOLAR SYSTEM.

star tracker a telescopic instrument on a spacecraft that locks onto a celestial body and gives guidance reference to the vehicle during flight. See LOCK.

star trail a track left by a star that appears on photographic film when a long exposure by a stationary camera enables the motion of stars to be seen.

stationary orbit an orbit in which a satellite revolves about the primary, or primary body, (such as the secondary, Earth, about its primary, the sun) at the regular rate at which the primary rotates on its axis. From the primary, the satellite thus appears to be stationary over a point on the primary. A stationary orbit with respect to Earth is commonly called a 24-hour orbit.

station keeping a sequence of maneuvers designed to maintain a vehicle in a predetermined orbit.

Station Tranquillitatis see ARMSTRONG, NEIL.

Stella Polaris see NORTH STAR.

stellar of or pertaining to stars.

stellar association a group of stars that have formed together, but are more loosely linked than a cluster. See STELLAR CLUSTER.

stellar cluster a localized region of enhanced star density. Notable examples are the Hyades, the Pleiades, Praesepe, and Coma Berenices.

stellar guidance see CELESTIAL GUIDANCE.

stellar inertial guidance guidance of a spacecraft by a combination of celestial and inertial guidance. See INERTIAL GUIDANCE.

stellar magnitude see MAGNITUDE.

stellar map matching a procedure during the flight of a spacecraft in which a chart of the stars that has been set into the spacecraft guidance system is automatically matched with the position of the stars observed through telescopes to assist in guiding the vehicle.

stellar nomenclature the system of naming stars. These names have their origin in antiquity. Distinctive star groups were given the names of mythological or legendary figures. The majority of the individual stars in each group were also given names, sometimes relating to their positions in the mythological or legendary figures. Most of the names retained today are of Greek, Latin, and Arabic origin, such as Altair, Aldebaran, and Betelgeuse. Since all early works written on astronomy were confined to the naked-eye (visual) stars, relatively few stars were identified by name.

Shortly after the invention of the telescope, the astronomer Bayer (1572–1625) introduced a new method of deignating the stars. The stars in each constellation were identified by the small letters of the Greek alphabet, for the most part beginning with alpha (α) as the brightest star, beta (ß) as the next brightest, and so on. Bayer identified a star further by putting after its Greek letter the genitive (possessive) case of the Latin name of the constellation. Thus, the brightest star in Taurus is called α Tauri or A Tauri. When several stars in a constellation were of about the same brightness, they were lettered in order of position, beginning at the head of the mythological figure.

The astronomer Flamsteed (1646–1719) developed a plan of numbering stars consecutively from west to east across each constellation. Today, most star maps use the Bayer designations as far as the Greek letters go together with the ancient names of most of the brightest stars. Additional stars bear the Flamsteed numbers, such as a Cygni (Deneb; 61 Cygni). As a result of the availability of alternative systems, a bright star may be identified, for example, as Aldebaran (Arabic name), A Tauri or Alpha Tauri (Bayer's method), or 87 Tau or 87 Tauri (Flamsteed's number).

stellar parallax the angular radius of Earth's orbit as seen from a star, used to express the distance of a star from the sun. The fundamental method of measuring this distance is by annual, or trigonometric, parallax.

Because of the motion of Earth in its orbit, a nearby star appears to move against the background of more distant stars, just as a stationary automobile, seen from a moving train, appears to move—in the opposite direction to the motion of the train—against the background of landscape. Thus, a nearby star, observed on a given date, will appear to be in a slightly different place when observed months later. By measuring this shift, the angle can be measured, and the distance of the star from the sun can be found by simple geometry. The greater the distance of the star from Earth, the smaller its parallax. See PARALLAX.

stellar populations in galaxies groupings of stars based on composition and age. Population I consists of young, bright stars (hot, blue or white) mostly composed of helium, hydrogen, and calcium. The stars near the sun are Population I. Population II includes red giants, older stars mostly composed of calcium, titanium, and zirconium.

stellar wind or **solar wind** a steady stream of matter—a flow of charged particles, mainly protons and electrons—ejected into space from a star's corona.

St. Elmo's fire a bluish electrical glow caused by corona discharge on masts and other high parts of a ship at sea before and during an electrical storm.

Stephan's Quintet a group of five galaxies located close to one another, observed by French astronomer M.E. Stephan in 1877. They appear to be spatially linked together by a bright bridge of material. The largest galaxy in the quintet is NGC 7320.

Stofler a walled plain in the 4th quadrant of the moon's near side, at -1° S and +5° E, southeast of Walter. It has a diameter of 145 kilometers. See WALTER.

Stonehenge a prehistoric ruin with built-in astronomical alignments, on Salisbury Plain, Wiltshire, England. Stonehenge comprises a set of standing giant stones—megaliths—each weighing about 25 tons and together forming a circle surrounding two horseshoe-shaped patterns. Some of the pairs of stones have massive stone cross-pieces raised 4 meters above the ground. The stones are believed to have been transported to the site from a location in Wales that is hundreds of miles away. When we consider that work on Stonehenge began almost 5000 years ago, our wonder increases.

The massive stones were aligned pointing to the sun's most northerly rising and setting points at the time of the summer solstice, and its most southerly rising and setting points at the time of the winter solstice. Through these alignments, the shortest and longest days of the year could be noted, along with the seasons and the length of the year. In addition, solar eclipses could be accurately determined.

If the megaliths marked only the extremes of the sun's apparent motions, then we might surmise that Stonehenge served primarily a religious function. Because Stonehenge also marks the extremes in the rising and setting points of the moon, however, it can also be considered a lunar observatory, used for predicting lunar eclipses. Since solar and lunar eclipses are awesome sights, they must have been particularly fearful to people in the Neolithic period.

stony-iron meteorite or **siderolite** a meteorite that is made of approximately 50% iron and 50% silicates.

stony meteorite or **aerolite** a meteorite composed of silicate (rocky) material with some nickel-iron. The two main subgroups are CHONDRITE and ACHONDRITE.

stopping point or **Hemmungspunkt** the end of the highly luminous path of a visual meteor.

Straight Range a mountain range at +48° N and -20° W, in the 2nd quadrant of the moon, forming the northern boundary of Mare Imbrium.

Straight Wall a lunar cliff 75 miles in length, 1200 feet high, north of Tycho Crater in the moon's 3rd quadrant. The Straight Wall slopes upward to the east at a 41° angle, making it one of the steepest lunar slopes known.

Strathmore meteorite the largest-ever Scottish meteorite fall, made of chondrite. It fell in 1917.

stream or **meteor stream** a group of meteoroids with nearly identical orbits. See METEOR STREAM.

streamer a long extension of the sun's corona, usually near the solar equator and shaped by the sun's magnetic field. A streamer may be several radii of the sun in length.

STS or **Space Transportation System** the launch system for the Space Shuttle, consisting of an expendable external tank and two solid rocket booster. See SPACELAB.

Sualocin the common name for the star Alpha Delphini in the northern constellation Delphinus, near Pegasus. It has a magnitude of 3.86 and lies 270 light-years from Earth. Its name is a reversal of Nicolaus, the first name of Venator, the Italian astronomer who selected the name Sualocin. See ROTANEV.

subduction zone a region on Earth where one crustal plate is forced under another, generally associated with earthquakes, volcanic activity, and the formation of deep ocean trenches.

subdwarf star a star that, owing to its small size, is less luminous than a main sequence star of the same spectral class.

subgiant star a star of luminosity between that of a normal giant and a main-sequence star of the same spectral class.

subgravity the condition in which the acceleration acting on a body in flight is less than normal, between 0 and 1 g.

subluminous star a type of star such as a white dwarf or the nucleus of a planetary nebula that is fainter than a main-sequence star.

sublunar point **1.** the geographical position of the moon;
2. the point on Earth at which the moon is at its zenith at a specific time.

suborbital of a type of flight in which a spacecraft enters space but does not go into orbit. Most suborbital flights, the Mercury and Gemini missions, for example, lasted only about 15 minutes.

Subra the common name for the yellow-white star Omicron Leonis, magnitude 3.3, east of Regulus in the constellation Leo.

subrefraction a refraction of less than normal, particularly related to atmospheric refraction.

subsonic in aerodynamics, pertaining to or dealing with speeds of less than acoustic velocity, as in *subsonic aerodynamics*. See SPEED OF SOUND.

sudden-commencement magnetic storm a magnetic storm characterized by worldwide commencement in a matter of minutes and showing no recurrence after 27 days, the period of rotation of the sun.

Sulaphat the Arabic name for tortoise, the star Gamma Lyrae, in the northern constellation Lyra, near the Ring Nebula. It is a blue-white star of magnitude 3.25, at 370 light-years from Earth.

Sulci (singular *sulcus*) intricate networks of linear depressions and ridges on Mars. Examples include Cyane Sulci, Gigas Sulci, Lycus Sulci, and Sulci Gordii.

summer solstice or **June solstice** **1.** the point on the ecliptic occupied by the sun at maximum northerly declination;

2. the instant at which the sun reaches the point of maximum northerly declination, about June 21.

summer triangle a large distinctive triangle in the northern sky, formed by three bright stars—Vega, Altair, and Deneb. These stars are the first ones visible during summer evenings in the Northern Hemisphere.

sun a star, the central body of a solar system (star system). The sun is composed mostly of hydrogen and helium: 78% hydrogen, 20% helium, 2% other gases. See STAR.

sundog or **parhelion** **1.** a bright circular spot on a solar halo;

2. one of the patches of shimmering light—images of the sun refracted by thin clouds of ice crystals in Earth's lower atmosphere—seen, for example, when the sun is at or near its highest point in the sky.

sungrazer a comet, for example, Ikeya-Seki (1965), that comes very close to the sun. Sungrazers become quite brilliant at perihelion, the point in the orbit closest to the sun. They are visible in full daylight within 2° to 4° of the sun. All sungrazers are long-period comets, for example, Kohoutek and the Donati Comet. See Fig. 85.

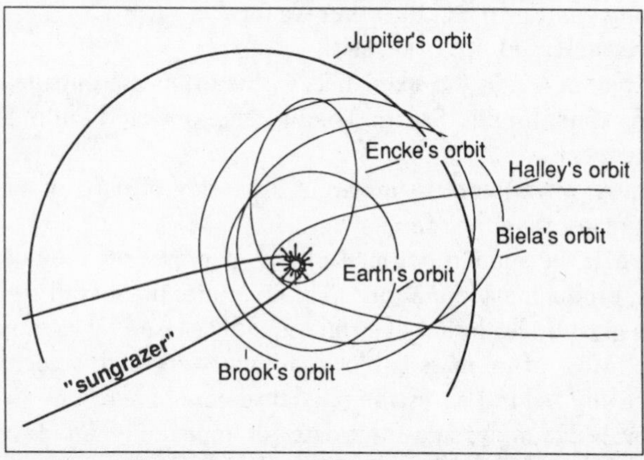

Fig. 85. **Sungrazer.** Don't be fooled by the impossibly close encounters shown here for the sungrazers. These comets come close to the sun only when one thinks in terms of astronomical distances.

sunrise the crossing of the visible horizon by the upper limb of the ascending sun.

sunset the crossing of the visible horizon by the upper limb of the descending sun.

sunspot one of the relatively dark markings that appear periodically on the photosphere of a sun and affect terrestrial magnetism and some other terrestrial phenomena. See SUNSPOT CYCLE.

sunspot cycle the cycle, with an average duration of 11.1 years, but varying between about 7 and 17 years, measured from a maximum degree of sunspot activity, down to a minimum, and back to a maximum. An approximate 11-year cycle has been found or suggested in terrestrial magnetism, frequency of aurora, and other ionospheric characteristics.

sun's revolution period the 230-million year period of the sun for one complete orbit around the Milky Way galaxy.

supercluster a loose cluster of galaxies, about 100 megaparsecs in size. An example is the Local Supercluster, which contains between 2 and 15 rich clusters of galaxies, including the Virgo cluster.

supergiant a very large and extremely luminous type of star, with a diameter 10 to 1000 times that of our sun. Three examples of supergiants are Rigel, Betelgeuse, and Antares.

supergranule a network of large-scale—30,000 km in diameter—connective cells in the solar photosphere. The spaces between these cells are the birthplaces of sunspots.

superior conjunction the conjunction of a planet and the sun when the sun is between Earth and the other planet.

superior transit see UPPER TRANSIT.

superior planet any of the six planets whose orbits are outside the orbit of Earth: Mars, Jupiter, Saturn, Uranus, Neptune, and Pluto. See INFERIOR PLANET.

superluminal expansion the apparent expansion of parts of a quasar at speeds greater than the speed of light.

supernova 1. the sudden outburst of energy blown off the outer layers of a star, producing a luminosity 10 billion times that of our sun;

2. the gigantic explosion of a star, possibly caused by its gravitational collapse. Most of its mass is blown away at very high velocity, sometimes leaving behind an extremely dense core. There are 400 known supernovae. Examples and their dates of appearance are Tycho's Star (1572), Kepler's Star (1604); and Crab Nebula (1054).

supernova remnant the gaseous residue of a star destroyed in a supernova. The remnant can be (a) seen in the sky, (b) detected from its radio emission, or (c) detected from its x-ray emission. The Crab Nebula, for example, can be detected all three ways.

supersonic greater than the speed of sound waves (acoustic velocity) through air.

surface the exterior boundary of any body, especially the outermost area of a planet.

surface boundary layer the thin layer of air adjacent to Earth's surface, extending approximately 300 feet up to the base of the Ekman layer. Also called surface layer and ground layer. See EKMAN LAYER.

surface brightness the brightness of a unit of area of the boundary surface of an object. For objects that are spread out, such as nebulae, the surface brightness determines the amount of contrast the object has against the background sky. It also determines whether the object's surface is bright enough to make an image on the human retina.

Surt an active volcano on Io (Jupiter's moon).

Swift Crater see DEIMOS.

Swift's Comet the great Comet of 1862, also called the Swift-Tuttle Comet, extremely bright and responsible for the Perseid meteor shower. It is a periodic comet that has made only one observed appearance, that of August 23, 1862. The comet, one of four that exhibit retrograde motion, was discovered by American astronomer Lewis Swift (1820–1923), who discovered 12 comets and 1200 nebulas.

synchronous orbit **1.** an orbit made by a spacecraft that has a revolution equal to the Earth's rotation;

2. an equatorial west-to-east satellite orbiting Earth at an altitude of approximately 35,900 kilometers, at which altitude it makes one revolution in 24 hours and is synchronous with Earth's rotation.

synchrotron radiation the radiation emitted by charged particles being accelerated in magnetic fields and moving at speeds near the speed of light.

synergic ascent an ascent of a spacecraft along a synergic curve. See SYNERGIC CURVE.

synergic curve a curve plotted for the ascent of a space vehicle that is calculated to give the craft its greatest fuel economy at its best achievable velocity. This curve, which is plotted to minimize air resistance, starts off vertically, but bends toward the horizontal between 20 and 60 miles altitude to minimize the thrust—therefore, the amount of fuel—required for vertical ascent.

synodic pertaining to a conjunction or to two successive conjunctions of three celestial bodies, often Earth, the sun, and a third body, such as another planet or the moon.

synodical month or **lunation** the average period of revolution of the moon about Earth with respect to the sun, a period of 29 days, 12 hours, 44 minutes, and 2.8 seconds. This period is sometimes called the *month of the phases*, since it extends from a new moon to the next new moon. See Fig. 79.

synodic period the interval of time between any planetary configuration of a celestial body, with respect to the sun, and the next successive same configuration of that body.

synodic satellite a hypothetical satellite of Earth, considered to be situated 0.84 of the distance to the moon on a line joining the centers of Earth and moon and having the same period of revolution as the moon.

Syrtis Major or **Syrtis Major Planitia** a surface feature of Mars, diameter 1262 km, appearing in the northern hemisphere as a dark triangular plateau, longitude 283° to 298° and latitude -1° S to 20° N, near the Martian equator and visible telescopically from Earth.

syzygy the point in the orbit of a planet or satellite at which it is in conjunction or opposition, the configuration arising when the sun, Earth, and either the moon or a planet lie approximately in a line. At such a time, the moon or planet is said to be at opposition or conjunction. The term is used chiefly in connection with the moon, when it refers to the points occupied by the moon at new and full phase. See CONJUNCTION.

T

Tacitus a crater in the 4th quadrant of the moon, west of Catharina Crater, at -16° S and +19° E, and some 40 kilometers in diameter.
tail the gases of a comet that are forced away from the head of the comet by the solar wind.
Talitha the common name for the topaz-yellow, north polar star Iota Ursae Majoris, in the right forepaw of the Great Bear. This A5-type star, 49 light-years from Earth, has an apparent magnitude of 3.1.
tandem missile a multistage configuration used in long-range boosted missiles. Stages are stacked together in a series and are discarded or staged after the propellant in each stage is exhausted. See STAGE.
tangential velocity 1. the component of a star's space velocity that is perpendicular to its radial velocity;
2. also called *transverse velocity*, a measure of the speed with which a star crosses the observer's line of sight.
Tania Australis the common name for the orange star Mu Ursae Majoris in the right hindfoot of Ursa Major, the Great Bear, a north polar constellation 160 light-years from Earth. Tania Australis has an apparent magnitude of 3.2.
Tania Borealis the common name for the white star Lambda Ursae Majoris in the left forepaw of Ursa Major, the Great Bear, a north polar constellation 120 light-years from Earth. Tania Borealis has an apparent magnitude of 3.5.
tankage the aggregate volume of tanks required to carry fuel and oxidizer for a liquid-propelled rocket.
Tarantula Nebula (NGC 2070) the largest diffuse nebula known anywhere in the universe, and the most striking single feature of the Large Magellanic Cloud. NGC 2070, also called 30 Doradus and the Great Looped Nebula, is visible to the naked eye at a distance of 190,000 light-years from Earth. Its diameter is some 800 light-years in extent; with its outer streamers included, the full extent is about 1800 × 1700 light-years. Its total mass is known to approach 500,000 solar masses. The Tarantula Nebula is extremely complex in form, with much structural detail taking the shape of extending filaments and streamers. In the center lies a cluster of over 100 supergiant stars, with the cluster covering an area some 100 light-years in diameter. See SOLAR MASS.
Tarazed or **Reda** the common names for the pale orange star Gamma Aquilae, in the body of the Eagle, the northern constellation Aquila,

near Aquarius. Tarazed is a 2.72 magnitude star. Of spectral type K3II, Tarazed is 340 light-years from Earth.

Taruntius a low-walled crater about 61 km in diameter on Mare Fecunditatis, which is at +5° N and +47° E in the first quadrant of the face of the moon. See MARE FECUNDITATIS.

T association an association of T Tauri stars found in the vicinity of open clusters of young stars. See ASSOCIATION.

Tau Ceti an orange star similar to the sun and thought to be the center of a planetary system. Tau is in the southern constellation Cetus, the Whale, just to the right of Deneb and 11.9 light-years from Earth.

Taurids a minor meteor shower visible between October 26 and November 16 and maximizing about November 8. Its meteors are seen as emanating from the Taurus constellation.

Taurus (Tau) the Bull, a large constellation found in the Northern Hemisphere near Orion. Its brightest star is Aldebaran (Alpha Tauri), a conspicuous red giant known as the follower of the Pleiades and as the eye of the Bull. El Nath, Beta Tauri, is the tip of the bull's horn and is known as the butting one,. The constellation also contains Hyades, the so-called rainy stars, and Pleiades, the Seven Sisters, both considered open clusters. Taurus also includes the supernova remnant of the Crab Nebula observed in China on July 4, 1054. In Greek myth Taurus was the bull that carried off Europa, beautiful daughter of the king of Phoenicia, to Crete.

Taurus dark clouds the large volume of dust-rich gas clouds near the constellation Taurus. It is the location of many T Tauri stars. See TAURUS.

Taygeta or **Taygete** the common name for 19 Tau (Taurus Constellation). Taygeta, one of the seven brightest stars of the Pleiades, has a spectral type B7 classification.

Taygete see TAYGETA.

T Coronae Borealis a recurrent nova that erupted in 1866 and 1946 in the northern constellation Corona Borealis, the Northern Crown, between Hercules and Boötes.

Tebbutt's Comet (1861 II) a comet that made a great sensation during the 19th century. It was discovered by astronomer John Tebbutt, of New South Wales, Australia, on May 13, 1861. The comet displayed a tail about 40° in length by June 11, when its nucleus was as bright as Saturn—about zero magnitude—and its main tail stretched 120° across the sky (0.34 AU). Jetlike appendages appeared that were 40° to 50° long.

So large and bright was the head, and so broad was the tail, that the comet was mistaken on one occasion for the rising moon. In late June and early July, the nucleus became visible for a few days in daytime as a starlike point. On June 29, John Herschel observed it to have a head far brighter than any star or planet except Venus. On June 29 and 30, the daylight comet appeared rather fuzzy, and the daytime sky took on a yellow hue so intense that candles were used to light homes in some places. The peculiar appearance of the sky continued into the night, giving the impression of a weak auroral display.

The cause of these effects became apparent: On June 29 and 30, the Earth had passed through the comet's tail at a distance of 2/3 of its length from the nucleus. See HERSCHEL, JOHN.

tectonic **1.** pertaining to the structure of Earth's crust;

2. relating to the forces and associated motion in the crust of a planet;

3. denoting the resulting disruption of planetary or satellite surfaces by large-scale mass movements, such as faulting.

Tejat Posterior the common name for the star Mu Geminorum, the back foot of the Twins, the northern constellation Gemini, between Cancer and Taurus. This orange red star, 150 light-years from Earth, has an apparent magnitude of 3.2.

Tejat Prior the common name for the star Eta Geminorum, the front foot of the Twins, the northern constellation Gemini, between Cancer and Taurus. This orange red star, 190 light-years from Earth, has an apparent magnitude of 3.4.

tektite any of small glassy bodies, composed of at least 65% silicon dioxide, that have traveled in Earth's atmosphere. These objects are thought to have been formed by meteorite impact, either on Earth or the moon. The large areas in which tektites are found are called *strewn fields*. They are named, as are minerals, with the suffix -ite, for example, *australite*, found in Australia; *billitonite*, *indochinite*, and *rizalite*, found in Southeast Asia; and *bediasite*, found in Texas. Microtektites are found in vast quantity on the floors of the Indian and Pacific Oceans.

telemetry the automatic measurement and transmission of data by radio waves from a satellite to a receiving station—called a tracking station—on Earth, where the transmission is recorded and analyzed.

telescope an optical instrument for making distant objects appear larger. Optical telescopes are essentially of two kinds, *refracting* and *reflecting*. In the former, light rays are brought to a focus by the action of a lens through which the rays pass; in the latter, the focus is effected by a concave mirror, either spherical or parabolic. See also RADIO ASTRONOMY and RADIO TELESCOPE.

telescopic double a star or other celestial object of less than 6th magnitude that cannot be seen without a telescope.

Telescopium (Tel) the Telescope, a small southern constellation between Ara and Corona Austrinus. This star group was originally called Tubus Astronomicus, which French astronomer Nicolas Lacaille (1713–1762) placed between Sagittarius and Ara. Telescopium contains no bright stars.

Telesto (1980 S25) a small shepherd satellite, or moon, of Saturn. Its diameter is 34 × 26 km, and its revolution period is 1888 days, the same as that of its companion moon, Tethys. See TETHYS.

tellurian terrestrial; of or characteristic of Earth or its inhabitants.

Telstar 1. one of an early series of privately financed United States active communications satellites first launched on July 10, 1962. These Telstars were placed in low elliptical orbits and were designed to carry 600 telephone circuits or one television channel. Telstar 1 carried the first transatlantic TV broadcast, linking the United States with Great Britain and France. Telstar later was replaced by geostationary satellites;

2. one of a later series of privately financed United States geostationary satellites under the name Telstar, beginning in 1983.

Tempe a region on Mars just east of Acidalia Planitia. It is associated with Tempe Fossa, an 1180-km (730-mile) so-called ditch, at 35° to 50° S and 82° to 62° W.

Tempe Fossa see TEMPE.

Tempel Comet a short-period comet discovered in 1867 by German astronomer Ernst Wilhelm Tempel (1821–1889), who discovered 6 asteroids, 60 nebulas, and 20 comets. It was studied in 1983 by the IRAS satellite. See IRAS.

Tempel-Tuttle Comet (Comet 1866) a periodic comet—with a period of 32.9 years—discovered by E.W. Tempel in 1865. The comet, associated with the Leonid meteors, is expected to return in 1998. Spectacular Leonid meteor storms have occurred at about the times of the comet's perihelion passage. See PERIHELION and TEMPEL COMET.

temperature a measure of the average speed with which the molecules of a substance (or atoms of a gas) are moving.

Tereshkova, Valentina V. (1937–) a Soviet cosmonaut and skydiving enthusiast and the first woman to make a space flight. In 1963, aboard Vostok 6, she orbited Earth 48 times. See VOSTOK.

terminator or **terminator line** a line of demarcation or boundary between the dark and sunlit hemispheres of the moon, a planet, or any spherical body that is illuminated from a radiant source.

terminator line see TERMINATOR.

terra the Latin word for Earth or land. Also used in reference to the moon. See HIGHLANDS, LUNAR.

Terra Sabaea see SABAEA TERRA.

terrestrial relating to the planet Earth, as distinguished from any other planet. See also TELLURIAN.

terrestrial latitude 1. latitude on Earth;

2. an angular distance from the equator.

terrestrial longitude 1. longitude on Earth;

2. the arc of a parallel, or the angle at the pole between the prime meridian and the meridian of a point on Earth.

terrestrial magnetism or **geomagnetism** the magnetism of Earth.

terrestrial planet any of the planets similar to Earth in density. They have a rocky surface, are small, and have limited atmosphere. The terrestrial planets are Mercury, Venus, Earth, Mars, and Pluto.

terrestrial pole a term used for any of the poles of Earth: a geographical pole, a geomagnetic pole, or a magnetic pole.

terrestrial radiation the total infrared radiation emitted from Earth's surface. Also called *Earth radiation* and *irradiation*.

terrestrial refraction any refraction phenomenon observed in the light originating from a source lying within Earth's atmosphere. See REFRACTION.

Tethys (S III) an intermediate-sized moon of Saturn that was discovered in 1684 by Italian astronomer Jean De Cassini (1615–1712), who also discovered three other moons of Saturn—Rhea, Dinoe, and Iapetus. Thetys orbits Saturn at a mean distance of 295,000 km. Its diameter is 1050 kilometers—about a third of the diameter of our moon—and its revolution period is 1888 days. It was photographed by Voyager 1 in 1980 and Voyager 2 in 1981. The heavily cratered surface of Tethys faces Saturn and includes a valley about 750 km (500 miles) long by 60 km (40 miles) wide.

Teton fireball an exceptionally bright meteor that can reach magnitudes of -15 or -20—brighter than the full moon. It was observed in broad daylight on August 10, 1972, from Grand Teton National Park, Wyoming. The fireball, believed to have reached magnitude -19, was visible for 101 seconds and was photographed. It was about 80 meters across and weighed about a million tons. It came within 58 km of hitting Earth's surface.

Tharsis Ridge a principal area of volcanic activity on Mars. Measuring 5000 km in diameter, the region—latitude -33° to -45° and longitude 125° to 101°—includes the four largest Martian volcanoes: Olympus Mons, Ascraeus Mons, Pavonis Mons, and Arsia Mons.

Thaumasia a region on Mars, at latitude -33° to -45° and longitude 100° to 85°, associated with the 802 km (500-mile) ditch called Thaumasia Fossae. Thaumasia is just south of Solis Planum.

Theaetetus an irregular-shaped crater on Palus Nebularum, in the 1st quadrant of the near side of the moon, northeast of the Archimedes Crater. Theaetetus has a diameter of 16 miles, and the highest point on its rim is 7700 feet.

Thebe (J14) a satellite of Jupiter discovered in 1980 by astronomer S.P. Synnott while studying photographs sent by Voyagers 1 and 2. Its orbit lies between the moons Amalthea and Io at a distance of 223,000 kilometers. Its orbital period is 0.674 day, and its diameter is 76 kilometers.

Theia Mons either of two volcanic-shield mountains on Beta Regio, at +30 N and 270° W, in the northern hemisphere of Venus. The mountains on Beta Regio—Rhea Mons and Theia Mons—have long tongues of rough material, apparently lava flowing from the summit and extending 500 km in irregular fashion. Theia Mons is at the junction of at least three major rift zones.

Themis (Asteroid 24) discovered in 1853 by de Gasparis. Its diameter is 234 km, perihelion 2.76 AU, aphelion 3.52 AU.

The Norc (Asteroid 1625) an asteroid of magnitude 14. It was named after the Naval Ordnance Research Calculator in Virginia.

Theon either of two bright-walled lunar craters ten miles in diameter, situated in a heavily cratered upland west of Mare Tranquillitatis. Theon Junior is at -2°S and +16° E; the highest point on its rim is 8900 feet. Theon Senior is at -1° S and +15° E, just north of Junior; the highest point on Senior's rim is 10,500 feet.

Theophilius Crater a magnificent crater 101 km in diameter in the 4th quadrant of the near side of the moon. The crater is part of a central mountain group at -11° S and +27 ° E, on the western edge of Mare Nectaris.

theory a set of ideas that are consistent with observed phenomena and serve to explain the phenomena.

theory of cosmological red shifts the theory that galaxies' red shifts are all due to recessional motion, increase with distance, and thus give an indicator of distance.

theory of star formation the theory that describes how stars form by the gravitational collapse of interstellar clouds of dust and gas.

thermal barrier or **heat barrier** the speed limitation within an atmosphere that is imposed by aerodynamic heating. An outstanding example is the rapid rise in temperature of a returning spacecraft, such as the Space Shuttle, as a consequence of friction or compression of atmospheric gases passing over its exterior surface.

thermal escape the escape of the fastest-moving gas atoms or molecules from the top of a planet's atmosphere by means of their thermal motion—the vertical air currents caused by heating of the terrain.

thermal tide the relatively small variation in atmospheric pressure due to the daily differential heating of the atmosphere by the sun.

thermocouple a thermoelectric device used for measuring the intensity of infrared radiation in order to measure temperature precisely. The thermocouple converts thermal energy (heat) into electricity. It consists of two dissimilar metals side by side that produce a current when heated; the strength of the current can then be read to obtain a temperature reading.

Theta Carinae a blue-white dwarf star in the southern constellation Carina, between Volans and Vela. Theta Carinae, 750 light-years from Earth, is associated with a bright open cluster. Theta's magnitude is 2.76.

Theta Orionis familiarly known as the Trapezium, a multiple star in the Orion Nebula. A line connecting its four main components resembles a trapezium, which is a four-sided plane figure with no two sides parallel. See TRAPEZIUM.

third quarter the phase of the moon when it is three-fourths of the way around its orbits from new moon. The third quarter moon, also called last quarter moon, is seen in the dawn sky with a straight terminator and half the disk illuminated. See TERMINATOR and Fig. 57, which is associated with the entry NEW MOON.

3C147 a strong, compact radio quasar that appears to be in the same region of the sky as the Perseus cluster of galaxies. In photographs taken with the Palomar telescope, it looks like a faint star.

3C273 the first-identified and brightest quasar, discovered in 1963. In photographs taken with the 5-meter Hale telescope at Palomar, 3C273 looks like a star of 13th magnitude, except for the faint jet that is visible out to about 20 seconds of arc (50,000 parsecs). This quasar, found during a lunar eclipse, is a source of x-rays as well as of visible light and radio radiation.

thrust the pushing or pulling force developed by a spacecraft as a reaction to the rearward ejection of fuel gases at high velocities. Thrust is also called momentum thrust.

Thuban a common name for the white giant star of the northern constellation Draco, known also as Alpha Draconis. Thuban is an A0-type star with an apparent magnitude of 3.7. It is 220 light-years from Earth.

Early astronomers, about 2750 BC, saw Thuban as the north star. Its position has since changed as a result of the precession of the equinoxes. See NORTH STAR and PRECESSION.

Thunder Moon see HAY MOON.

Thyle Chasma a 235-kilometer (146-mile) long, very large and straight canyon, at longitude 230° to 325° and latitude -69° to -73°, on the planet Mars.

tidal coupling the locking of the rotation of a body to its revolution around another body. A good example is the moon, which—because of tidal coupling—always shows the same face to observers on Earth.

tidal day see LUNAR DAY.

tidal force a force caused by the differential effect of the gravity from one celestial body being greater on the near side of a second body than on the far side. Thus, the pull of the moon's differential gravity results in the changes observed in Earth's ocean tides. For the same reason, Jupiter's moon Io seems to be hot—volcanically active—because of the changing tidal distortion caused by Jupiter's strong gravitational field (or tidal force).

tidal heating the heating of a planet or satellite because of internal friction caused by tides within a moon. An example is seen in Ganymede, which is closer to Jupiter than Callisto and therefore feels the effects of tidal heating, which tends to squeeze it out of spherical shape.

tidal recession the recession of the moon or other satellite from Earth or other planet that is caused by tidal forces. Tidal friction is currently slowing down Earth's rate of rotation (the length of Earth's day) by 16 seconds every million years and is at present causing the moon to recede from Earth by about 5 cm every year.

tidal stability limit see ROCHE LIMIT.

tidal wave see TSUNAMI.

tide 1. the deformation of a celestial body that is caused by gravitational forces exerted by other celestial bodies;

2. the periodic rise and fall of Earth's oceans and atmosphere. It results from the gravitational forces of the moon and sun acting upon the rotating Earth.

Timaeus a lunar crater 34 kilometers in diameter, at +64° N and 0°, just barely on the edge of Mare Frigoris.

time the hour of the day reckoned by the position of a celestial reference point relative to a reference celestial meridian. Time may be designated *solar*, *lunar*, or *sidereal* when the reference is, respectively, the sun, moon, or vernal equinox. Time may also be designated according to the reference meridian, either the local or Greenwich meridian.

time dilation the slowing of moving clocks or of clocks in strong gravitational fields. This idea is based on Einstein's theory of relativity. Time recorded on a clock that is moving at a certain velocity relative to an observer will pass more slowly than time recorded on a clock that is stationary. For example, during 1 hour recorded on the stationary observer's clock, 0.44 hour would pass on a clock moving at 0.9 times the speed of light; only 0.04 hour would pass on a clock that is moving at 0.999 times the speed of light. Thus, if an astronaut were to travel to and from a star 12.5 light-years distant at a constant speed of 0.999 times the speed of light, 25 years would elapse on Earth, but the astronaut would age only 1 year.

It is worth pointing out that the fastest speed attained thus far by an astronaut is that of a space shuttle, approximately 17,000 miles per hour. The speed of light is 186,000 miles per second.

time lag the total time between the application of a signal to a measuring instrument and the full indication of that signal within the uncertainty of the instrument.

time zone a zone on Earth's surface approximately 15° wide, within which the hour used is uniform.

Timocharis a lunar crater 35 km in diameter on the Mare Imbrium, southwest of the Archimedes Crater, at +27° N and -13° W.

Tiros (*T*elevision and *I*nf*r*ared *O*bservation *S*atellite) any of a series of 10 weather satellites launched beginning in 1965 to monitor heat flow from Earth into space and to photograph Earth's cloud cover. Tiros, equipped with 4 specially designed television cameras, viewed Earth from a 725-km (450-mile) orbit. See Fig. 86.

Tir Planitia a plain on Mercury located just south of the Caloris Basin.

Titan Saturn's largest moon, discovered by Dutch astronomer Christian Huygens (1629–1695) in 1655. Titan, with a diameter of 5800 kilome-

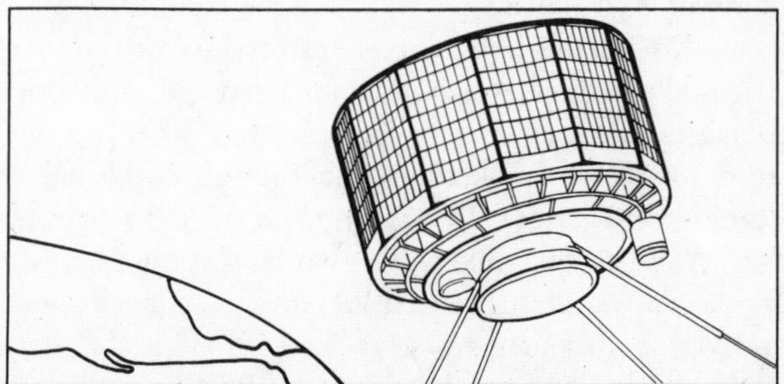

Fig. 86. **Tiros 1.** Launched in 1960, this satellite gave us the first weather pictures transmitted from space.

ters, is also the largest moon in the solar system and larger than the planet Mercury. Its smoggy reddish-orange atmosphere contains nitrogen and methane. The moon orbits Saturn in 15.95 days at a mean distance of 1,222,000 kilometers.

Titania the largest moon of Uranus, with a diameter of 1800 kilometers. Discovered in 1787 by English astronomer William Herschel (1738–1822), discoverer of Uranus, this satellite orbits Uranus in 8.71 days at a mean distance of 438,000 km.

Tithonia Catena a Martian crater chain, at latitude -06° to -05° and longitude 87° to 80°, extending from Valles Marineris to Tithonium Chasma.

Titius-Bode rule a simple series of steps that produces numbers approximately matching the sizes of the planetary orbits. See BODE'S LAW.

TLP see TRANSIENT LUNAR PHENOMENON.

tolerance the allowable variation in measurements within which the dimensions of an item are judged acceptable.

Toliman a common name, meaning grapevine shoot, for the star Alpha Centauri. Alpha Centauri is most commonly referred to as Rigel Kentaurus, meaning foot of the centaur. It is a triple star and the closest to the solar system. Alpha Centauri A is the primary star, and Alpha Centauri B is the secondary star. Both are approximately 4.34 light-years from our solar system. Alpha Centauri C, at 4.24 light-years, is slightly closer than the other two and so is also called Alpha Centauri Proxima. See RIGEL.

Tolstoy a crater, at latitude -15° and longitude 165°, on the planet Mercury that was photographed in 1974 by Mariner 10. It is 400 kilometers in diameter. Apart from the 625-km diameter crater Beethoven, at -20° and 124°, it is Mercury's largest named crater.

topocentric referring to measurements or coordinates when the position of the observer is on Earth.

T Orionis variables the irregular eruptive stars of Orion that have abrupt Algol-like fadings, which are connected with bright or dark diffuse nebulae. See ALGOL.

Toro (Asteroid 1685) an Apollo asteroid of magnitude 0.8 and a diameter of 5 kilometers (3 miles). It was discovered in 1948 by American astronomer A. Wirtanen while he was working at the Lick Observatory in California. Toro's orbit is remarkable for a resonance involving both Earth and Venus. Resonance is a gravitational effect that occurs when the orbital period of one object is an exact fraction of the period of a larger neighbor. This causes systematic tugs on the smaller object—the asteroid—that gradually chnage the orbit of the smaller object.

totality the state of an eclipse when it is deemed to be total.

Lunar totality occurs when the moon enters completely into the umbra of Earth's shadow. The maximum duration of totality is 1 hour and 42 minutes. The moon can usually be seen throughout totality, because it is illuminated by sunlight that is refracted by Earth's atmosphere into the shadow area. Since the bluer wavelengths are removed by scattering, the moon has a coppery-red color.

Solar totality occurs when the moon passes directly in front of the sun so that Earth lies in the moon's shadow. The moon moves in a general west-to-east direction over a narrow curved zone of the sun's surface, known as the path of totality, which can be up to 250 km wide, but averages about 160 km. An observer in the path of totality will experience a total eclipse, in which the sun is completely obscured. Totality begins when the sun disappears from sight. The maximum duration of totality is 7 minutes and 40 seconds, but it is usually much less. Totality ends just as the crescent sun emerges. During totality, the chromosphere and the corona can be studied.

total curvature the change in direction of a ray between object and observer as observed on the surface of a telescopic lens.

total eclipse 1. an eclipse in which the entire source of light is obscured;

2. an eclipse of the sun during which the disk of the moon completely covers the photosphere of the sun;

3. an eclipse of the moon during which the moon lies completely within the umbra of Earth's shadow. See UMBRA and Fig. 87, which is associated with that entry.

total radiation radiation over the entire spectrum of emitted wavelengths, both visible and invisible. See ELECTROMAGNETIC SPECTRUM.

towering a refraction phenomenon that is a special case of looming, in which the downward curvature of light rays due to atmospheric refraction increases with elevation so that the visual image of a distant object—for example, the sun, moon, or star—appears to be stretched in the vertical direction. See REFRACTION and LOOMING.

tracking the process of following the flight path of a satellite or spacecraft by optical, radio, or radar observations.

tracking station see TELEMETRY.

trail or **train** a temporary luminous streak produced by passage of a meteoroid through Earth's atmosphere.

train see TRAIL.

trajectory the curved path followed by a moving spacecraft, rocket, or projectile.

transfer ellipse See TRANSFER ORBIT.

transfer orbit 1. in interplanetary travel, an elliptical trajectory tangent to the orbits of both the departure planet and the target planet;

2. a flight path followed by a spacecraft moving from one orbit to another, such as moving from the orbit of one planet to that of another. The trajectory is generally an elongated ellipse, called a transfer ellipse, that intersects the new orbits.

Transient Lunar Phenomenon (TLP) a change, such as an emission of gas, observed on the moon. The area of the moon that has shown the most numerous transient lunar phenomena is the brilliant Aristarchus Crater, at +24° N and -47° W, in the moon's 2nd quadrant.

transit 1. the passage as seen from Earth of a planet, usually Mercury or Venus, across the sun's disk;

2. **the passage of a moon, such as one of Jupiter's Galilean satellites, across its planet's disk. See also** CULMINATION.

transition the movement of an electron from one atomic orbit to another.

transition maneuver a maneuver required in lifting flight to fly smoothly from one equilibrium glidepath to another, performed by changing aircraft attitude in some manner.

translation an intentional movement of a spacecraft from one position to another, usually in relation to a second spacecraft or other object.

translunar space the region of space lying beyond the orbit of the moon as seen from Earth at any moment.

transponder a radar, radio, or sonar combined receiver and transmitter whose function is to transmit signals automatically when triggered by an interrogator, a person who is stationed at the ground base, for example, at Houston Mission Control.

Trapezium a multiple star (six stars) that lies in and ionizes the Orion Nebula and is part of the Orion association. The four brightest stars form a trapezium and are visible with a small telescope. See THETA ORIONIS.

trapping a process by which radiation particles are caught and held in a radiation belt.

Triangle see METALLAH.

triangulation a process whereby an inaccessible side of a triangle may be determined from the measurement of accessible sides and angles. A method of calculating distances.

Triangulum (Tri) the Triangle, a small northern constellation between Pisces and Perseus. The star group can be found just under Andromeda, above Aries. Its main star is Rasalmothallah, which lies 59 light-years from Earth. Triangulum is noted for M33, a 6th-magnitude galaxy, one of the three spirals in the Local Group of galaxies. Ancients drew Triangulum as a triangle or equilateral. The Greek astronomer Aratos thought it was the celestial representation of the island of Sicily. See LOCAL GROUP.

Triangulum Australe (TrA) the Southern Triangle, a constellation between Pavo and Circinus, near Alpha Centauri. Triangulum Australe contains NGC 6205, which is a 7th-magnitude star cluster.

Triangulum Spiral (M33, NGC 598) a spiral galaxy in the constellation Triangulum and a member of the Local Group of galaxies. See LOCAL GROUP.

Triesnecker Crater a lunar crater 23 kilometers in diameter located in the Mare Vaporum area.

Trifid Nebula (M20, NGC 6514) an emission nebula at 2000 parsecs distance, in the Sagittarius constellation. The word *trifid* denotes a structure that is divided into 3 narrow parts or lobes, and the Trifid Nebula is divided into 3 rosy pink sectors by dark black dust lanes.

trigonometric parallax a determinant of stellar distance. The angular displacement of a nearby star's movement as seen from opposite ends of the diameter of Earth's orbit at right angles to the direction from the sun to the star. It is a direct measure of the star's parallax.

Triton the largest moon of Neptune, diameter 3800 kilometers. The satellite was discovered in 1846 by English astronomer William Lassell (1799–1880). Triton orbits Neptune in retrograde motion every 5.877 days at a mean distance of 354,000 kilometers.

Trojan group or **Trojan asteroids** or **Trojan minor planets** **1.** the moons and asteroids located near Jupiter;

2. two groups of minor planets that librate in long-period orbits around the stable Lagrangian points of the sun and Jupiter. An example is any asteroid that orbits the sun in approximately the same orbit as Jupiter but is located 60∞ ahead of or behind the planet as viewed from the sun. Beginning with the first Trojan to be discovered, Achilles in 1906, most have been named after heroes of the Trojan Wars. More than 1000 Trojan group members may be bright enough to be seen from Earth, but fewer than 2% of these have yet received official minor planet designations. They are all exceptionally dark bodies. See LAGRANGIAN POINT.

tropical in astronomy, of or pertaining to the vernal equinox.

tropical year a period of one revolution of Earth around the sun, approximately 365.25 days, beginning with a vernal equinox and ending with the next.

Tropic of Cancer the northern parallel of declination, approximately 23°

and 27 minutes from the celestial equator, reached by the sun at its maximum declination, or the corresponding parallel on Earth.

Tropic of Capricorn the southern parallel of declination, approximately 23° and 27 minutes from the celestial equator, reached by the sun at its maximum declination, or the corresponding parallel on Earth.

tropopause the boundary between the atmospheric layers called the *troposphere* and *stratosphere.*

troposphere the portion of the atmosphere from Earth's surface to the stratosphere, that is, the lowest 10 to 20 kilometers of the atmosphere.

true altitude or **observed altitude** the actual height above sea level or the actual altitude of a celestial body above the celestial horizon.

true meridian the great circle through the geographical poles, distinguished from the *magnetic meridian.*

true position or **geometric position** the position of a celestial body (or space vehicle) on the celestial sphere as computed directly from the elements of the orbit of Earth and the body concerned without allowance for light time.

Tsiolkovskii a formation on the far side of the moon. Because it has a dark floor and a major central peak, it seems to be intermediate between a mare and a crater—perhaps it should be thought of as a flooded crater. Tsiolkovskii was named after a Russian rocket pioneer, Konstantin E. Tsiolkovskii (1857–1935), who is regarded as the father of astronautics.

tsunami a large ocean wave generated by earthquake or volcanic activity. Tsunami is the correct name for a tidal wave.

T Tauri star a type of variable star, often shedding mass, believed to be still forming and contracting into a dwarf star of the main sequence.

T Tauri wind a supersonic, jet-like gas that flows from the polar regions of T Tauri stars. The T Tauri wind resembles the solar wind, but the amount of material lost is far greater.

T-time any specific time, minus or plus as referenced to zero or launch time, during a countdown sequence that is intended to result in the firing of a rocket propulsion unit that will launch a space vehicle.

Tucana (Tuc) the Toucan, a southern constellation between Octans and Phoenix, bordering the constellation known as the Small Magellanic Cloud. Tucana is known for its globular cluster 47 Tucanae (NGC 104). The constellation's brightest star is only of 3rd magnitude. The constellation's name, Tucana, is from the name of a bird of South America in the language of an Indian tribe living along the coasts of Brazil and Paraguay and in the Amazon River Valley.

Tunguska event a mysterious explosive event that occurred on June 30,

1908, in the Podkamennaya Tunguska river basin, in Central Siberia. An area 80 kilometers in diameter was devastated. No crater or remnant has ever been found, even though trees were blown outward for kilometers around and a tremendous explosion rocked the area. Calculations suggest that the Tunguska object, possibly a small comet or bolide, was 100 meters in diameter. See BOLIDE.

turbidity 1. any condition of the atmosphere of a planet that reduces its transparency to radiation, especially to visible radiation;

2. a cloud-free portion of Earth's atmosphere that is made turbid, or murky, by air molecules and suspensoids such as smoke, dust, and haze.

turbidity factor a measure of the atmospheric transmission of incident solar radiation.

turbulence a state of fluid flow in which the instantaneous velocities exhibit irregular and apparently random fluctuations so that in practice only statistical properties can be recognized and subjected to analysis.

Tureis a common name for the star Tau Carinae, in the top middle of the Carina (the Keel) constellation, close to Centaurus. Tureis, a yellow white star of magnitude 2.24, lies 650 light-years from Earth.

twenty-four hour satellite a synchronous satellite of Earth. Orbiting Earth equatorially from west to east at an altitude of 35,900 km, it makes 1 revolution in 24 hours, in synchrony with the rotation of Earth. Thus, the satellite is seen to hover over a single point on Earth, neither rising nor setting. GEOS is an example.

twilight a period of incomplete darkness following sunset (evening twilight) or preceding sunrise (morning twilight).

twinkle the apparent changes in the brightness and color of a star due to the motion of the Earth's atmosphere See SCINTILLATION.

twin paradox theory the seeming contradiction that is perceived when one Earth-born twin astronaut travels near the speed of light and returns younger than the astronaut's twin, who stayed behind. See TIME DILATION.

Twins the common name for the Gemini constellation.

two-body problem the problem in classical celestial mechanics that treats of the relative motion of two point masses under their mutual gravitational attraction. The motion of a planet around the sun is an example of the two-body problem as long as the attractive forces of the other planets are assumed to be negligible. Most theories of celestial motion use functions and principles such as semimajor axis, ascending node, eccentricity, perihelion, orbital velocity, and Kepler's laws. See entries for these.

Tycho one of the most nearly perfect of the moon's craters and the center of the most extensive ray system possessed by any lunar crater. Some of the rays are 1000 miles or more in length. This 3rd-quadrant crater, at -43° S and -11° W, is 100 km in diameter, and its walls rise 16,000 feet. Tycho was photographed in 1968 by Surveyor 7.

Tycho's star a supernova observed in 1572 AD in the northern constellation Cassiopeia. The star remained visible for 18 months. Danish astronomer Tycho Brahe (1546–1601) made careful observations of this star's position and magnitude (-4). The star, which remained visible for 18 months, is associated with a radio and x-ray source.

Tyl the common name for the star Epsilon Draconis, a yellow white star in the northern constellation Draco, near the celestial equator. This star has an apparent magnitude of 4.0.

Type I supernova a supernova whose distribution in all types of galaxies and whose lack of hydrogen in its spectrum make us think that it is an event in the development of low-mass stars, probably resulting from the collapse and incineration of a white dwarf in a binary system. See WHITE DWARF and BINARY SYSTEM.

Type II supernova a supernova associated with spiral arms and which has hydrogen in its spectrum, making us think that it is the explosion of a massive star.

Tyrrhena Terra a bright feature 55 km in diameter at latitude -22° and longitude 253°, in the southern hemisphere of Mars.

U

U Cephei an Algol-type eclipsing variable star in the northern constellation Cepheus, near Cassiopeia and Draco. The magnitude of this blue-white dwarf varies from 6.6 to 9.8. See ALGOL.

U Geminorum star or **SS Cygni star** any variable star, for example, a dwarf nova. Such stars are characterized by rapid outbursts, followed by a slower return to minimum activity until the next outburst.

Uhuru a NASA satellite, whose name means freedom in the Swahili language. Uhuru, launched in 1970, was the first artificial earth satellite—followed by IRIS, Skylab, and Ulysses—intended to make x-ray astronomical observations of the sky. The satellite discovered neutron stars in binary systems and distant galaxy clusters.

ultrabasic rock a rock of high density, low silica content, and high iron content, often derived from the upper mantle of a planet or satellite.

ultraviolet light radiation of wavelength too short to see, but longer than that of X-rays.

Ulysses the shuttle Discovery-launched ESA (European Space Agency) spacecraft, weighing 360 kg (810 pounds), that is intended to study the poles of the sun from a distance of 1.3 AU during a 27-month interplanetary voyage to the sun, which began in October 1990. While passing over the sun's poles, Ulysses will study the sun's environment. Ulysses is equipped with a variety of scientific instruments that will enable it to study the physics of the sun, the nature of the solar wind, and the locations of radio and x-ray emissions.

umbilical cord or **umbilical** any of the servicing electrical or fluid lines between the ground or a tower and a rocket vehicle standing upright before a launch.

umbilical tower a vertical structure supporting the umbilical cords running into a rocket in launching position.

umbra 1. the darkest part of a shadow in which light is completely cut off by an intervening object, for example, the darker central portion of a sunspot surrounded by the lighter penumbra;

2 at an eclipse, the part of the moon or Earth's shadow from which the solar disk is entirely hidden. See Fig. 87.

Umbriel (U2) a satellite of Uranus discovered in 1851 by English astronomer William Lassell (1790–1880), who also discovered Neptune's Triton satellite and Saturn's Hyperion satellite. Umbriel, diame-

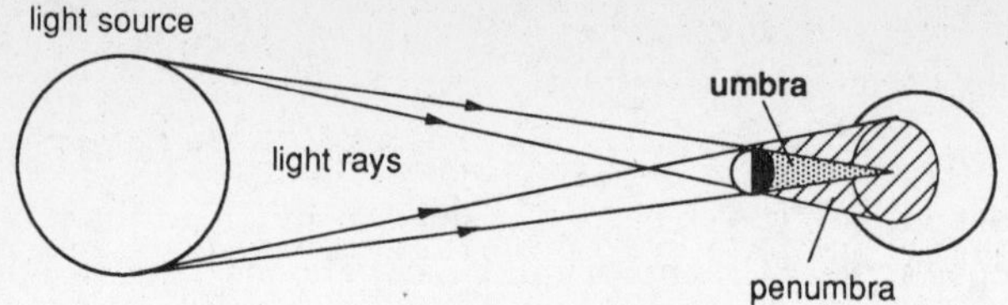

Fig. 87. **Umbra.**

ter 1000 kilometers, orbits Uranus at a mean distance of 267,000 kilometers. Its orbital period is 4.144 days.

Umkehr effect an anomaly of the relative zenith intensities of scattered sunlight at certain wavelengths in the ultraviolet as the sun approaches the horizon. The anomaly is that only the ultraviolets rays are scattered.

Undina (Asteroid 92) a minor planet discovered in 1867 by German astronomer Christian H. Peters, who was living then in the United States. Undina, with a period of 5724 years, has a diameter of 250 kilometers, making it one of the largest members of the asteroid swarm.

universality the assumption that the physical laws observed on Earth apply everywhere in the universe.

universal time (UT) or **Greenwich time** the time measured from midnight and defined by the rotational motion of Earth, and determined from the apparent diurnal motions that reflect this rotation.

universe the sum total of potentially knowable objects. The study of the universe on a grand scale is called *cosmology*.

upper culmination see UPPER TRANSIT.

upper limb the half of the outer edge of a celestial body, especially the moon, having the greatest altitude in contrast with the lower limb, the half having the least altitude.

upper transit the transit of the upper branch of the celestial meridian. Also called *superior transit* and *upper culmination*.

Uranius Patera a large—125-km—volcanic crater with irregular edges at latitude 26° and longitude 93° in the Tharsis Ridge region of the northern hemisphere of Mars.

Uranius Tholus a minor—65-km—Martian volcanic structure. It lies at latitude 26° and longitude 98°, near URANIUS PATERA.

Uranus the Jovian planet discovered in 1781 by German-born British astronomer William Herschel (1738–1822). Uranus, about half the size of Saturn, is seen through Earth-based telescopes as a tiny green disk that otherwise resembles Neptune. In January of 1986, the Voyager 2 spacecraft flew past Uranus and returned a rich dividend of photographs and measurements. Uranus has a ring system that, unlike the rings of Saturn, is dark and narrow. It has some 30 moons, the largest including Miranda, Ariel, Umbrial, Titania, Oberon, Cordelia, Ophelia, Bianca, Cressida, Desdemona, Juliet, Portia, Rosalind, Belinda, and Puck.

Uranus, the 7th planet from the sun, is unique among the planets on several counts: (1) It was the first planet to be discovered with the aid of a telescope; (2) it was discovered by accident; (3) it rotates about its own axis backward (clockwise); and (4) its equatorial plane is almost at right angles with its orbital planet. See VOYAGER.

Uranus, rings of a system of very narrow rings of dark particles—tiny rock dust grains to chunks as big as boulders—around Uranus and scarcely detectable from Earth.

Uranus, rotational axis of an axis notable for its almost right-angle tilt (obliquity) of 97° to the planet's orbital plane.

Uranus, satellites of a system of five large moons discovered from Earth, and another ten discovered by Voyager 2 in 1986. See URANUS for a listing of their names.

Ursa Major (UMa) the Great Bear, the most prominent northern constellation. Almost everyone living in the Northern Hemisphere can recognize the seven bright stars that make up the Big Dipper. These bright stars are Dubhe, Merak, Phecda, Megrez, Alioth, Mizar, and Alkaid (or Benetnash), known as the Pointers for the help they give us in finding Polaris, the North Star. Ursa Major is also called the Wagon and the Plow.

Ursa Minor (UMi) the Little Bear, the northernmost constellation, containing the so-called Little Dipper, the outermost of whose stars is Polaris. About 600 BC this constellation was suggested by Thales as a guide for Greek sailors. Some saw it as a dog's tail, revolving around its tip, which was Polaris. We see the dog's tail as the handle of the Little Dipper. The bright stars of Ursa Minor are Polaris (Stella Polaris, the north pole star), Kochab, Pherkad, and Yildun.

Ursid meteors a minor meteor stream that peaks on December 22 or 23. On December 22, 1945, a strong Ursid meteor shower occurred, with peak rates of about 100 meteors per hour. The Ursids are associated with comet Tuttle 1790 II. See TUTTLE.

UT see UNIVERSAL TIME.

Utopia Planitia a Martian plain, diameter 3276 km, longitude 310° and latitude 35° to 50°, located northwest of the Elysium Planitia volcanoes. It was selected as the landing site for the Viking 2 Lander in 1976.

UV *abbreviation of* ultraviolet.

UV Ceti an active red-dwarf flare star in the equatorial constellation Cetus (the Whale) that exhibits large flares every few hours.

UX Ursae Majoris stars a small group of eclipsing variable stars with Algol-like properties—darker companions periodically cut off the light of the brighter, winking stars—but extremely short periods. See ALGOL.

V

vacuum 1. any space filled with gas at pressures below atmospheric pressure;

2. in reference to satellite orbital parameters, without consideration of the perturbing effects of an atmosphere, as in *vacuum perigee* and *vacuum apogee*.

Valles Marineris a vast system of Martian canyons, latitude 1° N to -18° S and longitude 24° to 113°, that was photographed by the Mariner 9 spacecraft. The diameter of Valles Marineris is 5272 km. See MARINER VALLEY.

valleys, lunar numerous scattered features of the moon, varying all the way from very narrow rills to a mountain-walled plain named Schiller. Valleys are divided into five categories: (1) rills or clefts, for example, Schroter's Valley; (2) the Rheita valley, similar to a valley cutting through the southern part of Snellius, in the upper left-hand quadrant, containing sunken areas; (3) the Alpine Valley, length 75 miles, a graben that connects Mare Frigoris and Mare Imbrium; (4) the parallel gashes or valleys—roughly 150 miles long and ending in the right wall of Alphonsus—in the Ptolemaeus area, a narrow valley that appears to be gashes cut by fragments of an asteroid presumed to have struck in the nearby Mare Imbrium area; and (5) Schiller, a walled plain located near the lunar limb and so elongated that it borders on the valley type of lunar feature. See GRABEN.

Van Allen belt either of two radiation belts, together constituting the so-called magnetosphere, around the outer layer of Earth's atmosphere. The belts—one centered at an altitude of 3200 km, the other at an altitude between 9000 and 12,000 km—which trap high-speed charged particles, are named for their discoverer, American physicist James A. Van Allen (1914–). This zone of high-intensity particulate radiation surrounding Earth begins at an altitude of approximately 1000 km. The radiation is composed of protons and electrons temporarily trapped in Earth's magnetic field. The belts, which cause the polar auroras—Aurora Borealis in the north, Aurora Australis in the south—are also known as the Van Allen layer. See AURORA EXPLORER and Fig. 88.

Van Allen layer see VAN ALLEN BELT.

vapor any gas whose temperature is below its critical temperature, so that it can be condensed to the liquid or solid state by increase of pressure alone.

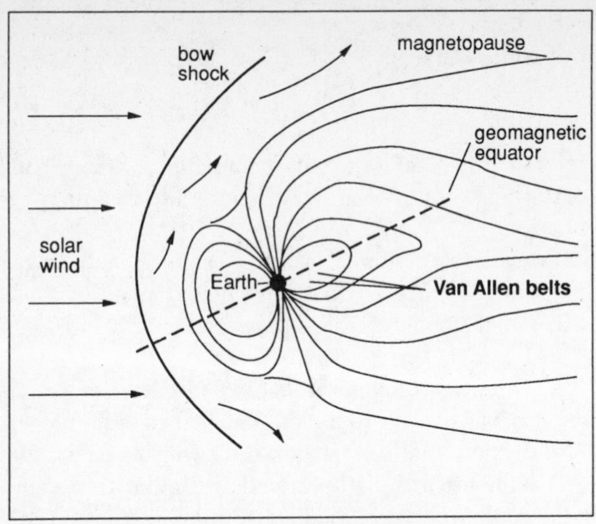

Fig. 88. **Van Allen belts.**

variable star 1. a star whose brightness varies with time. True variables—those that fluctuate in brightness because of processes going on in their interiors—include such stars as Mira Ceti and the Cepheids;

2. an Algol variable—an eclipsing binary in which the periodic variation in brightness is caused by the two stars in a binary system regularly eclipsing one another. See BINARY, NOVA, PULSAR, SUPERNOVA, ALGOL, and CEPHEID.

variable star nomenclature or **variable stellar nomenclature** Except for stars that carry Greek designations, variable stars are designated by a Roman capital letter, beginning with R and continuing through Z, and followed by the name of the constellation, given in the genitive (possessive) case, for example, R Andromedae. When more than nine variables were discovered in a constellation, double letters were introduced, for example, RR, RS, etc. to ZZ. Later, when additional discoveries were made, more letter combinations had to be introduced, so it continued with AA to AZ etc. With this method, 325 combinations are available. Today, since faint variable stars are being discovered in large numbers, any new variable found in a constellation that already has 324 variables is given a designation made of an Arabic number preceded by a Roman capital, for example, V 515 Persei.

variation or **magnetic declination** the angle between the magnetic and geographic meridians at any place, expressed in degrees east or west, to indicate the direction of magnetic north from true north.

variation of latitude the small periodic change in the astronomical latitude of points on Earth, due to wandering of the poles.

variometer an instrument for comparing magnetic forces, especially of Earth's magnetic field.

vector any quantity, such as force, velocity, or acceleration, that has both magnitude and direction at each point in space.

vector steering a method of steering rockets and spacecraft in which one or more thrust chambers are mounted so that the direction of the thrust force can be tilted in relation to the center of gravity of the vehicle to produce a turning movement.

Vega a blue-white star of the first magnitude in the Lyra constellation. Vega is the brightest star in the group and the fifth brightest in the heavens. It lies at a distance of 8.1 parsecs from Earth.

Veil Nebula see CYGNUS LOOP.

Vela (Vel) the Great Sail, a southern constellation, one of the subordinate constellations into which the ancient constellation Argo is divided. Vela, also known as the sail of Argo Navis, is found above Carina, the Keel. It contains several bright stars, but no Alpha or Beta, since these designations went to other constellations when Argo was split up. Gamma Velorum, which is also called Alsuhail, is a very hot star located at a distance of 520 light-years from Earth. See ARGO.

Vela pulsar the second optical pulsar discovered. Its flashes—period 89 milliseconds—were detected in 1977 during a general pulsar survey then under way at an observatory in New South Wales, Australia. The gamma-ray wavelengths of the Vela pulsar in the southern sky made it the brightest object in the entire sky. The pulsar may possibly be the remnant of a supernova.

velocity of escape or **escape velocity** or **escape speed** the initial speed an object must have at the surface of a celestial body to overcome the gravitational pull of that body and proceed out into space without being forced to return to the celestial body. The velocity of escape is an indication of a celestial body's ability to retain an atmosphere. The velocity of escape on the surface of Earth is almost 7 miles per second (neglecting air resistance).

velocity of light the speed of light, 186,000 miles per second.

Venera probes a series of 16 Soviet spaceprobes to Venus launched successfully in the 1960s. Most of these probes either crashed on Venus or sent a paucity of data before becoming disfunctional.

Venera 1—launched February 12, 1961, flew past Venus. Radio failure meant absence of data.

Venera 4—launched June 12, 1967, ejected 844-pound instrument capsule to planet, which transmitted atmospheric data back to Earth. It transmitted for 94 minutes on October 18, 1967: Venus temperature 900° F, composition carbon dioxide and sulfur dioxide, atmospheric pressure 1330 pounds per square inch.

Venera 9—sent first photographs of the planet on October 22, 1975, showing sharp angular rocks near the probe. The probe system operated on Venus for 53 minutes before being crushed by atmospheric pressure.

Venera 13 and 14—reached Venus in March of 1982. The lander returned color panoramas of the surface, made soil analyses, and transmitted atmospheric data.

Venera 15 and 16 orbited Venus in October of 1983, studied its atmosphere, and used radar to map the mountains and craters of the planet's northern hemisphere.

Venus the second planet from the sun. Venus has a rotation period of 243 days. The planet was visited by Mariner, Pioneer, and Venera probes. The properties of Venus include a hostile surface environment, extreme atmospheric conditions, absence of moons, and a surface gravity of 0.9 that of Earth. Venus, called both the evening star and the morning star, is covered with brilliant yellowish white clouds. Its surface temperature is nearly 1040°F because of the greenhouse effect at the planet, its clouds of sulfuric acid, and an atmosphere of 97% carbon dioxide. Other gases present are nitrogen, hydrogen sulfide, and water. Its air pressure is 1330 pounds per square inch. Venus, whose diameter is 0.95 that of Earth, was once called Phosphorus and Earth's Twin. Maxwell Montes is its highest point (nearly 7 miles in height). Venus, which exhibits phases like those of our moon, has a diameter of 12,140 km and rotates in the opposite direction from Earth. See MARINER, PIONEER, and VENERA PROBES.

vernal equinox or **March equinox** the point of intersection of the ecliptic and the celestial equator that is occupied by the sun as it changes from south to north declination, on or about March 21 each year.

vertical circle the great circle of the celestial sphere, through the zenith and the nadir.

vertical diameter the diameter of the lunar or solar disk which, at a given instant, is in a vertical position.

vertigo the sensation that the outer world is revolving about the person *(objective vertigo)* or that the person is moving in space *(subjective vertigo)*.

Vesta (Asteroid 4) the second largest asteroid, diameter 328 miles—the largest is Ceres, 579 miles—and one of the four brightest of the asteroids discovered thus far. Vesta was discovered in 1807 by German astronomer Heinrich Olbers (1758–1840), who discovered 7 comets and the Pallas asteroid.

vibration any motion due to a rapid and continuing change in the magnitude of an applied force that reverses its direction frequently with time.

Viking probe one of two unmanned United States spacecraft sent to orbit Mars, land, and operate on its surface. Two identical spacecraft, consisting of an orbiter carrying a lander, were launched in 1975 from Cape Kennedy.

Viking 1—launched August 20, 1975; began orbiting Mars on June 19, 1976; the lander separated from the orbiter and landed in Chryse Planitia on July 20.

Viking 2—launched September 9, 1975; began orbiting Mars on August 7, 1976; the lander soft-landed in Utopia Planitia on September 3.

Viking's primary mission ended on November 15, 1976, eleven days before Mars passed behind the sun. After conjunction in mid-December, telemetry and command communications were reestablished, and the extended mission operations began. Orbiter 1 continued working until the summer of 1980. Orbiter 2 ended its mission in July of 1978, and Lander 2 in April of 1980. Lander 1 had the longest occupational life, operating until November of 1982.

The Viking scientific instruments acquired more data than expected:

1. Biology experiments analyzed Martian soil and discovered chemical activity, but no evidence of life.

2. Measurements made of some physical and magnetic properties of the soil showed a high proportion of silicon and iron. Measurements also revealed the composition and physical properties of the upper atmosphere.

3. There was nearly continuous monitoring of weather at the landing sites, where surface temperatures ranged from -29° C (-20° F) in the afternoon to -84° C (-120° F) at night.

4. There were dust storms, but wind velocities were low.

5. The north polar ice cap was found to be composed of water ice.

6. The first color photographs showed that the Red Planet was truly red, the color being due to oxidized iron. The total number of pictures exceeded 4500 from the landers; 52,000 from the orbiters.

7. Maps were made of 97% of the Mars surface.

8. Detailed analysis of the Viking Lander experiments has led to the conclusion that there is no form of life on Mars.

See MARS, UTOPIA PLANITIA, and CHRYSE PLANITIA.

Vindemiatrix another name for the orange dwarf star Epsilon Eridani, magnitude 3.73, in the southern constellation Eridanus, between the stars Rana and Zibal. At a distance of 10.7 light-years from Earth, it is the 9th closest star to our planet. See VIRGO.

Virgo (Vir) the Virgin, a zodiacal constellation between Leo and Libra. Its bright stars include Spica, Alpha Virginis, an eclipsing variable; Zavijava, Beta Virginis; Porrima, Gamma Virginis, a double star; Vindemiatrix, Epsilon Virginis; Zaniah, Eta Virginis; and Syrma, Iota Virginis. The constellation Virgo was recognized in ancient Egypt as a maiden and seen as a woman in other early folklores. In classical myth, this constellation was called Astraea, goddess of justice and daughter of Jupiter and Themis.

Virgo Cluster a concentration of hundreds of galaxies seen near the constellation Virgo, at 60 million light-years from Earth. More than 20 members of the cluster have been catalogued by Messier. Examples are M58, a barred spiral galaxy; M59, an elliptical galaxy; and M61, a spiral galaxy.

visible binaries see BINARY.

visible radiation the electromagnetic radiation lying within the wavelength interval to which the human eye is sensitive.

visible spectrum the portion of the electromagnetic spectrum that is occupied by the wavelengths of visible radiation.

visual magnitude (m_V) the apparent brightness of a star or other celestial body as viewed by the unassisted human eye, usually in conjunction with an instrument by which brightness can be compared. The brighter the object, the lower its magnitude number. Visual magnitudes are now determined photographically and are called photovisual magnitudes.

visual trinary a system of closely associated stars, also known as *multiple stars*, moving in elliptical orbits. The stars are sufficiently separated from one another to be seen separately, either telescopically or with the naked eye.

VLA a Very Large Array radio interferometer consisting of 27 radio dishes placed in a Y-shaped pattern about 20 km on each leg. The signals from the dishes, combined by a computer, simulate a radio telescope 40 km in diameter, which can produce radio maps with a resolution of better than 1 second of arc, as good as the best photographs taken by the largest optical telescopes on Earth. See RADIO INTERFEROMETER.

VLBs the Very Long Baseline Arrays being built by astronomers. They form a series of matched radio dishes stretching from Puerto Rico to Hawaii. The dishes will be linked together to form a radio interferometer spanning nearly a fourth of Earth's circumference and having a resolving power better than 0.0003 second of arc, the equivalent of being able to read a newspaper 600 miles away. See RADIO INTERFEROMETER.

Volans (Vol) the Flying Fish, a southern constellation between the bright star Beta Carinae (Miaplacidus) and the Large Magellanic Cloud. It was named Piscis Volans, a flying fish, in 1603 by German astronomer Johann Bayer (1572–1625).

volcanism any of the natural processes that are associated with volcanoes—lava flows, hot springs, geysers, and fumaroles—although strictly speaking the term refers to volcanic activity, which is the eruption of magma at the surface of a planet or moon through the vents of volcanoes or through fissures in the crust, which are caused by rupturing of the rocks. Volcanism is related also to earthquakes, Marsquakes, and moonquakes. See MARS, VENUS, IO, MOON, PLUME 2.

Voskhod either of two Soviet spacecraft that were launched after the Vostok spacecraft. Voskhod 1—*voskhod* means sunrise—was launched on October 12, 1964. It was the first spacecraft to carry a sizeable crew. In addition to a medical doctor and a scientist, there were three cosmonauts aboard. They completed 16 Earth orbits. Voskhod 2 was launched on March 18, 1965, and during its 17-orbit flight Alexei Leonov, one of the two crew members, made the first spacewalk, which lasted 10 minutes. Total thrust of the Voskhod vehicle has been given as 1,443,000 pounds, and the weight of the spacecraft was probably 7 or 8 tons. See VOSTOK.

Vostok 1. the first Soviet space vehicle—*vostok* means east—launched April 12, 1961, with a one-man crew, Yuri Gagarin, the first man in space. He circled Earth once in a flight of 1.8 hours.

2. a series of six Soviet manned spacecraft that could carry a crew of one into orbit. Over time, flight duration was greatly extended in order to study the effects of prolonged weightlessness on the crew. The launching of Vostoks 3 and 4 in August of 1962, which made a close approach in orbit taught much about space rendezvous techniques. On Vostok 6, the last of the Vostok flights, Valentina Tereshkova became the first woman in space, completing 48 orbits and flying in tandem—and communicating—with Vostok 5, which completed 81 orbits. See VOSKHOD.

Voyager one of a series of United States space probes launched toward Jupiter with the goal of acquiring scientific information. The flyby of Jupiter occurred in 1979, the Saturn flyby in 1980, the Uranus flyby in

1986, and the Neptune flyby in 1989. Voyager spacecraft were more advanced than the Pioneer spacecraft and were able to send back magnificent photographs of the outer planets and their moons. Because the Pioneers passed very close to Jupiter, their electronics were somewhat damaged by the charged particles trapped in Jupiter's radiation belts.

Jupiter flybys. For protection against the electronics problems experienced by the Pioneer spacecraft when they went too near Jupiter, the Voyagers did not pass as close. Nevertheless, their improved imaging systems returned more detailed pictures than the Pioneers had returned. Voyager 1 was launched on September 5, 1977, and flew past Jupiter's cloud tops at a distance of 277,560 kilometers (172,100 miles) on March 5, 1979. Voyager 2 was launched on August 20, 1977, and flew by at a distance of 650,000 kilometers (403,400 miles) on July 9, 1979. Although Voyager 2 had been launched first, Voyager traveled a more direct trajectory and arrived at Jupiter first. Numerous discoveries were made by the Voyagers. They provided new information about the planetary atmospheres and also examined interactions among these regions. Lightning and auroras were found in Jupiter's atmosphere, and significant changes were noted during the four months separating the two encounters, as well as since the Pioneer flybys. The Galilean satellites of Jupiter were closely examined by the Voyagers, and three new satellites—Adrastea, Metis, and Amalthea—as well as the planet's ring system were discovered. Both Voyagers gained gravitational boosts from Jupiter and went on toward Saturn, but Voyager 2 was the only spacecraft to have explored all four gas giants—Jupiter, Saturn, Uranus, and Neptune.

Saturn flybys. Saturn was visited by both Voyagers. Voyager 1 passed through the Saturn system in November of 1980. A major objective was to photograph the satellite Titan, but its atmosphere was found to be opaque, like that of Venus, so Titan's surface was invisible. Voyager 1 passed only 4000 km above the clouds of Titan on November 11, 1980. On the next day, Voyager 1 made its closest approach to Saturn, at 124,000 km, and encountered many other satellites. Voyager 1 also obtained high-resolution photographs of Saturn's rings, revealing for the first time the extreme complexity of their structure. In addition, Voyager 1 observed a star as it was occulted by the rings, and this technique enabled detection of even finer details of ring structure than could be observed by photographing directly. Because of the nature of the trajectory of Voyager 1 through the Saturn system, the spacecraft could not be sent on to other planets.

Voyager 2 encountered Saturn on August 25, 1981. It passed only

32,000 km beyond the outer edge of the rings, a distance of 113,000 km from Saturn's cloud tops. The first pictures returned after the spacecraft's close passage through the ring plane were blank, and fears mounted that collisions with ring particles had damaged the imaging system. After Voyager 2 had left Saturn, the camera was unjammed and functioned normally during subsequent encounters with Uranus and Neptune. The August 1981 encounter gave the spacecraft the proper boost for a journey to the two planets.

Uranus flyby. Voyager 2 sped by Uranus at a velocity of 10 miles per second on January 24, 1986, nine and a half years after launch. Voyager 2 came within 81,600 km of the tops of the planet's clouds and transmitted numerous photographs of the planet, its rings, and its satellites. In addition to studying previously known objects, Voyager 2 discovered ten new satellites and two new rings. Because of the high obliquity of Uranus and the fact that its rings and satellites lie in its equatorial plane, Voyager 2 did not make the same leisurely cruise through the system that it had made at Jupiter and Saturn. Voyager's path resembled that of an arrow passing through a bull's-eye target, making its encounter sequence very rushed. In addition, only the southern hemispheres of Uranus and its satellites were seen, since their northern hemispheres were in darkness because of the tilt of the planet's axis—the axis lies practically in the plane of the planet's orbit. Uranus has its poles where the other planets have their equators.

Neptune flyby. Neptune is the most distant planet yet visited by spacecraft. Voyager 2 encountered the planet on August 24, 1989, just over twelve years after its launch from Earth. The spacecraft was aimed toward a point 29,500 km from the planet's center, about 4900 km above its cloud tops. Voyager skimmed over Neptune's north pole and then encountered the large satellite Triton from a distance of about 40,000 km. Nereid, the only previously known satellite of Neptune, was observed from a distance of 4.7 million kilometers. Six additional satellites were discovered, as well as several planetary markings, primarily in Neptune's southern hemisphere.

The most conspicuous feature found was the Great Dark Spot, at 20° south latitude, similar in location and circulation pattern to the Great Red Spot of Jupiter. The Great Dark Spot measures 12,000 by 8000 km. Because observations from Earth prior to the flyby had indicated the presence of a ring system, the trajectory was planned to avoid it. Voyager 2 not only succeeded in avoiding collisions with ring particles, but returned numerous photographs of the rings, enabling determination of their dimensions and other properties.

Because of the trajectory of Voyager 2, the majority of its observations were of features in Neptune's southern hemisphere. Cloud features of Neptune observed by Voyager 2 indicated that the atmosphere rotated in 18.4 hours far south of the planetary equator, and in 15.8 hours near the equator. Observations of the planet's internal radio emissions showed that the interior of Neptune rotates in just over 16 hours. This means that Neptune's atmosphere is rotating more slowly than its interior except in areas south of 53° south latitude. As a result, most of Neptune's winds blow in the east-to-west direction, opposite to the internal rotation. Neptune has the fastest east-to-west winds of any planet, 730 miles per hour. In areas near the south pole, atmospheric winds—moving west to east, the same direction in which the planet rotates—have speeds of 45 miles per hour.

Vulcan During the 19th century, an undiscovered planet, dubbed Vulcan, was suspected of causing discrepancies in Mercury's orbit. French astronomer Urbain Le Verrier (1811–1877), attempting to explain the discrepancies, invented this intra-Mercurial planet in 1859. A small planetoid was discovered inside Mercury's orbit in the spring of 1986 but was assigned only a catalog number.

Vulpecula (Vul) the Little Fox, a northern constellation between Cygnus, Delphinus, and Sagitta. It was originally called *Vulpecula cum Ansere*, the Fox with the Goose. This constellation was named by German astronomer Johannes Hevelius (1611–1687), who charted the lunar surface, catalogued many stars, observed sunspots, and studied the phases of Saturn. Vulpecula is best known as the location of the Dumbbell Nebula (M27). See DUMBBELL NEBULA.

W

Wabar Craters two small impact craters somewhere in Arabia that were produced by iron meteorites.

walled plain 1. any of the crater plains on the moon that are surrounded by raised rims,

2. any of the largest lunar craters that are surrounded by raised rims. Lunar craters consist of two types: (a) explosive *ringed plains* with external walls and (b) *mountain-walled plains* with small or no external walls.

Walter a walled plain 129 kilometers in diameter, sitting at -33° S and 0°, on the dividing line between the 3rd and 4th quadrants of the near side of the moon.

wandering of the poles a shifting of the body of Earth in relation to its axis of rotation.

wandering star a term once used for what we now call a planet. In contrast with stars, which appeared to be fixed in position in the sky, the planets were seen as wandering.

wane to become smaller. The visible lunar disk wanes during the interval from full moon to new moon. See WAX.

Wargentin Plateau a circular plateau 1000 feet above the surrounding surface, at -51° S and -64° E, in the 3rd quadrant of the near side of the moon, southwest of Schickard. It resembles an Earth feature and has a lava-filled basin 89 kilometers in diameter.

Wasat the common name for the pale white double star Delta Gemini. Wasat is situated in the body, or middle, of the Gemini constellation, which has two bright stars, Castor and Pollux. Wasat has a magnitude of 3.51 and lies 58 light-years from Earth.

Water Bearer the common name for the zodiacal constellation Aquarius, between Pisces and Capricornus.

water hole the interval of the radio spectrum between the 21-cm hydrogen radiation and the 18-cm hydrogen OH radiation. These are likely wavelengths to use in the search for extraterrestrial life, just as water holes are attractive to wild animals and to hunters of wild animals.

Watersnake the common name for the constellation Hydrus and sometimes for Hydra.

watt (W) the unit of power in the SI system of measurement.

wave a disturbance that is propagated in a medium in such a manner that at any point in the medium the quantity serving as the measure of disturbance is a function of time, while at any instant the displacement at a point is a function of the position of the point.

wave front or **phase front** the continuous line or surface of waves of light or other radiation that are in the same phase. An advancing wave front is always perpendicular to the direction of wave travel.

wavelength the distance, measured in the direction of propagation of a wave, between successive crests (or troughs) of a wave.

wave of darkening the seasonal variation in the shape and reflectivity of Martian features, once thought to be evidence of the existence of forms of life but now known to be caused by seasonal winds moving dust about the surface of the planet.

wax to grow larger. The visible lunar disk waxes during the interval from new moon to full moon. See WANE.

W Comae a faint quasar in Coma Berenices. W Comae was formerly regarded as a variable star.

WC stars see WOLF-RAYET STARS.

weather the prevailing atmospheric conditions—temperature, pressure, humidity, wind velocity, etc.

weathering the erosion of the landscape of a planet or other celestial body by rain, wind, frost, sunlight, etc.

weber (wb) the SI unit of magnetic flux.

weight 1. the force that gravitation (g) exerts on a body on Earth, equal to the product of the mass (m) of the body and the acceleration acting on it, expressed as m = wg;

2. the measure of the pull of gravity on an object on the surface of a planet or moon. Weight varies on the other planets in accordance with their gravity.

weightlessness or **zero gravity** the condition of being without apparent weight. Just as any object falling freely in a vacuum is weightless, an unaccelerated satellite orbiting Earth is weightless, although gravity affects its orbit.

Weizsacker's theory a theory proposed in 1944 by German astronomer Carl Friedrich von Weizsacker (1912–) for the accretion of the planets at the points of contact between turbulent eddies in the nebula that contracted to form the solar system.

Werner a crater 66 kilometers in diameter, located at -28° S and +3° E, in the 4th quadrant of the near side of the moon. Werner, which is northeast of WALTER, has multiple peaks, the highest being 2400 feet. The highest point on Werner's rim is 15,000 feet.

West Comet a comet visible without the help of a telescope that passed within 30 million kilometers of the sun in February of 1976. The nucleus of West Comet fragmented and sent out huge amounts of gas and dust.

Westphal's Comet a comet that was visible without the help of a telescope in 1852. Its period is 61.2 years, but it dimmed during its 1913 return and has not appeared since then.

west point a point on the celestial horizon that is located 270° from the north point, measured in a clockwise direction.

Wezen a common name for the light yellow star Delta Canis Majoris, in the southern constellation Canis Major, which lies between Puppis and Lepus. Wezen is an extremely luminous and remote star, magnitude -4.07 and 1956 light-years from Earth. Also known as Wezea.

Whale the common name for the constellation Cetus. See CETUS.

Whipple, Fred L. (1906–) American astronomer who did much of his work at the Harvard and Smithsonian observatories. He discovered 6 new comets and wrote on the theory of comet structure, especially the dirty snowball model advanced in 1950. According to this theory, a comet may be described as "dirty ice-ball" a few kilometers across, its nucleus made of ice of such molecules as water, carbon dioxide, ammonia, methane, and dust. When a comet is closest to the sun—approaching perihelion—these substances evaporate and a tail develops. Because of the solar wind, the tail always points more or less away from the sun.

Whipple's Comet a comet discovered in 1933 that started life with a near-circular orbit, period 10.3 years, but has been perturbed by Jupiter so that its period is now 7.5 years. The comet seems to be decreasing in magnitude at each return. Its most recent perihelion date was March 27, 1978.

Whirlpool Galaxy (M51) a spiral galaxy, also known as NGC 5194, in the northern constellation Canes Venatici, near Ursa Major and Boötes. Whirlpool has a nucleus that is not very obvious, but it also has open and prominent spiral arms. The galaxy appears in the winter sky almost face-on to Earth in the east, at a distance of 11.5 megaparsecs from Earth.

whistler the whistling sound sometimes heard on a radio, occurring during lightning, when a plasma disturbance travels out along the lines of force of Earth's magnetic field and ricochets back to its source. The disturbance may be trapped electromagnetically and converted to sound.

whistling meteor the name applied to a radio meteor when a detection system indicates the presence of the meteor by a rapidly changing audio-frequency radio signal. The audio-frequency beat, when amplified and fed to a speaker, enables the meteors to be heard as a high-pitched whistle that rapidly falls to zero frequency as the meteor trail becomes normal to the line of sight.

white dwarf a dying star that is very faint in color, having undergone gravitational collapse to about the size of Earth. Such a star has a mass below the 1.44 solar mass limit. A white dwarf is the final, degenerate stage of a star's life. The most famous white dwarf is Sirius B, a companion star of Sirius. See DWARF STAR and SIRIUS.

white hole a hypothetical celestial object once thought to be the counterpart of a black hole. Thus, if there were such a body, it would be a region in which matter would spontaneously appear. Space and time, severely distorted, would connect our universe with another through what is called an Einstein-Rosen bridge or *wormhole*. Any matter entering a black hole would appear in the other universe as an emergance of material through a white hole. Certain highly energetic objects, quasars for example, have been proposed as examples of white holes in our own universe. See BLACK HOLE.

white light light, also called visible light, seen by the eye as having the same color as ordinary sunlight at noon.

White Sands Missile Range a United States Army military rocket testing ground established in 1945 in White Sands, New Mexico. This was the site of the explosion of the first atomic bomb, in 1945. It now is used to provide C-band radar for near-Earth orbital mission support.

Widmanstatten figures orderly patterns of crystal bands seen in some meterorites when a polished section is etched. They usually cross one another in two or more directions.

Wild Duck Cluster (M11) a nickname for the fan-shaped (like a flight of ducks in a V formation) open star cluster in Scutum. See SCUTUM.

Wild's Trio three irregular spiral galaxies in the constellation Virgo. The galaxies appear to be connected by bridges of luminous material. Their differing radial velocities suggest that the group is disintegrating rapidly.

Wilhelm Humboldt a vast formation at -27° S and +86° E, in the 4th quadrant of the near side of the moon, but so near the limb that it cannot be seen well from Earth. The formation is 193 km in diameter and includes a system of clefts or rills. See RILL.

Wilson effect an apparent alteration in the appearance of a sunspot, changing from circular to elliptical when seen near the limb. The effect is due to foreshortening, an illusion of projection or extension in space. The term *Wilson effect* takes its name from English astronomer Alexander Wilson (1714–1786), who observed sunspots and found that they often are depressions in the surface of the sun.

Wilson-Harrington Comet a comet discovered in 1949, but not seen since then. Its period was estimated to be 2.3 years, which makes it the shortest known period.

wind, stellar see SOLAR WIND.

window or **atmospheric window** any region of the electromagnetic spectrum that can be transmitted through Earth's atmosphere without significant absorption or reflection by atmospheric constituents. See also LAUNCH WINDOW.

wind streaks the light or dark markings seen behind Martian surface features. They are believed to be caused by deposition of wind-blown material left behind by dust storms.

Winged Horse a common name for the constellation Pegasus. See PEGASUS.

winter the coldest of the four seasons, which extends in the Northern Hemisphere of Earth from the winter solstice (about December 21) to the vernal equinox (about March 21), in the Southern Hemisphere from about June 21 to about September 22. The actual dates may vary because of calendar irregularities, for example, leap years.

winter solstice the point on the ecliptic occupied by the sun at maximum southerly declination in the Northern Hemisphere, about December 22, the shortest day of the year. The winter solstice is sometimes called the December solstice. In the Southern Hemisphere, the winter solstice occurs on about June 22.

wispy terrain the light coloration seen by observers on Earth as existing on the trailing sides of some planetary satellites, for example, Dione, Iapetus, and Rhea—moons of Saturn. All of Saturn's moons are locked tidally to Saturn and orbit with one side leading and the other side trailing. Internal tidal heating of a small moon may cause eruptions of liquid water to resurface in the form of vented gas (water vapor), which crystallizes on the moon's surface, forming the wispy streaked terrain seen on the trailing side of the moon.

Wolf **1.** the common name for the southern constellation Lupus, between Norma and Centaurus;

2. a pear-shaped 3rd-quadrant lunar crater in the southwestern part of Mare Nubium, at -23° S and -16° W, approximately 15 miles in diameter. Wolf's flat floor is enclosed by clumps of hills.

Wolf Creek Crater an 820-meter wide crater in western Australia caused by the impact of an iron meteorite.

Wolff a lunar mountain, diameter 6.5 miles, in the 2nd quadrant, at +17° N and -7° W, on the Apennine crest. Elevations of 11,000 to 12,000 feet are reported.

Wolf number or **relative sunspot number** a number indicating the amount of sunspot activity. Wolf numbers provide an almost continuous record of sunspot activity back to the mid-19th century. The Wolf number Z = k(f + 10g), where g is the number of groups, f is the total number of individual spots, and k is a constant depending on the estimated efficiency, or calibre, of the observer. Wolf number was named for Swiss astronomer Rudolf Wolf (1816–1893), who discovered, in 1852, the parallelism between sunspots and magnetic variations. Also called Zurich relative sunspot number. See SUNSPOT CYCLE.

Wolf-Rayet star or **W-R star** or **W star** a very hot and luminous star in its early stages of evolution that ejects shells of gas at high velocity. Many stars of planetary nebulae are W-R stars. The existence of these stars, whose spectra contain entirely bright instead of entirely dark lines, was first recognized, in 1867, by the French astronomers Charles J. E. Wolf (1827–1918) and Georges Rayet (1839–1906). Gamma Velorum, in the Southern Hemisphere, is an example.

Wolf 359 a 13.66-magnitude star 2.32 parsecs from Earth, in the northern constellation Leo, between Cancer and Virgo.

Wollaston a 2nd-quadrant lunar crater, diameter 6.5 miles, near Aristarchus, located at +31° N and -47° W.

wrinkle ridge a crinkly type of lunar ridge, often a few kilometers across and 100 km or more in length and usually found in mare lava plains. Wrinkle ridges are found on the southwestern part of Mare Serenitatis, at +30° N and +17° E, in the 1st quadrant of the moon. Some of the ridges lie radial to the Imbrium basin. Tyrrhena Patera volcano on Mars, at latitude -22° and longitude +253°, is also laced by wrinkle ridges, and mare-like surfaces in the Caloris Basin of Mercury, at latitude +22° and longitude +180°, have wrinkle ridges. See MARE.

Wrottesley a lunar crater, diameter 40 miles, at -23° S and +57° E in the 4th quadrant, possessing multiple peaks. The highest peak is 1600 feet.

WR star see WOLF-RAYET STAR.

W Serpentis a red giant eclipsing variable star in the equatorial constellation Serpens, between Hercules and Boötes. W Serpentis has unusual light variations, between magnitudes of 8.9 and 10.3, and an average period of 14.153 days. The system consists of two stars of roughly the same size, but of different brightness, rotating about each other.

W star see WOLF-RAYET STAR.

W Ursae Majoris stars pairs of yellow-white stars that appear to almost touch as they orbit one another. These stars, of the northern constellation Ursa Major, near Draco and Leo, are of nearly identical brightness. See ALGOL.

Wurzelbauer a lunar crater 55 miles in diameter, in the 3rd quadrant, at -34° S and -15° W, near Tycho.

W Virginis stars pulsating, yellow to orange giant variable stars in the equatorial constellation Virgo, between Serpens and Crater, that are similar to Cepheids. See CEPHEID VARIABLES.

WW Aurigae an eclipsing binary, period 2.52 days, in the southern constellation Auriga, between Gemini and Perseus. See ECLIPSING BINARY.

WZ Sagittae an eclipsing star—magnitude 15.5 at minimum and 7.0 during outbursts—in the southern constellation Sagittarius, between Capricornus and Scorpius. It was once classified as a recurrent nova or dwarf nova, but now is considered to be similar to the U Geminorum class of dwarf novas. Outbursts have been observed thus far in 1913, 1946, and 1978. See U GEMINORUM STARS and NOVA.

X

Xenophanes a high-walled lunar crater 108 kilometers (67 miles) in diameter. The crater is located in the moon's west limb, at +56° N and -80° W, in the Roris region.

X-Persei a massive x-ray binary, magnitude 6.0 to 6.7 and a period of 580 days, in the northern constellation Perseus, between Auriga and Andromeda.

x-ray a form of high-energy electromagnetic radiation lying between gamma ray radiation and ultraviolet radiation in the electromagnetic spectrum.

x-ray astronomy the study of distant stars, galaxies, and quasars. This branch of astronomy had its inception when a cosmic x-ray source, Scorpius X-1, was discovered in 1962 by American astronomer Riccardo Giacconi and colleagues.

x-ray binary a binary neutron star that gives off x-ray pulses. One of the most widely known luminous x-ray sources is called SS433, from its number in a star catalog.

x-ray burster or **x-ray burst source** or **burster** a celestial source of cosmic x-ray flashes. It was discovered in 1975.

x-ray galaxy a galaxy or quasar that is a powerful emitter of X-rays and also often a strong radio source.

x-ray pulsar see CENTAURUS X-3.

x-ray satellite any of the manned satellites designed to observe cosmic x-ray emissions. The first of these was NASA's Uhuru, which was launched in 1970. See UHURU.

x-ray source any of the luminous sources of x-ray emission that are found far outside the solar system. Many of the celestial objects emitting x-rays are binary systems where mass is transferred. A few examples are Scorpius X-1, Cygnus X-1, Centaurus X-3, and Hercules X-1. See BINARY SYSTEM.

x-ray star a star, usually a binary, that emits x-rays. The detection of x-rays from an extremely luminous star usually indicates the presence nearby of a binary system, where matter is transferred from the extended atmosphere of one star to the surface of a smaller, denser companion, which may be a neutron star or perhaps a black hole. Most x-ray stars are part of a binary star system. In the case of less luminous stars, such as SS Cygni, the companion is more likely to be a white dwarf. See X-RAY BINARY and X-RAY SOURCE.

x-ray transient a bright cosmic x-ray source that develops in a matter of days and can be observed for several weeks or months. The brightest ever seen was Nova Mon, in 1975. It disappeared in the following year.

XUV astronomy the study of celestial objects that lie outside the solar system and emit radiation between the wavelengths of x-rays and ultraviolet radiation. The first partial sky survey in the XUV (*x*-ray and *u*ltra*v*iolet radiation) was carried out in the Apollo-Soyuz mission in 1975, which found a number of intense sources, including HZ43 and Feige 24 (both hot white dwarf stars), and Proxima Centauri.

Y

yaw a rotational or oscillatory movement of an aircraft, rocket, or spacecraft about a vertical axis.

yawing moment a yawing action that tends to rotate a craft about its vertical axis. This moment is considered positive when it causes clockwise rotation. See ATTITUDE.

year the time required for one revolution of Earth around the sun. A *sidereal year* is one revolution relative to the fixed stars (365.25636 mean solar days). A *tropical year* or *solar year* is one revolution relative to the equinoxes (365.24219 days). An *anomalistic year* is one revolution relative to perihelion (365.25964 days). A *civil year* or *calendar year* averages 365.2425 days. A *lunar year* is 12 synodic months or about 354 days. An *eclipse year* is one revolution relative to the same node of the moon's orbit (346.62003 days).

year (Jupiter) the time it takes for Jupiter to orbit the sun once, 11.86 years, or 11.86×365 days.

year (Mars) the time it takes for Mars to orbit the sun once, 686.98 days.

year (Pluto) the time it takes for Pluto to orbit the sun once, 248.6 years.

year (Venus) the time it takes for Venus to orbit the sun once, 224.70 days.

Yed Posterior the common name for the deep yellow star Epsilon Ophiuchi, in the equatorial constellation Ophiuchus, near Hercules and Scorpius. This K0 star has a luminosity 35 times that of the sun, is of apparent magnitude of 3.3, and lies 90 light-years from Earth.

Yed Prior the common name for the orange-red giant star Delta Ophiuchi. This M0 star, with an apparent magnitude of 3.0 and a luminosity 130 times that of the sun, lies 140 light-years from Earth. Epsilon and Delta Ophiuchi form a naked-eye pair, Epsilon lying southeast of Delta. See YED POSTERIOR.

Y-feature of Venus a recurring dark horizontal feature on Venus discovered in 1957 by French amateur astronomer Charles Boyer. While recording sequences of ultraviolet images of Venus, Boyer noticed a feature that was apparent at four-day intervals. He came to believe that a retrograde atmospheric circulation was occurring every four days. In 1974 Mariner 10 flew by Venus and confirmed Boyer's observation.

Yildun another name for the star Pherkard (Delta Ursa Minoris). Yildun is an A0 star, magnitude 4.44, and 233 light-years from Earth.

Young an irregular 4th-quadrant lunar crater at -40° S and +54° E, near

Tycho. Young, which apparently is an extremely old crater, is approximately 45 miles in diameter, and the Rheita Valley cuts through it.

YY Geminorum the eclipsing binary star also known as Castor C, made up of two faint red dwarfs found in the Gemini constellation.

YY Orionis stars two irregular variable stars that apparently constitute subclass of T Tauri stars. They may represent a protostar, a star undergoing contraction.

Z

Zach an irregular lunar crater in the 4th quadrant, in the Southern Highlands, at -61° S and +6° E, near the north wall of Tycho. It has a diameter of 44 miles, and the highest point on the crater wall is 11,800 feet.

Zagut a heavily battered lunar crater in the 4th quadrant, at -32° S and +22° E, close to Theophilus. Zagut, considered to be a very old feature, has a diameter of 53 miles, and the highest point on the crater wall is 9800 feet.

Z Andromedae a prototype star of a class of peculiar variable stars. The star is made up of two stars that are close together, one a hot dwarf and the other a red giant. Other examples of such variables are the hot dwarf V Sagittae and the red giant R Aquarii.

Zaniah the common name for the star Eta Virginis, in the constellation Virgo, close to the celestial equator and near Leo and Libra. Zaniah is an A0 star of magnitude 4.00, at 142 light-years from Earth.

zap crater or **zap pit** a minute micrometeorite crater in rock.

Zaurak or **Zurak** a common name for the star Gamma Eridani. Zaurak is an M0 III giant of magnitude 2.96 and is sometimes called the bright star of the boat on the river. It lies 160 light-years from Earth.

Zavijah a common name for the star Beta Virginis, in the constellation Virgo, in the equatorial region, near Leo and Libra. It is an F8 star with an apparent magnitude of 3.8. This star is also called Zavijava and Alaraph.

Z Camelopardalis stars a small group of eruptive variable stars known as dwarf novas. The first members of this group were discovered in the northern constellation Camelopardalis, the Giraffe, near Ursa Major and Cassiopeia. Most are classified as U Geminorum stars, of which the brightest member is SS Cygni.

Zeehaen Rupes a major ridge on Mercury, at latitude +50° and longitude 158°, just east of the Caloris Basin.

Zeeman effect the splitting or broadening of spectral lines, which indicates the presence and strength of magnetic fields at the source.

zenith a point on the celestial sphere directly over the head of the observer. See NADIR and CELESTIAL SPHERE.

zenithal hourly rate (ZHR) the number of meteors one can expect to see from a meteor shower under ideal observing conditions, that is, on a clear, cloudless night. Shower rates fluctuate from night to night and year to year.

zenith attraction the effect of Earth's gravity on a meteoric body, which increases the velocity of the meteoric body and moves the meteor's radiant toward the zenith. See ZENITH.

zenith stars those stars that come to culmination on the zenith. See ZENITH.

Zeno a heavily battered and deformed lunar crater in the 1st quadrant, at +46° N and +75° E, near the moon's eastern limb. Zeno's major feature is a low, broad peak.

zenographic referring to positions on Jupiter measured in latitude from Jupiter's equator and in longitude from a reference meridian.

zero-g see WEIGHTLESSNESS.

zero gravity see WEIGHTLESSNESS.

Zeta the sixth letter in the Greek alphabet, used in stellar nomenclature usually to designate the sixth-brightest star in a constellation. See next four entries.

Zeta Aurigae an eclipsing binary in the northern constellation Auriga, near the bright star Capella. The brighter component is a hot blue B star, and the secondary is a cool orange K5 II giant over 50 times the size of its companion. See ECLIPSING BINARY.

Zeta Herculis a binary star system in the Hercules constellation, with a period of 34 years. The components—Zeta Herculis (A) is a yellow subgiant star; Zeta Herculis (B) is a dwarf orange-red star—are of magnitudes 3.1 and 5.6, respectively. The old name of Zeta Herculis is Rutilicus.

Zeta Ophiuchi a star in the equatorial constellation Ophiuchus that is 520 light-years from Earth and 5000 times as luminous as the sun.

Zeta Puppis the brightest star in the constellation Puppis. It is one of the most luminous and hottest—30,000 to 60,000 K—blue-white superbeacons of the night sky. The star, of spectral type O5 and magnitude 2.25, lies 2400 light-years from Earth. Zeta Puppis, in the stern of Argo, the Ship, is sometimes called Naos, meaning stern of the ship.

Zeta Tauri a third-magnitude star in the constellation Taurus, 1° south of the Crab Nebula. Zeta Tauri is also known as Heka.

Zibel a common name for Zeta Eridani, an A3 type star, 4.9 apparent magnitude. See ERIDANUS.

zodiac a band on the celestial sphere that is centered on the ecliptic and contains twelve constellations: Aries, Taurus, Gemini, Cancer, Leo, Virgo, Libra, Scorpius, Sagittarius, Capricornus, Aquarius, and Pisces. The sun, moon, and navigational planets are always within this band, with the occasional exception of Venus.

zodiacal dust the interplanetary dust orbiting the sun in a disk that is roughly symmetrical about the ecliptic plane. Sunlight scattered from the dust produces zodiacal light. Most of the zodiacal dust lies in the asteroid belt and has a banded structure. The dust is probably formed as a result of asteroid collisions as well as from material released from comets. See ZODIACAL LIGHT.

zodiacal light a faint light seen along the ecliptic possibly due to sunlight being scattered by interplanetary dust. It is seen only from tropical latitudes on Earth for a few hours after sunset or a few hours before sunrise.

Zollner a 4th-quadrant lunar crater, at -8° S and +20° E, northwest of the Theophilus Crater, that is shaped like a peach stone and contains multiple peaks. The walls of the crater are broken on the north and south rims.

zonal winds the east-to-west winds on Jupiter and Saturn, which were measured in 1977 by Voyagers 1 and 2. Jupiter's zones appear to contain warm, moist, rising atmosphere, and the belts of Jupiter appear to contain cool, dry, falling Jovian air. Masses of atmosphere from the tops of the zones spread toward the equator and poles, but Coriolis forces—the bending of the paths of moving objects as a result of a planet's rotation—cause the flow to turn 90°. Flow toward the poles is forced east, and flow toward the equator is turned west. Thus, the atmosphere in Jupiter's banded regions flows around the planet, somewhat in the manner of Earth's trade winds. The same holds true for Saturn. See CORIOLIS FORCES.

Zond probes a series of Soviet interplanetary and lunar probes. Zond 1, launched in April of 1964, and Zond 2, launched in November of 1964, did not return data. Zond 3, in 1965, photographed the far side of the moon, obtaining the first high-quality pictures of the far side and successfuly transmitting them from a distance of 20 million miles. Zond 4, in 1968, may have been an unsuccessful attempt at a circumlunar flight. Zond 5 and Zond 6, in 1968; Zond 7, in 1969; and Zond 8, in 1970, made successful circumlunar flights and were recovered on Earth.

zone **1.** a part of the surface of a sphere included between two parallel planes;

2. any of the bands in the cloud layers of the giant planets—Jupiter has seven very bright and distinct bands, but those of Saturn, Uranus, and Neptune are too dim to be distinguished.

zone of avoidance a region toward the center of a galaxy where few, if any, galaxies are seen, since they are obscured by clouds of gas and dust. The zone of avoidance coincides approximately with the belt of the Milky Way.

Zosma a common name for Delta Leonis, in the northern constellation Leo, the Lion, between Virgo and Cancer. Zosma, the so-called girdle of the lion, is a 2.57-magnitude, pale yellow star at 82 light-years from Earth.

Zuben Elakrab or **Zubenelakrab** the common name for Gamma Librae, the so-called scorpion's claw, a giant G6 star of magnitude 4.02 at 109 light-years from Earth.

Zubenelgenubi the common name for Alpha Libra, a double star, called the southern claw of the scorpion. Zubenelgenubi is a pale yellow star, magnitude 2.76, lying 66 light-years from Earth.

Zubeneschemali the common name for Beta Librae, the so-called northern claw of the scorpion, a 2.61-magnitude blue-white star of spectral type B8V and lying 140 light-years from Earth.

Zucchius Crater an irregular lunar crater in the 3rd quadrant, at -62° S and -53° W, in the Schiller area of the Southern Highlands. The crater is 26 kilometers in diameter, and the highest point in its wall is 10,500 feet.

Zupus Crater an irregular lunar depression, 21 miles by 28 miles, with low walls broken in many places. Zupus, at -17° S and -53° W, in the 3rd quadrant of the moon, appears to be a very old lunar feature.

Zurak see ZAURAK.

Zurich number (R) see WOLF NUMBER.

APPENDICES

APPENDIX A

ASTRONOMICAL UNITS

NAME OF PLANET	ASTRONOMICAL UNITS (AU)	AVG. DISTANCE FROM SUN (IN MILES)
Mercury	0.3871	36,000,000
Venus	0.7233	67,000,000
Earth	1.000	93,000,000
Mars	1.5237	142,000,000
Jupiter	5,2028	484,000,000
Saturn	9.5388	885,000,000
Uranus	19.1914	1,780,000,000
Neptune	30.0611	2,790,000,000
Pluto	39.5294	3,660,000,000

APPENDIX B

ASTEROIDS
MINOR PLANETS "ASTEROIDS"

NO.	NAME	DISCOVERY YEAR	PERIOD (YEARS)	PERIHELION (AU)	APHELION (AU)	INCL (°)	DIAMETER (KM)
1	Ceres	1801	4.60	2.55	2.98	10.6	1003
2	Pallas	1802	4.61	2.11	3.42	34.8	608
3	Juno	1804	4.36	1.98	3.35	13.0	247
4	Vesta	1807	3.63	2.15	2.57	7.1	538
5	Astraea	1845	4.14	2.10	3.06	5.3	117
6	Hebe	1847	3.78	1.93	2.92	14.8	201
7	Iris	1847	3.69	1.84	2.94	5.5	209
10	Hygica	1849	5.59	2.84	3.46	3.8	450
15	Eunomia	1851	4.30	2.14	3.14	11.7	272
31	Euphrosyne	1854	5.61	2.45	3.86	26.3	370
433	Eros	1898	1.76	1.13	1.78	10.8	23
588	Achilles	1906	11.90	4.44	5.98	10.3	50
944	Hidalgo	1920	14.04	2.00	9.64	42.5	15
1221	Amor	1932	2.66	1.08	2.76	11.9	0.5
1566	Icarus	1949	1.12	0.19	1.97	23.0	1
1862	Apollo	1932	1.78	0.65	2.29	6.3	1
2060	Chiron	1977	50.68	8.51	18.88	6.9	300?
2062	Aten	1976	0.95	0.79	1.14	18.9	1
	Adonis	1936	2.56	0.44	3.30	1.4	0.3
	Hermes	1937	2.10	0.62	2.66	6.2	0.5

APPENDIX C

CELESTIAL EVENTS
METEOR SHOWERS

SHOWER	DATES	HOURLY RATE	RADIANT R.A.	RADIANT DEC	ASSOCIATED COMET
Quadrantids	Jan. 2–4	30	$15^h 24^m$	50°	
Lyrids	April 20–22	8	$18^h 4^m$	33°	1861 I
∂ Aquarids	May 2–7	10	$22^h 24^m$	0°	Halley
∂ Aquarids	July 26–31	15	$22^h 36^m$	-10°	
Perseids	Aug. 10–14	40	$3^h 4^m$	58°	1982 III
Orionids	Oct. 18–23	15	$6^h 20^m$	15°	Halley
Taurids	Nov. 1–7	8	$3^h 40^m$	17°	Encke
Leonids	Nov. 14–19	6	$10^h 12^m$	22°	1866 I
Temp					
Geminids	Dec. 10–13	50	$7^h 28^m$	32°	

PERIODIC COMETS

OBSERVED BY OR NAMED FOR	YEAR OF DISCOVERY	PERIOD (YEARS)	PERIHELION (AU)
Gunn	1970	6.80	2.44
Wolf	1884	8.43	2.51
Harrington-Abell	1955	7.19	1.77
Schaumasse	1911	8.18	1.20
Klemola	1965	11.0	1.76
d'Arrest	1851	6.23	1.17
Pons-Winnecke	1819	6.34	1.25
Kojima	1970	6.19	1.63
Johnson	1949	6.77	2.20
Dutoit-Neujmin	1941	6.31	1.67
Van Houten	1961	15.75	3.94
Kopff	1906	6.42	1.57
Faye	1843	7.39	1.62
Grigg-Skjellerup	1902	5.12	1.00
Encke	1786	3.30	0.39
Temple I	1867	5.50	1.50
Arend-Rigaux	1951	6.84	1.44
Temple II	1873	5.26	1.36
Wolf-Harrington	1924	6.55	1.62
Whipple	1933	7.47	2.48
Tsuchinshan I	1965	6.64	1.50
Comas-Sola	1926	8.55	1.77

Daniel	1909	7.09	1.66
Tsuchinshan II	1965	6.80	1.78
Van Biesbroeck	1954	12.41	2.41
Halley	240 BC	76.1	0.59

LUNAR ECLIPSES
SOME TOTAL LUNAR ECLIPSES 1986 TO 2000

DATE	LOCATION
1986 April 24	New Hebrides
1986 October 17	Arabian Sea
1992 December 10	Sahara
1993 June 4	New Hebrides
1993 November 29	Mexico City
1996 April 4	Gulf of Guinea
1997 September 16	Indian Ocean
2000 January 21	West Indies
2000 July 16	Coral Sea

TOTAL SOLAR ECLIPSES FROM 1988 THROUGH 2030

DATE	DURATION OF TOTALITY (MIN)	WHERE VISIBLE
1988 March 18	4.0	Philippines, Indonesia
1990 July 22	2.6	Finland, Arctic Regions
1991 July 11	7.1	Hawaii, Central America, Brazil
1992 June 30	5.4	South Atlantic
1994 November 3	4.6	South America
1995 October 24	2.4	South Asia
1997 March 9	2.8	Siberia, Arctic
1998 February 26	4.4	Central America
1999 August 11	2.6	Central Europe, Central Asia
2001 June 21	4.9	Southern Africa
2002 December 4	2.1	South Africa, Australia
2003 November 23	2.0	Antarctica
2005 April 8	0.7	South Pacific Ocean
2006 March 29	4.1	Africa, Asia Minor, USSR
2008 August 1	2.4	Arctic Ocean, Siberia, China
2009 July 22	6.6	India, China, South Pacific
2010 July 11	5.3	South Pacific Ocean
2012 November 13	4.0	Northern Australia, South Pacific
2013 November 3	1.7	Atlantic Ocean, Central Africa
2015 March 20	4.1	North Atlantic, Arctic Ocean

2016 March 9	4.5	Indonesia, Pacific Ocean
2017 August 21	2.7	Pacific Ocean, USA, Atlantic Ocean
2019 July 2	4.5	South Pacific, South America
2020 December 14	2.2	South Pacific, South America, South Atlantic Ocean
2021 December 4	1.9	Antarctica
2023 April 20	1.3	Indian Ocean, Indonesia
2024 April 8	4.5	South Pacific, Mexico, Eastern
2026 August 12	2.3	Arctic, Greenland, North Atlantic, Spain
2027 August 2	6.4	North Africa, Arabia, Indian Ocean
2028 July 22	5.1	Indian Ocean, Australia, New Zealand
2030 November 25	3.7	South Africa, Indian Ocean, Australia

APPENDIX D

SPACE TECHNOLOGY HIGHLIGHTS

SPACE VEHICLE	LAUNCH DATE	COUNTRY	SPECIAL FEATURES
Sputnik 1	Oct. 4, 1957	USSR	First artificial satellite
Sputnik 2	Nov. 3, 1957	USSR	First animal in space—dog, Laika
Explorer 1	Jan. 31, 1958	USA	First US satellite; discovered Van Allen radiation belts
Vanguard 2	Feb. 17, 1959	USA	First satellite to send weather information to Earth
Luna 2	Sept. 12, 1959	USSR	First spacecraft to hit the moon
Transit 1B	Apr. 13, 1960	USA	First navigational satellite
Vostok 1	Apr. 12, 1961	USSR	First person in orbit—Yuri Gagarin
Mercury-Redstone 3	May 5, 1961	USA	First American in rocket flight—Alan Shepard
Mercury-Atlas 6	Feb. 20, 1962	USA	First American in orbit—John Glenn
Telstar 1	July 10, 1962	USA	First satellite to relay TV programs between USA and Europe
Mariner 2	Aug. 26, 1962	USA	First spacecraft to reach another planet successfully—Venus, Dec. 14, 1962
Vostok 6	June 16, 1963	USSR	First woman in orbit—Valentina Tereshkova
Mariner 4	Nov. 28, 1964	USA	First spacecraft to send data and photos from Mars, July 14, 1965
Luna 9	Jan. 31, 1966	USSR	First soft landing on the moon, Feb. 3, 1966; radioed 27 pictures of the moon to Earth
Luna 10	Mar. 31, 1966	USSR	First spacecraft to orbit the moon
Zond 5	Sept. 14, 1968	USSR	First spacecraft to

			orbit the moon and return to Earth
Apollo 8	Dec. 21, 1968	USA	First astronauts to orbit the moon
Apollo 11	July 16, 1969	USA	First person to walk on the moon—Neil Armstrong, July 20, 1969
Venera 7	Aug. 17, 1970	USSR	First spacecraft to transmit data from the surface of Venus; landed Dec. 15, 1970
Salyut	Apr. 19, 1971	USSR	First scientific space laboratory in Earth orbit
Mars 3	May 28, 1971	USSR	First soft landing on Mars, Dec. 2, 1971
Mariner 9	May 30, 1971	USA	First spacecraft to orbit another planet—Mars, Nov. 13, 1971
Apollo 15	July 26, 1971	USA	First use of vehicle to explore surface of the moon—lunar rover
Pioneer 10	Mar. 2, 1972	USA	First spacecraft to fly by Jupiter, Dec. 3, 1973; sent back data and photos; first spacecraft to leave the solar system, June 13, 1983
Apollo 17	Dec. 7, 1972	USA	Most recent moon visit by astronauts
Pioneer Saturn	Apr. 6, 1973	USA	First spacecraft to fly by Saturn, Sept. 1, 1979, after flying by Jupiter, Dec. 2, 1974; sent back data and photos
Skylab	May 14, 1973	USA	First American scientific space laboratory in Earth orbit
Mariner 10	Nov. 3, 1973	USA	First spacecraft to fly by two planets—Venus and Mercury; sent back data and photos
Venera 9	June 8, 1975	USSR	First spacecraft to photograph surface of Venus; landed Oct. 22, 1975
Viking 1	Aug. 22, 1975	USA	Landed on Mars, June 20, 1976; sent back data

			and photos; sampled soil; found no signs of life
Voyager 2	Aug. 20, 1977	USA	Flew past Jupiter, July 1979, and Saturn, Aug. 1981; sent back data and photos; flew by Uranus, Jan. 1986; flew by Neptune,Sept. 1989
Voyager 1	Sept. 9, 1977	USA	Flew past Jupiter, Mar. 5, 1979, and Saturn, Nov. 12, 1980; made many new discoveries of the planets and their moons
Pioneer Venus 1	May 20, 1978	USA	Using radar, mapped surface of Venus from orbit, Dec. 4, 1978
Pioneer Venus 2	Aug. 8, 1978	USA	Entered and studied the atmosphere of Venus
Columbia	Apr. 12, 1981	USA	First flight of the Space Shuttle
Venera 13	Oct. 30, 1981	USSR	First spacecraft to send back color photos of surface of Venus; analyzed soil; landed Mar. 1, 1982
IRAS (Infrared Astronomy Satellite)	Jan. 25, 1983	USA	Orbiting infrared telescope; made many discoveries of objects in space
COBE (Cosmic Background Explorer)	Dec. 1987	USA	While in Earth orbit, hunts for evidence of the beginning of the universe
GRO (Gamma Ray Observatory)	Mar. 1988	USA	In Earth orbit, gathers data on the chemistry of stars, the working of galaxies, black holes, quasars, and supernovas
VRM (Venus Radar Mapper)	1991	USA	Will orbit Venus and map its hidden surface using radar
Galileo	Oct. 1989	USA	Two-part space probe—one part to descend through Jupiter's atmosphere, second part to orbit Jupiter; both parts

			to relay data to Earth
Hubble Space Telescope	1990	USA	Orbit Earth and relay photos of objects in space; to reveal objects impossible to see from Earth
Shuttle Infrared Telescope Facility	No date set	USA	Will detect objects in space 100 times fainter than can be seen from Earth
Lunar Geoscience Orbiter	No date set	USA	Will orbit the moon and collect data on its makeup
Space station	No date set	USA	Will orbit Earth and be home base for scientific research, construction projects in space, and other space efforts
Mars Climatology /Geoscience Orbiter	No date set	USA	Will orbit Mars and study its climate and other features
Titan atmospheric probe/flyby	No date set	USA	Will study Saturn's moon Titan
Human exploration of Mars	No plan set	USA	Scientists will roam over Martian surface
Space colony	No plan set	Joint venture	Artificial Earth in space will hold thousands of people, may be used to mine the moon and asteroids and to manufacture a wide variety of products

APPENDIX E

PLANETS: ORBITAL PROPERTIES

Planet	Semimajor Axis (a) (AU)	(10^6 km)	Orbital Period (P) (y)	(days)	Average Orbital Velocity (km/sec)
Mercury	0.3871	57.9	0.24084	87.96	47.89
Venus	0.7233	108.2	0.61515	224.68	35.03
Earth	1	149.6	1	365.26	29.79
Mars	1.5237	227.9	1.8808	686.95	24.13
Jupiter	5.2028	778.3	11.867	4334.3	13.06
Saturn	9.5388	1427.0	29.461	10,760	9.64
Uranus	19.1914	2871.0	84.014	30,685	6.81
Neptune	30.0611	4497.1	164.793	60,189	5.43
Pluto	39.44	5900	247.7	90,465	4.74

PLANETS: PHYSICAL PROPERTIES (EARTH =O)

Equatorial Planet	Radius (km)	Mass (O =. 1)	Density (g/cm³)	Average Gravity (O = 1)	Escape Velocity (km/sec)
Mercury	2439	0.38	0.0554	5.44	4.2
Venus	6052	0.95	0.815	5.24	10.3
Earth	6378	1.00	1.00	5.497	11.2
Mars	3398	0.53	0.1075	3.9	5.0
Jupiter	71,900	11.18	317.83	1.34	61
Saturn	60,330	9.42	95.147	0.7	37
Uranus	26,145	4.11	14.54	1.19	22
Neptune	24,750	3.93	17.23	1.66	25
Pluto	1120	0.18	0.002?	1.84	1.2?

PLANETS

Planet	Sidereal Period	Orbit Perihelion (AU)	Aphelion (AU)	Oblateness	Albedo
Mercury	87.97d	0.31	0.47	0.0	0.06
Venus	224.70d	.072	0.73	0.0	0.72
Earth	365.26d	0.98	1.02	0.0034	0.39
Mars	686.98d	1.38	1.67	0.009	0.16
Jupiter	11.86y	4.95	5.45	0.063	0.70
Saturn	29.46y	9.01	10.07	0.098	0.75
Uranus	84.01y	18.28	20.09	0.01	0.90
Neptune	164.79y	29.80	30.32	0.02	0.82
Pluto	247.7y	29.6	49.3	?	0.9?

APPENDIX F

SATELLITES OF THE SOLAR SYSTEM

Planet	Satellite	Radius (km)	Distance from Planet (10^3 km)	Orbital Period (days)	Orbital Eccentricity	Orbital Inclination
Earth	Moon	1738	384.4	27.322	0.055	5°8′43"
Mars	Phobos	14 X 10	9.38	0.3189	0.018	1°.0
	Deimos	8 X 6	23.5	1.262	0.002	2°.8
Jupiter J16	Metis	20	126	0.29	0.0	0°.0
J15	Adrastea	18	128	0.294	0.0	0°.0
J5	Amalthea	135 X 78	182	0.4982	0.003	0°.45
J14	Thebe	38	223	0.674	0.0	1°.3
J1	Io	1820	422	1.769	0.000	0°.3
J2	Europa	1565	671	3.551	0.000	0°.46
J3	Ganymede	2640	1071	7.155	0.002	0°.18
J4	Callisto	2420	1884	16.689	0.008	0°.25
J13	Leda	~4	11,110	240	0.146	26°.7
J6	Himalia	~85	11,470	250.6	0.158	27°.6
J10	Lysithea	~10	11,710	260	0.12	29°
J7	Elara	~30	11,740	260.1	0.207	24°.8
J12	Ananke	8?	20,700	617	0.169	147°
J11	Carme	12?	22,350	692	0.207	163°
J8	Pasiphaë	14?	23,300	735	0.40	147°
J9	Sinope	10?	23,700	758	0.275	156°
Saturn S15	Atlas	25 X 10	137.7	0.601	0.002	0°.3
S14	(1980 S27)	70 X 40	139.4	0.613	0.003	0°.0
S13	(1980 S26)	55 X 35	141.7	0.629	0.004	0°.05
S11	Epimetheus	70 X 50	151.42	0.694	0.009	0°.34
S10	Janus	110 X 80	151.47	0.695	0.007	0°.14
S1	Mimas	196	185.54	0.942	0.020	1°.5
S2	Enceladus	250	238.04	1.370	0.004	0°.0
S3	Tethys	530	294.67	1.888	0.000	1°.1
S16	Calypso	17 X 11	294.67	1.888	0.0	~1°?
S17	Telesto	17 X 13	294.67	1.888	0.0	~1°?
S4	Dione	560	377	2.737	0.002	0°.0
S12	Helene	18 X 15	377	2.74	0.005	0°.15
S5	Rhea	765	527	4.518	0.001	0°.4
S6	Titan	2575	1222	15.94	0.029	0°.3
S7	Hyperion	205 X 110	1484	21.28	0.104	~0°.5
S8	Iapetus	730	3562	79.33	0.028	14°.72
S9	Phoebe	110	12,930	550.4	0.163	150°
Uranus	Cordelia	25	49.8	0.3333	~0	~0°
	Ophelia	25	53.8	0.375	~0	~0°

	Bianca	25	59.1	0.433	~0	~0°
	Cressida	30	61.8	0.462	~0	~0°
	Desdemona	30	62.7	0.475	~0	~0°
	Juliet	40	64.4	0.492	~0	~0°
	Portia	40	66.1	0.512	~0	~0°
	Rosalind	30	69.9	0.558	~0	~0°
	Belinda	30	75.2	0.621	~0	~0°
	Puck	85 ± 5	85.9	0.762	~0	~0°
U5	Miranda	242 ± 5	129.9	1.414	0.017	3°.4
U1	Ariel	580 ± 5	190.9	2.520	0.003	0°
U2	Umbriel	595 ± 10	266.0	4.144	0.003	0°
U3	Titania	805 ± 5	436.3	8.706	0.002	0°
U4	Oberon	775 ± 10	583.4	13.463	0.001	0°
Neptune	Triton	~1700	355.5	5.877	0.00	160°
	Nereid	~470	5567	359.4	0.76	27°.7
Pluto	Charon	665 ± 60	17	6.38718	~0	120°

APPENDIX G

STARS

CLASSIFICATION OF STARS BY SPECTRAL TYPE

Spectral Type	Prominent Bands in Spectrum	Color	Temperature	Example of Star	Constellation
O	Ionized helium, nitrogen and oxygen	Bluish white	50,000° C.	Cephei	Cepheus
B	Neutral helium with weak oxygen and nitrogen bands	Bluish white	25,000° C.	Rigel	Orion
A	Prominent hydrogen and ionized calcium	White	11,000° C.	Vega and Sirius	Lyra and Canis Major
F	Weak hydrogen with stronger calcium bands	Yellowish white	7500° C.	Procyon	Canis Minor
G	Calcium bands with strong development of metallic bands	Yellow	6000° C.	Sun	—
K	Maximum ionized calcium and strong bands of neutral metallic atoms	Orange	5000° C.	Arcturus	Boötes
M	Neutral metallic bands, some of them very strong, plus intense titanium oxide	Red	3500° C.	Betelgeuse	Orion

THE NEAREST STARS

Name	R.A. h	R.A. m	Decl. °	Decl. ′	Parallax π ″	Distance ly	Spectral Type	Apparent Magnitude V	Absolute Magnitude M_V	Luminosity (L° = 1)
1 Sun							G2 V	-26.72	4.85	1.0
2 Proxima Cen	14	30.0	-62	40	0.763	4.3	M5.5 V	11.05	15.49	0.00006
α Cen A	14	39.6	-60	50	.750	4.3	G2 V	-0.01	4.37	1.6
α Cen B							K1 V	1.33	5.71	.45
3 Barnard's star	17	57.9	+04	41	.549	5.9	M3.8 V	9.54	13.22	0.00045
4 Wolf 359 (CN Leo)	10	56.7	+07	00	.421	7.8	M5.8 V	13.53	16.65	0.00002
5 BD + 36°2147 = HD95735 (Lalande 21185)	11	03.4	+35	58	.400	8.2	M2.1 V	7.50	10.50	0.0055
6 Sirius A	6	45.1	-16	43	.376	8.7	A1 V	-1.46	1.42	23.5
Sirius B							DA	8.3	11.2	0.003
7 L 726-8 = A	1	38.8	-17	57	.372	8.8	M5.6 V	12.52	15.46	0.00006
UV Cet = B								13.02	15.96	0.00004
8 Ross 154 (V1216 Sgr)	18	49.7	-23	49	.346	9.4	M3.6 V	10.45	13.14	0.00048
9 Ross 248 (HH And)	23	41.9	+44	10	.313	0.4	M4.9 V	12.29	14.78	0.00011
10 ø Eri	3	32.9	-09	28	.303	10.8	K2 V	3.73	6.14	0.30
11 Ross 128 (FI Vir)	11	47.6	+00	48	.301	10.8	M4.1 V	11.10	13.47	0.00036
12 61 Cyg A	21	06.9	+38	45	.295	11.1	K3.5 V	5.22	7.56	0.082
61 Cyg B							K4.7 V	6.03	8.37	0.039
13 Procyon A	7	39.3	+05	14	.292	11.2	F5 IV-V	0.37	2.64	7.65

25 BRIGHTEST STARS

Star	Position (1975) α	δ	Apparent magnitude (m_v)	Distance (parsecs)	Proper Motion (″/yr)	Spectral Type	Absolute Magnitude (M_v)
Sirius, α CMa	$6^h44.0^m$	-16°41′	-1.5*	2.7	1.32	A1 V	+1.4
Canopus, α Car	6 23.6	-52 41	-0.7	30	0.02	F0 Ib	-3.1
α Centauri	14 38.0	-60 44	-0.3*	1.31	3.68	G2 V	+4.2
Arcturus, α Boo	14 14.5	+19 19	-0.1	11	2.28	K2III	-0.3
Vega, α Lyr	18 36.0	+38 46	0.0	8.1	0.34	A0 V	+0.5
Capella, α Aur	5 14.8	+45 52	0.1*	14	0.44	G0 III	-0.6
Rigel, β Ori	5 13.3	-8 14	0.1*	270	0.00	B8 Ia	-7.1
Procyon, α CMi	7 38.0	+5 17	0.3*	3.5	1.25	F5 IV-V	+2.7
Achernar, α Eri	1 37.8	-57 22	0.5	35	0.10	B5 V	-2.2
β Centauri	14 02.1	-60 15	0.6*	130	0.04	B1 III	-5.0
Altair, α Aql	19 49.5	+8 48	0.8	5.1	0.66	A 7 I V-V	+2.3
Betelgeuse, α Ori	5 53.8	+7 24	0.8†	180	0.03	M2 lab	-5.9
Aldebaran, α Tau	4 34.0	+16 28	0.8*	21	0.20	K5 III	-0.8
α Crucis	12 25.2	-63 00	0.9*	80	0.04	B1 IV	-3.7
Spica, α Vir	13 23.9	-11 01	1.0†	65	0.05	B1 V	-3.1
Antares, α Sco	16 27.8	-26 22	1.0†	130	0.03	MI Ib	-4.7
Pollux, β Gem	7 43.8	+28 05	1.2	11	0.62	KO III	+1.0
Fomalhaut, α PsA	22 56.2	-29 45	1.2	7	0.37	A3 V	+1.9
Deneb, α Cyg	20 40.6	+45 11	1.3	430	0.00	A2 Ia	-7.2
β Crucis	12 46.2	-59 33	1.3	130	0.05	BO.5 IV	-4.3
Regulus, α Leo	10 7.0	+12 5	1.3*	26	0.25	B7 V	-0.8
Adhara, ε CMa	6 57.7	-28 56	1.5	200	0.00	B2 II	-5.0
Castor, α Gem	7 33.0	+31 56	1.6	14	0.20	A1 V	+0.8
Shaula, λ Sco	17 31.8	-37 5	1.6	96	0.03	B2 IV	-3.3
Bellatrix, γ Ori	5 23.8	+6 20	1.6	140	0.02	B2 III	-4.1

*Multiple star: m_v is integrated magnitude
†Variable star

NEARBY STARS THAT MAY POSSESS PLANETS

Name	Constellation	Distance (light-years)	Remarks
Barnard's Star	Ophiuchus	5.9	2 planets M_1 = 0.8; P_1 = 11.7 years M_2 = 0.4; P_2 = 20 years
Lalande 21185	Ursa Major	8.2	1 large planet M = 30; P = 420 days
Luyten 726-8	Cetus	7.9	2 planets M_1 = 1.1; P_1 uncertain M_2 = 1.4; P_2 uncertain
Ross 248	Andromeda	10.3	1 planet M uncertain; P = 8 years
ε Eridani	Eridani	10.7	1 planet M between 6 and 50; P = 25 years
61 Cygni	Cygnus	11.1	1 planet M = 1.6; P = 5 years
BD + 5°1668	Canus Minoris	12.3	1 planet M = 60; P = 7 years
BD + 20°2465	Leo	15.50	1 planet M = 30; P uncertain

•M = mass of the presumed planet relative to Jupiter
P = period of revolution of the presumed planet

LONG-PERIOD VARIABLES

Position 1900	1970	Desig- nation	Maximum	Minimum	1964	Period (days)
001755	002256	T Cas	6.7	12.7	7.8	445
001838	002238	R And	5.0	15.3	7.0	2
021403	021703	O Cet	2.0	10.1	3.4	332
022813	023213	U Cet	6.7	13.0	7.5	235
050953	051354	R Aur	6.6	13.8	7.7	459
054920	055420	U Ori	5.2	12.9	6.3	372
061702	062102	V Mon	6.0	14.0	7.0	335
070122	070523	R Gem	5.9	14.1	7.1	370
070310	070710	R CMi	7.0	11.8	8.0	313
081112	081512	R Cnc	6.1	11.9	6.8	362
094211	094612	R Leo	4.4	11.6	5.8	313
103769	104369	R Uma	6.2	13.6	7.5	302
122001	122401	SS Vir	5.9	10.0	6.8	355

SHORT-PERIOD VARIABLES

Position 1900	Position 1970	Designation	Maximum	Minimum	Type	Period (days)
005381	005982	U Cep	6.7	9.8	Eclipsing	2.49
030140	030640	ß Per	2.1	3.3	Eclipsing	2.87
035512	035912	λ Tau	3.5	4.0	Eclipsing	3.95
184633	184933	ß Lyr	3.4	4.3	Eclipsing	12.93
025838	030339	ρ Per	3.3	4.0	Semiregular	33–55
060822	061322	η Gem	3.1	3.9	Semiregular	233.0
153738	154039	RR CrB	7.1	8.6	Semiregular	60.0
171014	171314	α Her	3.0	4.0	Semiregular	100.0
061907	062407	T Mon	6.4	8.0	Classical Cepheid	27.02
065820	070221	ζ Gem	4.4	5.2	Classical Cepheid	10.15
194700	195101	η Aql	4.1	5.2	Classical Cepheid	7.18
222557	222858	δ Cep	4.1	5.2	Classical Cepheid	5.37
192242	192543	RR Lyr	6.9	8.0	Cluster Cepheid	0.56
083610	083910	VZ Cnc	7.6	8.3	Cluster Cepheid	0.18
154428	154728	R CrB	5.8	14.8	R Coronae Borealis	—

APPENDIX H

NEBULAE

DIFFUSE NEBULAE

NGC number	Constellation	Angular size (minutes)	Distance (light-years)
I 1499 (California Nebula)	Per	145 X 40	1,950
1976 (M42, the Great Nebula in Orion)	Ori	66 X 60	975
1982 (M43)	Ori	20 X 15	975(?)
I 434 (Horsehead Nebula)	Ori	60 X 10	1,300
2024	Ori	30 X 30	1,300
2068 (M78)	Ori	8 X 6	(?)
2237 (Rosetta Nebula)	Mon	64 X 61	3,850
2264 (Cone Nebula)	Mon	60 X 30	3,260
6514 (M20, the Trifid Nebula)	Sgr	27 X 29	2,200
6523 (M8, the Lagoon Nebula)	Sgr	35 X 60	2,500
6611 (M16)	Ser	35 X 28	4,550
6618 (M17, the Omega Nebula)	Sgr	46 X 37	3,250
6960	Cyg	190 X 8	1,300
I 5067 (The Pelican Nebula)	Cyg	85 X 75	910

PLANETARY NEBULAE

NGC number	Constel- lation	Angular size (minutes)	Magnitude Nebula	Magnitude Star	Distance (light- years)	Class
40	Cas	1 X .6	10	11	3,250	3
246	Cet	4 X 3.5	9	11	1,500	3
650-1	Per	2.6 X 1.5	12	17	8,200	5
(M76, the Little Dumbbell Nebula)						
I 289	Cas	.7 X .5	12	15	8,500	4
1514	Tau	2 X 1.5	11	10	4,300	5
1535	Eri	.3 X .3	9	11	2,140	4
I 418	Lep	.2 X .2	12	11	7,450	4
1952	Tau	6 X 4	8	16	910	6
(M1, the Crab Nebula)						
2392	Gem	.8 X .7	9	11	1,360	3
2438	Pup	1.1 X 1.1	11	17	5,400	4
2440	Pup	.9 X .3	12	17	6,500	5
3132	Ant	1.6 X .9	8	11	1,300	4
3242	Hya	.7 X .6	9	11	1,800	3
3587	UMa	3.4 X 3.3	12	14	7,500	3
(M97, the Owl Nebula)						
4361	Crv	1.3 X 1.3	11	13	4,300	3
I 3568	Cam	.3 X .3	12	12	6,200	2
6153	Sco	.5 X .4	12		5,950	1
6210	Her	.3 X .2	10	11	2,580	2

6309	Oph	.3 X .2	12	14	6,200	3
6543	Dra	.3 X .4	9	11	1,700	3
6572	Oph	.3 X .2	10	12	2,480	2
6567	Sgr	.2 X .1	12	15	6,500	2
6720	Lyr	1 X 1.4	9	15	2,150	4
(M57, the Ring Nebula)						
6818	Sgr	.2 X .3	10	15	2,850	4
6853	Vul	8 X 4	8	13	975	3
(M27, the Dumbbell Nebula)						
6905	Del	.7 X .6	12	14	7,100	3
7009	Aqr	.7 X .4	8	12	1,430	3
(The Saturn Nebula)						
7027	Cyg	.3 X .2	10	17	3,600	6
7293	Aqr	15 X 12	7	13	590	4
(The Helical Nebula)						
7662	And	.5 X .5	9	13	1,800	3,4

APPENDIX I

CONSTELLATIONS

THE CONSTELLATIONS

		Approximate Position	
		R. A. (h)	Decl. (°)
Andromeda (And)	The Princess	1	+40
Antlia (Ant)	The Air Pump	10	-35
Apus (Aps)	The Bird of Paradise	16	-75
Aquarius (Aqr)	The Water Bearer	23	-15
Aquila (Aql)	The Eagle	20	+5
Ara (Ara)	The Altar	17	-55
Aries (Ari)	The Ram	3	+20
Auriga (Aur)	The Charioteer	6	+40
Boötes (Boo)	The Bear Driver	15	+30
Caelum (Cae)	The Sculptor's Chisel	5	-40
Camelopardus (Cam)	The Giraffe	6	+70
Cancer (Cnc)	The Crab	9	+20
Canes Venatici (CVn)	The Hunting Dogs	13	+40
Canis Major (CMa)	The Greater Dog	7	-20
Canis Minor (CMi)	The Smaller Dog	8	+5
Capricornus (Cap)	The Sea Goat	21	-20
Carina (Car)	The Keel	9	-60
Cassiopeia (Cas)	The Seated Queen	1	+60
Centaurus (Cen)	The Centaur	13	-50
Cepheus (Cep)	The King	22	+70
Cetus (Cet)	The Whale	2	-10
Chamaeleon (Cha)	The Chameleon	11	-80
Circinus (Cir)	The Compasses	15	-60
Columba (Col)	The Dove	6	-35
Coma Berenices (Com)	Berenice's Hair	13	+20
Corona Australis (CrA)	The Southern Crown	19	-40
Corona Borealis (CrB)	The Northern Crown	16	+30
Corvus (Crv)	The Crow	12	-20
Crater (Crt)	The Cup	11	-15
Crux (Cru)	The Southern Cross	12	-60
Cygnus (Cyg)	The Swan	21	+40
Delphinus (Del)	The Dolphin	21	+10
Dorado (Dor)	The Swordfish	5	-65
Draco (Dra)	The Dragon	17	+65
Equuleus (Equ)	The Foal	21	+10
Eridanus (Eri)	The River	3	-20
Fornax (For)	The Laboratory Furnace	3	-30
Gemini (Gem)	The Twins	7	+20
Grus (Gru)	The Crane	22	-45

Hercules (Her)	Hercules	17	+30
Horologium (Hor)	The Clock	3	-60
Hydra (Hya)	The Water Serpent	10	-20
Hydrus (Hyi)	The Water Snake	2	-75
Indus (Ind)	The American Indian	21	-55
Lacerta (Lac)	The Lizard	22	+45
Leo (Leo)	The Lion	11	+15
Leo Minor (LMi)	The Lion Cub	10	+35
Lepus (Lep)	The Hare	6	-20
Libra (Lib)	The Scales	15	-15
Lupus (Lup)	The Wolf	15	-45
Lynx (Lyn)	The Lynx	8	+45
Lyra (Lyr)	The Lyre	19	+40
Mensa (Men)	The Table Mountain	5	-80
Microscopium (Mic)	The Microscope	21	-35
Monoceros (Mon)	The Unicorn	7	-5
Musca (Mus)	The Fly	12	-70
Norma (Nor)	The Carpenter's Square	16	-50
Octans (Oct)	The Octant	22	-85
Ophiuchus (Oph)	The Serpent Holder	17	0
Orion (Ori)	The Great Hunter	5	0
Pavo (Pav)	The Peacock	20	-65
Pegasus (Peg)	The Winged Horse	22	+20
Perseus (Per)	The Hero	3	+45
Phoenix (Phe)	The Phoenix	1	-50
Pictor (Pic)	The Painter's Easel	6	-55
Pisces (Psc)	The Fishes	1	+15
Piscis Austrinus (PsA)	The Southern Fish	22	-30
Puppis (Pup)	The Stern	8	-40
Pyxis (Pyx)	The Compass Box	9	-30
Reticulum (Ret)	The Net	4	-60
Sagitta (Sge)	The Arrow	20	+10
Sagittarius (Sgr)	The Archer	19	-25
Scorpius (Sco)	The Scorpion	17	-40
Sculptor (Scl)	The Sculptor's Workshop	0	-30
Scutum (Sct)	The Shield	19	-10
Serpens (Ser)	The Serpent	17	0
Sextans (Sex)	The Sextant	10	0
Taurus (Tau)	The Bull	4	+15
Telescopium (Tel)	The Telescope	19	-50
Triangulum (Tri)	The Triangle	2	+30
Triangulum Australe (TrA)	The Southern Triangle	16	-65
Tucana (Tuc)	The Toucan	0	-65
Ursa Major (UMa)	The Greater Bear	11	+50
Ursa Minor (UMi)	The Smaller Bear	15	+70
Vela (Vel)	The Sail	9	-50
Virgo (Vir)	The Maiden	13	0
Volans (Vol)	The Flying Fish	8	-70
Vulpecula (Vul)	The Fox	20	+25

APPENDIX J

CHRONOLOGY OF ASTRONOMY AND SPACE SCIENCE

5000–4001 BC:	The Egyptian calendar, regular by sun and moon: 360 days, 12 months of 30 days each
3000–2501 BC:	(1) Beginning of systematic astronomical observations in Egypt, Babylonia, India, and China (2) Egypt introduces calendar of 365 days without adjustments (2772BC) (3) Cheops Pyramids conform in layout and dimensions to astronomical measurements
2500–2001 BC:	Equinoxes and solstices determined in China; lunar year of 360 days changes to variable sun-moon cycle
1500–1001 BC:	(1) Obelisks in Egypt serve as sun dials (2) Height of sun in relation to incline of polar axis measured in China
1000–901 BC:	(1) Indian lunar year has 360 days adjusted at random to coincide with solar year (2) King AdadnirarI II of Assyria starts new chronology (verified in connection with solar eclipse of June 15, 763 BC)
800–701 BC:	(1) Babylonian and Chinese astronomy understands planetary movements; new calendar confirmed (2) Romulus, first king of Rome, divides year into 10 months
700–601 BC:	(1) King Assurbanipal's famous library, with over 22,000 clay tablets, covers history, medicine, astronomy; movement of planets and signs of zodiac are recorded (2) Water clocks in Assyria
600–501 BC:	(1) Prediction of solar eclipse by Thales of Miletus, presumed to be first in occidental astronomy (2) Babylonian astronomy begins to conform to present reckonings; lunar year has 354 days regulated into 12 months alternating between 29 and 30 days
500–451 BC:	Babylonian astronomer Naburiannu determines length of lunar month (500 BC)
250–201 BC:	Eratosthenes (c. 276–194 BC) suggests that Earth moves around the sun and maps out the course of the Nile River; he also makes close estimates of Earth's circumference
200–151 BC:	Hipparchus of Nicaea makes important astronomical discoveries and invents trigonometry (160 BC)
151–101 BC:	Crates of Mallus forms his great globe of the world (140 BC)
250–300 AD:	The first form of a compass may have been used in China (271 AD)
451–500:	Aryabhata, Hindu astronomer, mathematician and writer on powers and roots of numbers (476 AD) compiles his manual of astronomy
813:	School of Astronomy at Baghdad
828:	The *Astronomical System* of Ptolemy (c. 178) translated into Arabic as *Almagest*
878:	The Arab astronomer al-Battani begins his observations

963:	*The Book of Fixed Stars* by Al Sufi mentions Andromeda Nebula
1050:	Astrolabes arrive in Europe from Eastern countries
1080:	Toledan table of position of stars
1091:	Walcher of Malvern notes eclipse of the moon in Italy
1512:	Nicolaus Copernicus writes *Commentariolus*, stating that Earth and the other planets turn around the sun
1520:	Magellan passes through the Straits of Magellan into Pacific Ocean; discovers Large Magellanic Cloud (Galaxy) and the Small Magellanic Cloud (Galaxy)
1512–1594:	Gerardus Mercator states that Earth has a magnetic pole
1572:	Tycho Brahe discovers the New Star in the Milky Way
1576:	Robert Norman discovers magnetic dip, or inclination, of Earth
1581:	Galileo Galilei discovers isochronous property of the pendulum
1590:	Galileo's *De Motu* describes experiments on various bodies (Law of Falling Objects)
1596:	(1) Galileo invents thermometer (2) Johann Kepler publishes *De admirabili proportione coelestium orbium*
1598:	Tycho Brahe's *Astronomical Instauratae Mechanica* provides an ccount of his discoveries and description of his instruments
1600:	Hans Lipperchey invents telescope
1602:	(1) Thomas Blondeville's *Theories of the Planets* appears (2) Tycho Brahe gives plans of 777 fixed stars
1606:	Galileo invents proportional compass
1608:	The telescope is invented by Hans Lippershey: Galileo constructs astronomical telescope
1610:	(1) Galileo observes Jupiter's satellites, naming them *sideria Medicea*; sunspots are discovered by Galileo (2) Thomas Harriott discovers sunspots (3) Nicolas Pieresc (1580–1637) discovers Orion nebula
1611:	Marco de Dominis publishes scientific explanation of rainbow
1612:	Simon Marius rediscovers Andromeda nebula
1616:	Willebrord Snellius discovers the law of refraction
1618:	J. Kepler's *Harmonices mundi* states the third law of planetary motion
1619:	John Bainbridge publishes his "An Astronomical Description of the Late Comet"
1621:	Johann Kepler's *The Epitome of the Copernican Astronomer* is banned by the Catholic Church
1627:	Johann Kepler compiles the Rudolphine Tables, giving locations of 1005 fixed stars
1643:	Evangelista Torricelli invents the barometer
1651:	Giovanni Riccioli introduces in his map of the moon many of the modern names of lunar features
1655:	Huygens discovers the first satellite of Saturn (Titan)
1656:	Huygens discovers rings around Saturn
1665:	(1) Giovanni Cassini determines rotations of Jupiter, Mars, and Venus (2) Francis Grimaldi's *Physicomathesis de lumine* explains diffraction of light (3) Isaac Newton experiments on gravity

1666: Newton measures the moon's orbit
1668: Newton constructs reflecting telescope
1671: Cassini discovers a satellite of Saturn (Iapetus)
1672: Cassini discovers a satellite of Saturn (Rhea)
1675: (1) Olaus Romer discovers the finite velocity of light
(2) Cassini observes the division in Saturn's rings
1678: Christiaan Huygens records his discovery of the polarization of light
1679: Edmund Halley publishes *Catalogus stellarum australium*
1682: Edmund Halley observes a comet, which later becomes known as Halley's Comet
1683: Newton explains mathematical theory on tides under gravitational attraction of sun, moon, Earth
1687: Newton publishes the *Principia*, which defines the law of gravitation
1704: Isaac Newton's *Optics* defends the emission theory of light
1705: Edmund Halley correctly predicts the return in 1758 of the comet seen in 1682
1706: Olaus Romer's catalogue of astronomical observations appears
1714: Fahrenheit constructs mercury thermometer with temperature scale
1728: James Bradley discovers aberration of light of fixed stars
1739: John Winthrop publishes *Notes on Sunspots*
1742: Anders Celsius invents centigrade thermometer
1750: (1) Nicolas de Lacaille leads expedition to Cape of Good Hope to determine solar and lunar parallax
(2) Johann Tobias Mayer publishes *Map of the Moon*
1761: Mikhail V. Momonosov discovers the atmosphere of Venus
1768: P.S. Pallas travels through Russia to Chinese frontier to observe transit of Venus
1781: (1) William Herschel discovers the planet Uranus
(2) Messier's catalog of nebulae and star clusters is published
1784: George Atwood accurately determines acceleration of a free-falling body
1786: William Herschel publishes his *Catalogue of Nebulae*
1787: Herschel discovers two satellites of Uranus (Titania and Oberon)
1788: Pierre Simon de Laplace publishes *Laws of the Planetary System*
1789: Herschel discovers two satellites of Saturn (Mimas and Enceladus)
1797: H.W.M. Olbers publishes his method of calculating the orbits of comets
1800: William Herschel discovers existence of infrared solar rays
1801: (1) J.J. Lalande catalogs 47,390 stars
(2) First asteroid (Ceres) is discovered by Guiseppe Piazzi (Italy)
1802: William Herschel discovers binary stars
1814: Joseph Fraunhofer first observes the dark lines of the sun's spectrum
1818: (1) F.W. Bessel publishes his catalog of 3,222 stars
(2) J.F. Encke discovers orbit of Encke's Comet
1819: Hans C. Oersted discovers electromagnetism
1823: Fraunhofer observes the dark lines in the spectra of stars
1838: F.W. Bessel makes the first definite parallax measurement for fixed star

1841:	F.W. Bessel deduces a value for the ellipticity of Earth
1842:	C.J. Doppler publishes a paper "On the Colored Light of Binary Stars" (Doppler effect)
1843:	Heinrich Schwabe discovers the waxing and waning cycle of sunspots
1846:	(1) Urbain Leverrier and John C. Adams calculate the position of a new planet, Neptune: Johann Galle locates it telescopically (2) William Lassell discovers a satellite of Neptune (Triton)
1848:	W. Bond discovers a satellite of Saturn (Hyperion)
1849:	Armand Fizeau measures speed of light
1851:	Lassell discovers two satellites of Uranus (Ariel and Umbriel)
1857:	James Maxwell proves that Saturn's rings consist of small particles
1862:	Léon Foucault successfully measures the speed of light
1877:	(1) Giovanni V. Schiaparelli observes Mars' canals (2) Asaph Hall discovers the two moons of Mars (Phobos and Deimos)
1889:	(1) G.V. Schiaparelli discovers synchronous rotations of Mercury and Venus (2) George E. Hale invents the spectroheliograph
1892:	C.D. Perrin discovers the fifth satellite of Jupiter
1895:	Konstantin Isiolkovski formulates the principle of rocket reaction propulsion
1898:	William Pickering discovers a satellite of Saturn (Phoebe)
1904:	Perrin discovers the sixth satellite of Jupiter
1905:	(1) Albert Einstein formulates Special Theory of Relativity: establishes law of mass-energy equivalence; creates Brownian theory of motion and formulates the photon theory of light (2) Percival Lowell calculates the position of a new planet (later proved to be Pluto) (3) Perrin discovers the seventh satellite of Jupiter
1908:	R. Melotte discovers the eighth satellite of Jupiter
1910:	Halley's comet observed
1912:	Viktor F. Hess discovers cosmic radiation
1913:	H.N. Russell formulates his theory of stellar evolution
1914:	Seth Nicholson discovers Jupiter's ninth satellite
1915:	Arthur Eddington investigates the physical properties of stars
1917:	A 100-inch reflecting telescope is installed at Mount Wilson, California
1918:	Harlow Shapley discovers the true dimensions of the Milky Way
1919:	(1) Observations of the total eclipse of the sun bear out Albert Einstein's theory of relativity (2) Robert H. Goddard publishes "A Method of Reaching Altitudes"
1920:	(1) Max Wolf shows the true structure of the Milky Way for the first time, in an early application of photography to the discovery of asteroids (2) V.M. Slipher defines the meaning of red shift in the spectra of galaxies
1921:	Hermann J. Oberth writes "The Rocket into Interplanetary Space"
1922:	W.W. Coblentz obtains accurate measurements of the relative thermal intensities of star images
1923:	(1) L.A. Bauer analyzes Earth's magnetic field

	(2) Edwin P. Hubble discovers a distance-indicating cepheid variable star in the Andromeda Nebula
	(3) Frederick Lindemann, Lord Cherwell, investigates the size of meteors and the temperature of the upper atmosphere
1924:	(1) Henry Draper's Catalogue—the spectra of 225,000 stars—is published
	(2) Eddington discovers that the luminosity of a star is related to its mass
1925:	A solar eclipse is seen in New York, the first in 300 years
1926:	Robert H. Goddard fires the first liquid fuel rocket
1929:	Edward Hubble measures large red shifts in the spectra of extragalactic nebulae
1930:	(1) Clyde Tombaugh locates the planet Pluto, employing the calculations of Percival Lowell
	(2) Bernard Lyot invents the coronagraph
1931:	Karl Jansky discovers radio waves coming from outer space
1932:	(1) Jansky establishes a foundation for the development of radio astronomy
	(2) Theodore Dunham and Walter Adams discover the presence of carbon dioxide in the atmosphere of Venus
1936:	The first radio telescope designed solely for the study of astronomy is built in Wheaton, Illinois
1938:	Seth Nicholson discovers satellites 10 and 11 of Jupiter
1945:	Appleton discovers that sunspots emit radio waves
1946:	Z. Bay bounces radar waves off the moon in the first successful use of radar astronomy
1947:	U.S. airplane first flies at supersonic speeds
1948:	(1) A 200-inch Mount Palomar reflecting telescope is dedicated
	(2) Gerard Kuiper discovers a satellite of Uranus (Miranda)
1949:	(1) Kuiper discovers carbon dioxide in the atmosphere of Mars
	(2) Kuiper discovers a satellite of Neptune (Nereid)
1953:	(1) Cosmic ray observatory erected on Mount Wrangell, Alaska
	(2) A rocket-powered U.S. plane is flown at more than 1,600 mph
1957:	USSR launches Sputnik 1 and 2, first artificial Earth satellites
1958:	(1) USA launches artificial Earth satellite Explorer 1
	(2) USA establishes NASA to administer scientific exploration of space
	(3) USA launches first moon rocket; it failed to reach moon but traveled 79,000 miles from Earth
	(4) Space probes reveal Van Allen radiation belts around Earth
1959:	(1) USSR launches rocket with two monkeys aboard
	(2) USSR's Lunik reaches moon, the first Earth object to reach another body in space; Lunik 3 photographs moon
	(3) The first photographs of the far side of the moon are received on Earth (Luna 3)
1960:	(1) Laser device developed
	(2) First weather satellite, Tiros 1, launched by USA to transmit TV images of cloud cover around the world
1961:	(1) Yuri Gagarin orbits Earth in 6-ton satellite
	(2) Alan Shepard makes first US space flight

	(3) USSR begins its program of launching space probes to Venus
1962:	(1) Astronauts Glenn, Carpenter, and Schirra orbit Earth separately
	(2) Telstar satellite launched from Cape Canaveral
	(3) Mariner 2 launched as Venus probe; flies past Venus within 21,000 miles
1963:	(1) Valentina Tereshkova makes a 3-day flight in space, becoming the first female astronaut
	(2) Astronaut Gordon Cooper complete 22 orbits in Atlas rocket
	(3) Maarten Schmidt discovers quasars
1964:	(1) Ranger 7, launched from Cape Kennedy, returns close-up photographs of the moon's surface
	(2) Both USA and USSR initiate programs to send space probes to fly by Mars
	(3) Radar astronomy reveals that Venus rotates in retrograde motion
1965:	(1) Cosmonaut Leonov leaves spacecraft Voskhod 2 and floats in space for 10 minutes
	(2) Astronaut Edward White walks in space from Gemini 4 for 21 minutes
1966:	(1) Luna 9 makes successful soft landing on the moon
	(2) Surveyor I makes soft landing on moon and transmits more than 11,000 TV images of the terrain
	(3) Two dogs sent into orbit aboard Soviet satellite Cosmos 11
	(4) Edwin E. Aldrin steps out of the Gemini 12 spacecraft for 129 minutes
	(5) First space vehicle (Venus 3) to reach another planet is crash-landed on Venus
1967:	(1) Cosmonaut Vladimir M. Komarov killed during reentry of Soyuz I
	(2) Russia launches Luna 13 toward moon
	(3) U.S. manned space flights are suspended after death of three astronauts in fire on launching pad
	(4) Audouin Dolfus discovers a satellite of Saturn (Janus)
1968:	(1) Surveyor 7 lands on the moon successfully
	(2) Two unmanned Soviet satellites find each other by radar while in Earth orbit
	(3) Apollo 7, with three astronauts aboard, launched from Cape Kennedy; makes 11-day orbiting flight with splashdown in Atlantic Ocean
	(4) Intelsat 3A, first of new series of communication satellites, is put into Earth orbit
	(5) Apollo 8, with three astronauts aboard, launched on flight to moon, orbits the moon and splashes down in Pacific Ocean
	(6) Hewish and Bell discover pulsating radio sources (pulsars)
1969:	(1) The Concorde supersonic aircraft aircraft makes its first test flight
	(2) Apollo 10 astronauts bring lunar module within 9.4 miles of moon's surface
	(3) Apollo 11 lands lunar module on the moon's surface July 20,
1969;	
	Neil Armstrong steps out on the moon July 21, and Apollo 11 returns

with its crew July 24

(4) Astronauts Charles Conrad and Alan Bean land on moon in Apollo 12 lunar module; return to Earth with samples of material from the lunar surface

(5) Two Mariner space probes send back pictures of surface of Mars

1970: (1) Apollo 13 launched from Cape Kennedy

(2) Luna 16, unmanned Soviet spacecraft, returns from moon with rock samples; Luna 17 lands a self-propelled 8-wheel vehicle on the moon

(3) Venera 7 lands on Venus

(4) The 150-inch reflecting telescope at Kitt Peak Observatory (Tucson, Arizona) is completed.

1971: (1) Apollo 14 and 15 crews become the third and fourth groups to explore the moon's surface

(2) Mariner 9 orbits Mars

(3) Three cosmonauts die when their Soyuz 11 capsule develops an air leak while reentering Earth's atmosphere

(4) USSR soft-lands a space capsule on Mars

(5) American astronomers discover two galaxies adjacent to Earth's own galaxy, the Milky Way

1972: (1) Apollo 16 astronauts John Watts and Charles Duke spend 71 hours on the surface of the moon; Apollo 17 crew, Eugene Cernan and Harrison Schmitt, later stay a record 74 hours, 59 minutes

(2) Venus 8 soft-lands on Venus

1973: (1) Skylab 1 (unmanned), 2, and 3 (manned) space missions completed successfully; Skylab 2 astronauts spend 28 days in space; Skylab 3, 59.5 days; Skylab 4 sets out for record flight

(2) Pioneer 10 transmits TV pictures from within 81,000 miles of planet Jupiter

1974: March 29, Mariner 10 takes first close-up photographs of Mercury during flyby

1975: (1) July, Apollo and Soyuz, in first international space mission, dock in orbit

(2) Viking 1 and 2 spacecraft sent to Mars

(3) August, Venera 9 sends back first photographs of Venus

(4) Nova Cygni observed

1976: Viking 1 and 2 reach Mars; orbiters photograph planet; landers carry out scientific experiments in search for life, results negative

(1) Chiron, the outermost asteroid discovered, orbits between Saturn and Uranus

(2) Rings of Uranus discovered by James Elliot and colleagues aboard Kuiper Airborne Observatory

(3) Voyager 2 launched on Grand Tour of Giant Planets (Jupiter, Saturn, Uranus, and Neptune)

(4) Salyut 6, USSR space station, launched into Earth orbit

1978: James W. Christy discovers Charon, Pluto's moon

1979: (1) March 5, Voyager 1 passes Jupiter; returns color photographs; discovers ring system

(2) July 9, Voyager 2 passes Jupiter; photographs planet and moon system

(3) July 11, Skylab, US space station, destroyed when it plunges through Earth's atmosphere into the Indian Ocean; fragments land in western Australia

(4) September 1, Pioneer 11 becomes first spacecraft to reach Saturn; photographs planet during flyby

1980: (1) Voyager 1 passes Saturn; returns photographs

(2) Voyager 2, in Grand Tour mission, continues on to Uranus and Neptune

1981: (1) April 12, Columbia, first Space Shuttle, launched

(2) Voyager 2 passes Saturn; returns photographs

1982: Venera 13 and 14, USSR spacecraft, land on Venus; take first photographs of planet's surface

1983: (1) June 18, Dr. Sally K. Ride, member of five-person crew aboard Challenger Space shuttle, becomes first American woman in space

(2) Venera 15 and 16, USSR spacecraft, orbiting Venus, begin radar mapping of planet

(3) November, Spacelab launched into Earth orbit by Columbia Space Shuttle

1984: (1) Partial ring system of Neptune detected

(2) Solar Maximum Mission launched by Challenger Space Shuttle

1986: (1) January, Voyager 2 becomes first spacecraft to reach Uranus and flies on to Neptune

(2) January 28, Challenger Space Shuttle explodes 73 seconds after launch, killing crew of seven

(3) Cosmonauts Leonid Kizim, Vladimir Solovyov, and Oleg Atkov, aboard USSR orbiting space station Salyut 7, accomplish longest stay in space, 237 days

1987: (1) Water ice discovered on Charon, Pluto's moon

(2) Supernova 1987A observed by Ian Shelton while photographing the Large Magellanic Cloud

1989: Voyager 2 becomes first spacecraft to reach Neptune; photographs southern hemisphere of the planet; discovers the Great White Spot and a large family of moons

1990: (1) Hubble Space Telescope launched into Earth orbit

(2) Columbia Space Shuttle (STS-35) becomes the first shuttle mission dedicated to astronomical experiments; deploys Astro-l payload; collects more than 900 images of supernovae, planetary nebulae, and galaxies; a live Space Classroom is conducted during the mission with students in Alabama and Maryland

1991: (1) Venus Radar Mapper discovers large volcano and canyon system surface of Venus

(2) Columbia Space Shuttle (STS-40) becomes first Spacelab mission fully dedicated to life science

THE AUTHOR

Dianne F. Moore—one of the few teachers of astronomy in the Arkansas public education system—received her undergraduate degree at East Texas State University, at Texarkana, Texas; her master's degree at Henderson University, at Arkadelphia, Arkansas. She teaches in the Hot Springs (Arkansas) Public Schools, for 19 years specializing in astronomy, Earth science, and physical science.

As an amateur astronomer from an early age, and a teacher dedicated to the interests of her students of astronomy, she has attended NASA Aerospace Educational Workshops on such topics as future space missions, the "grand tour," the space shuttle, the new aerospace plane, and Lunar Briefing Certification. She has published numerous articles, including "Sounds of Science," "Arkansas Ghost Towns," "Panning for the King of Metals," and "Cerrogordo's Spanish Cave of Silver."